Inorganic Chem

KING'S SCHOOL, ELY

PUPIL'S NAME	COST	DATE PURCHASED	OFFICE USE
	£5-00		

Butterworths Intermediate Chemistry is a new series of three books—
Physical Chemistry, Organic Chemistry and Inorganic Chemistry—
giving a comprehensive coverage of all modern A-level syllabuses. The
treatment is designed to consolidate the student's knowledge after each
new topic has been dealt with, by means of concise summaries and
pertinent examination questions at the end of each chapter. The authors
avoid unnecessary confusion by adopting throughout the latest
recommendations on nomenclature of the Association for Science
Education. In addition to their particular suitability for students
preparing for A-level, the rigorous, modern and concise treatment of
the subject that the books provide makes them an ideal introduction
for first-year university students and those reading chemistry as a
subsidiary subject.

Inorganic Chemistry

C. Chambers, BSc, PhD, CChem, MRSC
Senior Science Master, Bolton School

A. K. Holliday, PhD, DSc, CChem, FRSC
*Grant Professor of Inorganic Chemistry,
The University of Liverpool*

Butterworth Scientific
London Boston Sydney Wellington Durban Toronto

First published in this edition 1982
(Published as *Modern Inorganic Chemistry* 1975)

© **Butterworth & Co (Publishers) Ltd 1982**

British Library Cataloguing in Publication Data

Chambers, C.
 Inorganic chemistry — (Butterworths intermediate chemistry)
 1. Chemistry, Inorganic
 I. Title   II. Holliday, A. K.
 546   QD151.5

 ISBN 0-408-10822-3

Filmset by Mid-County Press, London SW15
Printed and bound by Mansells Bookbinders Ltd, Witham, Essex

Preface

This book, the second of three volumes in the new Butterworth Intermediate Chemistry series, is intended as a successor to the authors' previous book *Modern Inorganic Chemistry*, of which it is in effect a new edition. The new book, like its predecessor, should also be of value in first-year tertiary level chemistry courses. We have tried in the first four chapters — the periodic table; structure and bonding; energetics; and acids and bases with oxidation and reduction — to provide the necessary grounding for the later chapters on the main groups, the first transition series and the lanthanides and actinides. Although a similar overall treatment has been adopted in all these later chapters, each particular group or series has been treated distinctively, where appropriate, to emphasize special characteristics or trends. Most chapters end with a summary and selection of recent questions taken from A-level, S-level or University of Liverpool first-year examination papers.

A major difficulty in an inorganic text is to strike a balance between a short readable book and a longer, more detailed text which can be used for reference purposes. In reaching what we hope is a reasonable compromise between these two extremes, we acknowledge that both the historical background and industrial processes have been treated very concisely. We must also say that we have not hesitated to simplify complicated reactions or other phenomena — thus, for example, the treatment of amphoterism as a pH-dependent sequence between a simple aquo-cation and a simple hydroxo-anion neglects the presence of more complicated species but enables the phenomena to be adequately understood at this level.

We are grateful to the following examination boards for permission to reproduce questions (or parts of questions) set in recent years in Advanced level (A), Special or Scholarship (S), and Nuffield (N) papers: Joint Matriculation Board (JMB), Oxford Local Examinations (O), University of London (L) and Cambridge Local Examination Syndicate (C). We also thank the University of Liverpool for permission to use questions from various first-year examination papers. Where appropriate, data in the questions have been converted to SI units, and minor changes of nomenclature have been carried out; we are indebted to the various Examination Boards and to the University of Liverpool for permission for such changes.

C.C.
A.K.H.

v

Contents

Chapter 1
The periodic table

1.1 Development of ideas

1.1.1 Metals and non-metals

We now know of the existence of over one hundred elements. A century ago, more than sixty of these were already known, and naturally attempts were made to relate the properties of all these elements in some way. One obvious method was to classify them as metals and non-metals; but this clearly did not go far enough.

Among the metals, for example, sodium and potassium are similar to each other and form similar compounds. Copper and iron are also metals having similar chemical properties but these metals are clearly different from sodium and potassium — the latter being soft metals forming mainly colourless compounds, whilst copper and iron are hard metals and form mainly coloured compounds.

Among the non-metals, nitrogen and chlorine, for example, are gases, but phosphorus, which resembles nitrogen chemically, is a solid, as is iodine which chemically resembles chlorine. Clearly we have to consider the physical and chemical properties of the elements and their compounds if we are to establish a meaningful classification.

1.1.2 Relative atomic masses

By 1850, values of atomic weights (now called relative atomic masses) had been ascertained for many elements, and a knowledge of these enabled Newlands in 1864 to postulate a *law of octaves*. When the elements were arranged in order of increasing relative atomic mass, each successive eighth element was 'a kind of repetition of the first'. A few years later, Lothar Meyer and Mendeléef, independently, suggested that the *properties of elements are periodic functions of their relative atomic masses*. Lothar Meyer based his suggestion on the physical properties of the elements. He plotted 'atomic volume' — the volume (cm^3) of the relative atomic mass of the solid element against relative atomic mass. He obtained the graph shown in *Figure 1.1*.

Mendeléef drew up a table of elements, in the order of their relative atomic masses, but also based on their chemical properties, notably the valencies they exhibited in their oxides and hydrides. He found that the elements could then be classified into vertical columns called *groups* and into horizontal

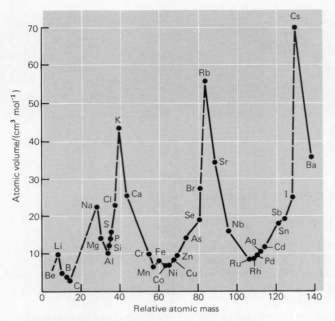

Figure 1.1 Atomic volume curve (Lothar Meyer)

rows called *periods* or *series*. These terms are used to describe the columns and rows in the modern form of the *Periodic Table*, shown on the inside cover.

1.2 Periodicity of physical and chemical properties

Although regularities are clearly observable 'atomic volume' has no single meaning for all the elements — certainly it does *not* measure atomic size, a quantity which depends on the state of aggregation of the element. There are, however, more fundamental physical properties which show periodicity. One of these is the first ionization energy. This is the energy needed to remove one electron from a free atom of the element in the gaseous state, i.e. for the process:

$$M(g) \rightarrow M^+(g) + e^-$$

where M is the element atom. A plot of first ionization energy against atomic number is shown in *Figure 1.2* (units of ionization energy are kJ mol^{-1}). In 1913 the English physicist Moseley examined the spectrum produced when X-rays were directed at a metal target. He found that the frequencies v of the observed lines obeyed the relationship

$$v = a(Z-b)^2$$

where a and b are constants. Z was a number, different for each metal, found to depend upon the position of the metal in the periodic table. It increased by

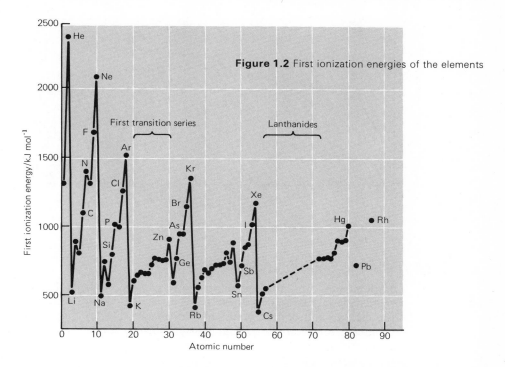

Figure 1.2 First ionization energies of the elements

one unit from one element to the next, for example magnesium 12, aluminium 13. Z was called the *atomic number*; it was found to correspond to the charge on the nucleus of the atom (made up essentially of protons and neutrons), a charge equal and opposite to the number of extranuclear electrons in the atom. Here then was the fundamental quantity on which the periodic table was built.

Clearly the general tendency is for metals to have low ionization energies and non-metals to have rather high ionization energies. We should also note that the first ionization energies *rise* as we cross a period, although not quite regularly, and *fall* as we descend a group, for example lithium to caesium. The fall in ionization energy as we descend a group is associated with the change from non-metallic to metallic character and is very clearly shown by the Group IV elements, carbon, silicon, germanium and tin. Here then is a link between the physicochemical property ionization energy and those chemical properties which depend on the degree of metallic (electropositive) character of the elements in the group.

If we consider the *successive* (first, second, third ...) ionization energies for any one atom, further confirmation of the periodicity of the electron quantum levels is obtained. *Figure 1.3* shows a graph of $\log_{10}$ (ionization energy) for the successive removal of 1, 2, 3, ...19 electrons from the potassium atom (the logarithmic scale is used because the changes in energy are so large). The stabilities of the noble gas configurations at the 18 (argon), 10 (neon) and 2 (helium) levels are clearly seen. The subject of ionization energies is further discussed in Chapters 2 and 3.

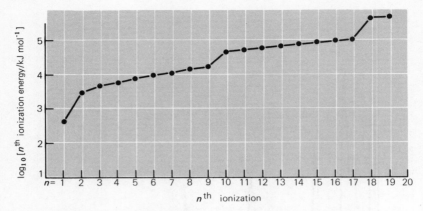

Figure 1.3 Successive ionization energies for potassium

1.2.1   Melting and boiling points

Both melting and boiling points show some periodicity but observable
regularities are largely confined to the groups. In Group 0, the noble gases,
the melting and boiling points of the elements are low but rise down the
group as shown in *Figure 1.4*. Similarly in Group VII, the halogens, the same
trend is observed (*Figure 1.5*). In contrast the metals of Group I (and II) have
relatively high melting and boiling points and these *decrease* down the
groups. These values are shown in *Figure 1.6*.

If we look at some of the compounds of these elements we find similar
behaviour. Thus the hydrides of Group VII elements (excepting hydrogen
fluoride, p. 45) show an increase in melting and boiling points as we go down

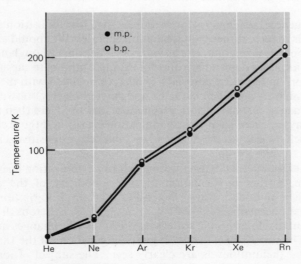

Figure 1.4 The noble gases

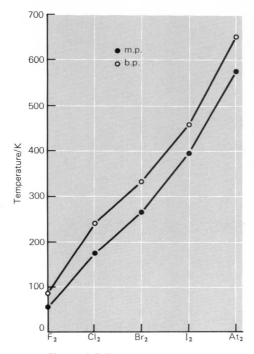

Figure 1.5 The halogens

the group. These are generally low, in contrast to the melting and boiling points of the Group I metal chlorides (except lithium chloride) which are high and decrease down the group. The values are shown in *Figure 1.7(a)* and *1.7(b)*.

Clearly the direction of change — increase or decrease — down the group depends on the kind of bonding. Between the free atoms of the noble gases there are weak forces of attraction which increase with the size of the atom (Chapter 12) and similar forces operate between the molecules of the hydrogen halides HCl, HBr and HI. The forces between the atoms in a metal and the ions in a salt, for example sodium chloride, are very strong and result in high melting and boiling points. These forces decrease with increasing size of atom and ion and hence the fall in melting and boiling points.

1.2.2 Chemical character

In any group of the periodic table we shall see that the number of electrons in the outermost shell is the same for each element and the ionization energy falls as the group is descended. This immediately predicts two likely properties of the elements in a group: (a) their general similarity and (b) the trend towards metallic behaviour as the group is descended. We shall see that these predicted properties are borne out when we study the individual groups.

Increasing metallic — electropositive — behaviour down a group also

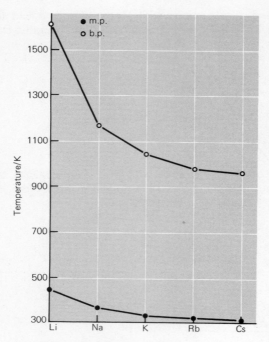

Figure 1.6 The alkali metals

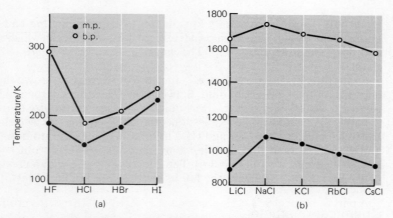

Figure 1.7 Melting and boiling points of (a) the halogen hydrides and (b) alkali metal chlorides

implies a change in the character of the oxides. They will be expected to become more basic as we descend the group and a change from an acidic oxide, i.e. an oxide of a non-metal which readily reacts with OH^- or oxide ions to give oxoacid *anions*, to a basic oxide, i.e. one which readily yields *cations*, in some groups. The best example of such a change is shown by the Group IV elements; the oxides of carbon and silicon are acidic, readily forming carbonate and silicate anions, whilst those of tin and lead are basic giving such ions as Sn^{2+} and Pb^{2+} in acidic solution. Metallic character diminishes across a period and in consequence the oxides become *more* acidic as we cross a given period. This is clearly demonstrated in Period 3:

Na_2O MgO Al_2O_3 SiO_2 $(P_2O_5)_2$ SO_3 Cl_2O_7

← ——Basic ——————————Amphoteric ——————————Acidic———————→

Similar trends are shown by all periods except Period 1.

1.2.3   Valency

Mendeléef based his original table on the valencies of the elements. Listed in *Tables 1.1* and *1.2* are the highest valency fluorides, oxides and hydrides formed by the typical elements in Periods 3 and 4.

Table 1.1 Period 3

Group	I	II	III	IV	V	VI	VII
Fluorides	NaF	MgF_2	AlF_3	SiF_4	PF_5	SF_6	ClF_3
Oxides	Na_2O	MgO	Al_2O_3	SiO_2	$(P_2O_5)_2$	SO_3	Cl_2O_7
Hydrides	NaH	MgH_2	(AlH_3)	SiH_4	PH_3	SH_2	ClH

Table 1.2 Period 4

Group	I	II	III	IV	V	VI	VII
Fluorides	KF	CaF_2	GaF_3	GeF_4	AsF_5		
Oxides	K_2O	CaO	Ga_2O_3	GeO_2	$(As_2O_5)_2$	SeO_3	
Hydrides	KH	CaH_2	GaH_3	GeH_4	AsH_3	SeH_2	BrH

From the tables it is clear that elements in Groups I—IV can display a valency equal to the group number. In groups V—VII, however, a group valency equal to the group number (x) can be shown in the oxides and fluorides (except chlorine) but a lower valency ($8 - x$) is displayed in the hydrides. This lower valency ($8 - x$) is also found in compounds of the head elements of Groups V—VII.

A part of Mendeléef's table is shown in *Figure 1.8*. Most of the groups were further divided into sub-groups, for example Groups IA, IB as shown. The element at the top of each group was called the 'head' element. Group VIII contained no head element, but was made up of a group of three elements of closely similar properties, called 'transitional triads'. Many of these terms, for example group, period and head element, are still used, although in a slightly different way from that of Mendeléef.

The periodic table of Mendeléef, and the physical periodicity typified by Lothar Meyer's atomic volume curve, were of immense value to the development of chemistry from the mid-nineteenth to early in the present

Group		I			II	III	IV	V	VI	VII		VIII		
		Li										—		
		Na										—		
A sub-group	{ K Rb Cs Fr*		Cu Ag Au	} B sub-group								Fe Ru Os	Co Rh Ir	Ni Pd Pt

*   Francium, unknown to Mendeléef, has been added.

Figure 1.8 Arrangement of some elements according to Mendeléef

century, despite the fact that the quantity chosen to show periodicity, the relative atomic mass, was not ideal. Indeed, Mendeléef had to deliberately transpose certain elements from their correct order of relative atomic mass to make them 'fit' into what were the obviously correct places in his table; argon and potassium, 39.9 and 39.1 respectively, were reversed, as were iodine and tellurium, relative atomic masses 126.9 and 127.5. This rearrangement was later fully justified by the discovery of isotopes. Mendeléef's table gave a means of recognizing relationships between the elements but gave no fundamental reasons for these relationships.

1.3   Atomic spectra and atomic structure

Studies of atomic spectra confirmed the basic periodic arrangement of elements as set out by Mendeléef and helped to develop this into the modern table shown in the figure in the inside cover of this book. When atoms of an element are excited, for example in an electric discharge or by an electric arc, energy in the form of radiation is emitted. This radiation can be analysed by means of a spectrograph into a series of lines called an *atomic spectrum*. Part of the spectrum of hydrogen is shown in *Figure 1.9*. The lines in the visible region are called the Balmer series after their discoverer. Several series of lines are observed, all of which fit the formula

$$\frac{1}{\lambda} = R\left(\frac{1}{n_1^2} - \frac{1}{n_2^2}\right)$$

where R is a constant (the Rydberg constant), λ the wavelength of the radiation, and n_1 and n_2 have whole number values dependent upon the

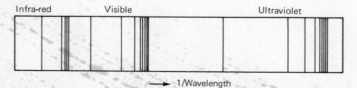

Figure 1.9 Part of the atomic spectrum of hydrogen

Table 1.3

Series	n_1	n_2
Lyman	1	2,3,4,...
Balmer	2	3,4,5,6,...
Paschen	3	4,5,6,7,...
Brackett	4	5,6,7,8,...

series studied, as shown in *Table 1.3*. The spectra of the atoms of other elements also consist of similar series, although much overlapping makes them less simple in appearance.

To explain these regularities, the Danish physicist Bohr in 1913 suggested that the electrons existed in an atom in certain definite *energy levels* (also called quantum levels) each level being characterized by a whole number n, called the *quantum number*. In the hydrogen atom, the electron is in the lowest quantum level — sometimes called the *ground state* — for which $n = 1$. By absorbing heat or light energy, the electron can be excited to higher quantum levels for which $n = 2,3,4...$. The excited electron can lose energy by falling to a lower quantum level, the energy being emitted as radiation. If the quantum level to which the electron returns is termed n_1, and the level from which it falls is n_2, then clearly several series of emitted radiation can be expected for different values of $n_2 - n_1$. *Figure 1.10* shows how the different series of lines in the hydrogen emission spectrum arise from such transitions.

As a model for the energy levels, Bohr envisaged the electron to be moving in circular orbits, each orbit corresponding to a particular energy state. Using this model, he was able to calculate a value for the Rydberg constant for the spectrum of hydrogen which agreed closely with the experimental value.

Improved spectroscopic methods showed that the spectrum of hydrogen contained many more lines than was originally supposed and that some of these lines were split further into yet more lines when the excited hydrogen was placed in a magnetic field. An attempt was made to explain these lines using a modified Bohr model with elliptical orbits but this was only partially successful and the model was eventually abandoned.

1.4   Wave mechanics

With the failure of the Bohr model it was found that the properties of an electron in an atom had to be described in wave-mechanical terms (p. 47). Each Bohr model energy level corresponding to $n = 1, 2, 3, ...$ is split into a group of subsidiary levels designated by the letters s, p, d, f. The number n therefore becomes the number of a quantum level made up of a set of *orbitals* (p. 47). Interpretation of the effect of a magnetic or electric field on the spectra require that the p, d and f orbitals must also be subdivided so that finally each 'subdivision energy level' can accommodate only two electrons, these being described by the symbols ↑ and ↓ (representing electrons of opposite spin). Each electron can have, therefore, a unique description, its spin and its energy

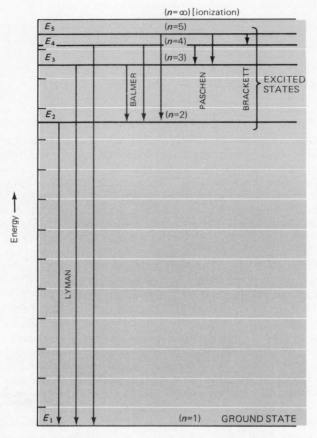

Figure 1.10 Energy level diagram for the hydrogen atom

[Reproduced by permission from Cartmell and Fowles 'Valency and Molecular Structure', 4th Edn, Butterworths]

level or orbital. We can summarize the data for the first three quantum levels briefly as shown in *Table 1.4*.

The maximum number of electrons that any quantum level can accommodate is seen to be given by the formula $2n^2$ where n is the number of the quantum level. For example, when $n = 3$ the maximum number of electrons is 18.

An orbital is characterized by having a single energy level able to accommodate two electrons. The three p orbitals and five d orbitals are given symbols to differentiate them, for example p_x, p_y, p_z representing three orbitals at right angles each capable of containing two electrons.

1.5 The modern periodic table

The close similarity of the atomic spectra of other atoms to that of hydrogen indicates that, as we progressively increase the number of protons

Table 1.4 Electrons in the first three quantum levels

	Quantum level		
Orbital	1	2	3
s	↑↓	↑↓	↑↓
p		↑↓↑↓↑↓	↑↓↑↓↑↓
d			↑↓↑↓↑↓↑↓↑↓
Total	2	8	18

in the nucleus and the extranuclear electrons in the atom for a series of elements of increasing atomic number, the additional electrons enter orbitals of the type originally suggested by wave mechanics for hydrogen. The orbitals are filled in order of ascending energy and when several equivalent energy levels are available, each is occupied by a single electron before any pairing of electrons with opposed spin occurs (Hund's rule).

The order of increasing energy for the orbitals can be deduced from the modern periodic table although for elements of high atomic number (when the electron energy levels are close together) the precise positioning of an electron may be rather uncertain. The filling of the energy levels for the first ten elements, hydrogen to neon, atomic numbers 1—10, is shown in *Table 1.5*.

Table 1.5 Electronic configurations of the elements hydrogen to neon

Atomic number	*Element*	*1s*	*2s*	*2p*		
1	H	↑				
2	He	↑↓				
3	Li	↑↓	↑			
4	Be	↑↓	↑↓			
5	B	↑↓	↑↓	↑		
6	C	↑↓	↑↓	↑	↑	
7	N	↑↑	↑↓	↑	↑	↑
8	O	↑↓	↑↓	↑↓	↑	↑
9	F	↑↓	↑↓	↑↓	↑↓	↑
10	Cl	↑↓	↑↓	↑↓	↑↓	↑↓

We notice here that the first energy level, quantum number $n=1$, is complete at helium and there is only one orbital, the 1s (first quantum level, s type orbital). When this is full ($1s^2$), we may call it the helium core. Filling of the second quantum level begins at lithium; at beryllium the 2s orbital is filled and the next added electron must go into a 2p orbital. All three 2p orbitals have the same energy in the absence of a magnetic or electric field and fill up singly at first — elements boron to nitrogen — before the electrons 'pair up'. (The effect of pairing on the ionization energy is further discussed on page 26.) The $n=2$ quantum level is completed at neon, and again we may use 'neon core' for short.

Table 1.6 Electronic configurations of the elements sodium to argon

Atomic number	Element	1s	2s	2p	3s	3p	Notation
11	Na	↑↓	↑↓	↑↓↑↓↑↓	↑		Ne core $3s^1$
12	Mg		i.e. neon core		↑↓		Ne core $3s^2$
13	Al				↑↓	↑	Ne core $3s^23p^1$
14	Si				↑↓	↑↓	Ne core $3s^23p^2$
15	P				↑↓	↑↑↑	Ne core $3s^23p^3$
16	S				↑↓	↑↓↑↑	Ne core $3s^23p^4$
17	Cl				↑↓	↑↓↑↓↑	Ne core $3s^23p^5$
18	Ar				↑↓	↑↓↑↓↑↓	$1s^22s^22p^63s^23p^6$

For the next elements, sodium to argon, the $n = 3$ quantum level fills up in the same way as the $n = 2$ quantum level. This is shown in *Table 1.6.*

Reference to the modern periodic table shows that we have now completed the first three periods — the so-called 'short' periods. But we should note that the $n = 3$ quantum level can still accommodate 10 more electrons.

The element of atomic number 19 is potassium, strongly resembling both sodium and lithium in its physical and chemical properties. The atomic spectrum of potassium also confirms its position as a Group I element with an electronic configuration resembling that of sodium. These facts indicate that the extra electron in potassium must be placed in a new quantum level and it is therefore ascribed the electronic configuration $1s^22s^22p^63s^23p^64s^1$ (i.e. 2, 8, 8, 1). Similar reasoning leads to calcium being given an electronic configuration of $1s^22s^22p^63s^23p^64s^2$ (i.e. 2, 8, 8, 2).

The following series of 10 elements, atomic numbers 21—30 inclusive, are all metals, indicating that they probably have the outer electronic configuration of a metal, i.e. 4 or less outer electrons. This is only possible if these electrons are placed in the inner $n = 3$ quantum level, entering the vacant 3d orbitals and forming a series of 'transition' metals. We should note that at zinc, atomic number 30, the $n = 3$ quantum level is complete and filling of the $n = 4$ quantum level is resumed with electrons entering the 4p orbitals. The electronic configurations for elements atomic numbers 19—36 are shown in *Table 1.7.*

Krypton is found to be an extremely unreactive element indicating that it has a stable electronic configuration despite the fact that the $n = 4$ quantum level can accommodate 24 more electrons in the d and f orbitals.

Chemical properties and spectroscopic data support the view that in the elements rubidium to xenon, atomic numbers 37—54, the 5s, 4d, 5p levels fill up. This is best seen by reference to the modern periodic table. Note that at the end of the fifth period the $n = 4$ quantum level contains 18 electrons but still has a vacant set of 4f orbitals.

The detailed electronic configurations for the elements atomic numbers 55—86 can be obtained from the periodic table and are shown in *Table 1.8.*

Note that the filling of the 4f orbitals begins after lanthanum (57) and the 14 elements cerium to lutetium are called the *lanthanides* (Chapter 15). The

Table 1.7 Electronic configuration of the elements potassium to krypton

Atomic number	Element	1s2s3s3p	3d					4s	4p		
19	K							↑			
20	Ca							↑↓			
21	Sc		↑					↑↓			
22	Ti		↑	↑				↑↓			
23	V		↑	↑	↑			↑↓			
24*	Cr		↑	↑	↑	↑	↑	↑			
25	Mn		↑	↑	↑	↑	↑	↑↓			
26	Fe		↑↓	↑	↑	↑	↑	↑↓			
27	Co	Argon	↑↓	↑↓	↑	↑	↑	↑↓			
28	Ni	core	↑↓	↑↓	↑↓	↑	↑	↑↓			
29*	Cu		↑↓	↑↓	↑↓	↑↓	↑↓	↑			
30	Zn		↑↓	↑↓	↑↓	↑↓	↑↓	↑↓			
31	Ga		↑↓	↑↓	↑↓	↑↓	↑↓	↑↓	↑		
32	Ge		↑↓	↑↓	↑↓	↑↓	↑↓	↑↓	↑	↑	
33	As		↑↓	↑↓	↑↓	↑↓	↑↓	↑↓	↑	↑	↑
34	Se		↑↓	↑↓	↑↓	↑↓	↑↓	↑↓	↑↓	↑	↑
35	Br		↑↓	↑↓	↑↓	↑↓	↑↓	↑↓	↑↓	↑↓	↑
36	Kr		↑↓	↑↓	↑↓	↑↓	↑↓	↑↓	↑↓	↑↓	↑↓

*   The tendency to attain either a half filled or fully filled set of *d* orbitals at the expense of the outer *s* orbital is shown by both chromium and copper and should be noted. This apparent irregularity will be discussed in more detail in Chapter 13.

   Note. The electronic configuration of any element can easily be obtained from the periodic table by adding up the numbers of electrons in the various quantum levels. We can express these in several ways, for example electronic configuration of nickel can be written as $1s^2 2s^2 2p^6 3s^2 3d^8 4s^2$, or more briefly ('neon core') $3d^8 4s^2$, or even more simply as 2, 8, 14, 2.

electronic configuration of some of the newly discovered elements with atomic numbers greater than 95 are uncertain as the energy levels are close together. Filling of the 5*f* orbitals does begin after actinium (89) and the remaining elements are generally referred to as *actinides* (Chapter 15).

1.6   Features of the periodic table

1   Chemical, physical and spectroscopic data all suggest a periodic table as shown on the inside cover.

2   The maximum number of electrons which a given quantum level can accommodate is given by the formula $2n^2$ where *n* is the quantum level number.

3   Except for the $n = 1$ quantum level the maximum number of electrons in the outermost quantum level of any period is always eight. At this point the element concerned is one of the noble gases (Chapter 12).

4   Elements in the *s* and *p* blocks of the table are referred to as *typical elements* whilst those in the *d* block are called *transition elements* and those in the *f* block are called *actinides* and *lanthanides* (or 'rare earth' elements).

5   Elements with the same number of electrons in the outermost quantum level are put in the same vertical column or *group*.

Table 1.8 Electronic configurations of the elements caesium to nobelium

Element	Atomic number	1s	2s	2p	3s	3p	3d	4s	4p	4d	4f	5s	5p	5d	5f	6s	6p	6d	6f	7s
Cs	55	2	2	6	2	6	10	2	6	10		2	6			1				
Ba	56	2	2	6	2	6	10	2	6	10		2	6			2				
La	57	2	2	6	2	6	10	2	6	10		2	6	1		2				
Ce	58	2	2	6	2	6	10	2	6	10	(2)	2	6			(2)				
Pr	59	2	2	6	2	6	10	2	6	10	(3)	2	6			(2)				
Nd	60	2	2	6	2	6	10	2	6	10	(4)	2	6			(2)				
Pm	61	2	2	6	2	6	10	2	6	10	(5)	2	6			(2)				
Sm	62	2	2	6	2	6	10	2	6	10	6	2	6			2				
Eu	63	2	2	6	2	6	10	2	6	10	7	2	6			2				
Gd	64	2	2	6	2	6	10	2	6	10	(7)	2	6	(1)		2				
Tb	65	2	2	6	2	6	10	2	6	10	(8)	2	6	(1)		2				
Dy	66	2	2	6	2	6	10	2	6	10	(10)	2	6			(2)				
Ho	67	2	2	6	2	6	10	2	6	10	(11)	2	6			(2)				
Er	68	2	2	6	2	6	10	2	6	10	(12)	2	6			(2)				
Tm	69	2	2	6	2	6	10	2	6	10	13	2	6			2				
Yb	70	2	2	6	2	6	10	2	6	10	14	2	6			2				
Lu	71	2	2	6	2	6	10	2	6	10	14	2	6	1		2				
Hf	72	2	2	6	2	6	10	2	6	10	14	2	6	2		2				
Ta	73	2	2	6	2	6	10	2	6	10	14	2	6	3		2				
W	74	2	2	6	2	6	10	2	6	10	14	2	6	4		2				
Re	75	2	2	6	2	6	10	2	6	10	14	2	6	5		2				
Os	76	2	2	6	2	6	10	2	6	10	14	2	6	6		2				
Ir	77	2	2	6	2	6	10	2	6	10	14	2	6	7		2				
Pt	78	2	2	6	2	6	10	2	6	10	14	2	6	9		1				
Au	79	2	2	6	2	6	10	2	6	10	14	2	6	10		1				
Hg	80	2	2	6	2	6	10	2	6	10	14	2	6	10		2				
Tl	81	2	2	6	2	6	10	2	6	10	14	2	6	10		2	1			
Pb	82	2	2	6	2	6	10	2	6	10	14	2	6	10		2	2			
Bi	83	2	2	6	2	6	10	2	6	10	14	2	6	10		2	3			
Po	84	2	2	6	2	6	10	2	6	10	14	2	6	10		2	4			
At	85	2	2	6	2	6	10	2	6	10	14	2	6	10		2	5			
Rn	86	2	2	6	2	6	10	2	6	10	14	2	6	10		2	6			

Z	El	1s	2s	2p	3s	3p	3d	4s	4p	4d	4f	5s	5p	5d	5f	6s	6p	6d	7s
87	Fr	2	2	6	2	6	10	2	6	10	14	2	6	10		2	6		1
88	Ra	2	2	6	2	6	10	2	6	10	14	2	6	10		2	6		2
89	Ac	2	2	6	2	6	10	2	6	10	14	2	6	10		2	6	(1)	(2)
90	Th	2	2	6	2	6	10	2	6	10	14	2	6	10		2	6	(2)	(2)
91	Pa	2	2	6	2	6	10	2	6	10	14	2	6	10	(2)	2	6	(1)	(2)
92	U	2	2	6	2	6	10	2	6	10	14	2	6	10	(3)	2	6	(1)	(2)
93	Np	2	2	6	2	6	10	2	6	10	14	2	6	10	(5)	2	6		(2)
94	Pu	2	2	6	2	6	10	2	6	10	14	2	6	10	(6)	2	6		(2)
95	Am	2	2	6	2	6	10	2	6	10	14	2	6	10	(7)	2	6		(2)
96	Cm	2	2	6	2	6	10	2	6	10	14	2	6	10	(7)	2	6	(1)	(2)
97	Bk	2	2	6	2	6	10	2	6	10	14	2	6	10	(8)	2	6	(1)	2
98	Cf	2	2	6	2	6	10	2	6	10	14	2	6	10	(10)	2	6		2
99	Es	2	2	6	2	6	10	2	6	10	14	2	6	10	11	2	6		2
100	Fm	2	2	6	2	6	10	2	6	10	14	2	6	10	12	2	6		2
101	Md	2	2	6	2	6	10	2	6	10	14	2	6	10	13	2	6		2
102	No	2	2	6	2	6	10	2	6	10	14	2	6	10	14	2	6		2

6   The periodic table also contains horizontal *periods* of elements, each period beginning with an element with an outermost electron in a previously empty quantum level and ending with a noble gas. Periods 1, 2 and 3 are called *short* periods, the remaining are *long* periods; Periods 4 and 5 containing a series of transition elements whilst 6 and 7 contain both a transition and a 'rare earth' series.

7   In noting changes of properties down the typical element groups I—VII of the periodic table, it soon becomes apparent that frequently the top or *head element* in each group does not fall into line with the other elements below it. This was clearly seen when we considered the melting points and boiling points of elements and their compounds (p. 6), and when we come to look at the properties of the individual groups in detail we shall see that the head element and its compounds are often exceptional in both physical and chemical properties. It will be sufficient to note here that *all* the head elements in Period 2, namely lithium, beryllium, boron, carbon, nitrogen, oxygen and fluorine, have one characteristic in common — they cannot expand their electron shells. The elements of Periods 3 onwards have vacant *d* orbitals, and we shall see that these can be used to increase the valency of the elements concerned — but in Period 2 the valency is limited.

      Unlike 'typical element' groups the 'transition metal' groups do not have head elements.

8   Although the head element of each group is often exceptional in its properties, it does often show a resemblance to the element one place to its right in the period below, i.e. Period 3. Thus lithium resembles magnesium both physically and chemically. Similarly beryllium resembles aluminium and boron resembles silicon but the resemblances of carbon to phosphorus and nitrogen to sulphur are less marked. Oxygen, however, does resemble chlorine in many respects. These are examples of what is sometimes called the *diagonal relationship* in the periodic table.

9   By reference to the outline periodic table (inside cover) we see that the metals and non-metals occupy fairly distinct regions of the table. The metals can be further sub-divided into (*a*) 'soft' metals, which are easily deformed and commonly used in moulding, for example, aluminium, lead, mercury; (*b*) the 'engineering' metals, for example iron, manganese and chromium, many of which are transition elements; and (*c*) the light metals which have low densities and are found in Groups IA and IIA.

1.7   Uses of the periodic table

The most obvious use of the table is that it avoids the necessity for acquiring a detailed knowledge of the individual chemistry of each element. If, for example, we know something of the chemistry of (say) sodium, we can immediately predict the chemistry of the other alkali metals, bearing in mind the trends in properties down the group, and the likelihood that lithium, the head element, may be unusual in certain of its properties. In general, therefore, a knowledge of the properties of the third period elements sodium, magnesium, aluminium, silicon, phosphorus, sulphur, chlorine and argon, is most useful in predicting the properties of the typical elements below Period 3.

As regards the transition elements, the first row in particular show some common characteristics which define a substantial part of their chemistry; the elements of the lanthanide and actinide series show an even closer resemblance to each other.

One of the early triumphs of the Mendeléef Periodic Table was the prediction of the properties of elements which were then unknown. Fifteen years before the discovery of germanium in 1886, Mendeléef had predicted that the element which he called 'ekasilicon' would be discovered, and he had also correctly predicted many of its properties. In *Table 1.9* his predicted properties are compared with the corresponding properties actually found for germanium.

Table 1.9 Predicted properties of germanium

Property	Predicted for Ekasilicon (Es) 1871	Found for Germanium 1886
Relative atomic mass	72	72.32
Density/g cm^{-3}	5.5	5.47 at 293 K
Colour	Dirty grey	Greyish-white
Heat in air	White EsO_2	White GeO_2
Action of acids	Slight	None by HCl(aq)
Preparation	EsO_2 + Na	GeO_2 + C
Tetrachloride	b.p. 373 K, density 1.9 g cm^{-3}	b.p. 360 K, density 1.89 g cm^{-3}

Until relatively recently there were other obvious gaps in the periodic table, one corresponding to the element of atomic number 87, situated at the foot of Group IA, and another to the element of atomic number 85, at the foot of the halogen group (VIIB). Both of these elements were subsequently found to occur as the products from either natural radioactive decay or from artificial nuclear reactions. Both elements are highly radioactive and even the most stable isotopes have very short half lives; hence only minute quantities of the compounds of either francium or astatine can be accumulated.

Francium being taken as an example, it was *assumed* that the minute traces of francium ion Fr^+ could be separated from other ions in solution by coprecipitation with insoluble caesium chlorate(VII) (perchlorate) because francium lies next to caesium in Group IA. This assumption proved to be correct and francium was separated by this method. Similarly, separation of astatine as the astatide ion At^- was achieved by coprecipitation on silver iodide because silver astatide AgAt was also expected to be insoluble.

It is an interesting speculation as to how much more difficult the isolation of these two elements might have been if the periodic classification had not provided us with a very good 'preview' of their chemistries.

Summary

Some properties of the chemical elements are found to show a regular variation, originally related to the relative atomic masses of the elements and later (and more fundamentally) to the *atomic numbers* — the numbers of extra-nuclear electrons in the atoms of the elements. These properties include atomic structure, ionization energies, melting and boiling points, chemical character and valencies. The modern periodic table sets out the elements in the order in which successive *energy levels* in the atoms are filled by electrons. The behaviour of these electrons is expressed in terms of *orbitals* described by the letters *s*, *p*, *d* and *f* and the variations in many properties (physical and chemical) of the elements can be accounted for in terms of these energy levels and orbitals which are occupied by electrons.

In the periodic table, elements with the same outer electronic configurations are placed in vertical columns called *groups*, and the horizontal rows of elements are called *periods*. Elements where *s* and *p* levels are being filled are called *typical*; those whose *d* levels are being filled are called *transition*, and there are two sets of elements (the *lanthanides* and *actinides*) in which *f* levels are being filled.

The periodic table enables predictions about *unknown* elements and compounds to be made from the properties of known elements.

Questions

1   What do you regard as the important oxidation states of the following elements:
(a) chlorine
(b) lead
(c) sulphur
(d) iron?
Illustrate, for each valency given, the electronic structure of a compound in which the element displays that valency.
Discuss, as far as possible, how far the valencies chosen are in agreement with expectations in the light of the position of these elements in the Periodic Table.

L,S

2   How, and why, do the following vary along the period sodium to argon:
(a) the relative ease of ionization of the element,
(b) the physical nature of the element,
(c) the action of water on the hydrides?

C,A

3   A century ago, Mendeléef used his new periodic table to predict the properties of 'ekasilicon', later identified as germanium. Some of the predicted properties were: metallic character and high m.p. for the element; formation of an oxide MO_2 and of a volatile chloride MCl_4.

(a) Explain how these predictions might be justified in terms of modern ideas about structure and valency.

(b) Give as many other 'predictions' as you can about the chemistry of germanium, with reasons.

Liverpool B.Sc., Part I

4   The graph shows the variation in atomic radius with increasing atomic number:

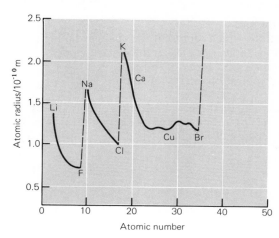

(a) What deduction can you make from this graph?

(b) Continue the graph to element 60 (Nd), and mark on it the approximate positions of the elements
   (i)   Ag (element 47),
   (ii) I (element 53),
   (iii) Ba (element 56).

(c) Explain briefly
   (i)   the decrease in atomic radius from Li to F,
   (ii) the increase in atomic radius from F to Br,
   (iii) the very large radii of the alkali metals, Li to K.

JMB,A

5   Give the electronic configurations of elements with atomic numbers 7, 11, 17, 20, 26, 30 and 36.
In each case give the oxidation state (or states) you expect each element to exhibit.

6   Explain the terms,
   (a) typical element,
   (b) transition element,
   (c) rare earth element,
   (d) group,
   (e) period,

(f) diagonal relationship,
as applied to the periodic table of elements.
In each case give examples to illustrate your answer.

7   (a) A metal ion M^{3+} has the following electronic configuration in the
           ground state:

           $1s^2 2s^2 2p^6 3s^2 3p^6 3d^3$

           Name the metal ion.
       (b) Give the equations which represent the changes taking place when the
           following ionization energy measurements are made:
           (i)   the first ionization energy of sodium,
           (ii) the second ionization energy of sodium.
       (c) Explain
           (i)   why helium has the highest ionization energy of any element,
           (ii) why the first ionization energy of potassium is less than the first
                 ionization energy of lithium.

                                                                        JMB,A

Chapter 2
Structure and bonding

2.1 The nature of the problem

A very superficial examination of a large number of chemical substances enables us to see that they differ widely in both physical and chemical properties. Any acceptable theory of bonding must explain these differences and enable us to predict the properties of new materials. As a first step towards solving the problem we need to know something of the arrangement of atoms in chemical substances. The structure of a solid can be investigated using a beam of X-rays or neutrons. From the diffraction patterns obtained it is possible to find the arrangement of the particles of which it is composed. Measurement of the amount of heat needed to melt the solid yields information concerning the forces of attraction between these particles, whilst the effect of an electric current and simple chemical tests on the solid may tell if it is a metal or a non-metal. Should the material be a non-conducting solid, we can determine whether it is composed of ions by investigating the effect of an electric current on the molten material.

Results of such investigations suggest that there are four limiting kinds of structure and these will be briefly considered.

2.1.1 The metallic lattice

In a pure metal the atoms of the solid are arranged in closely packed layers. There is more than one way of achieving close packing but it is generally true to say that each atom is surrounded by as many neighbouring atoms as can be accommodated in the space available. *Figure 2.1* shows two common ways in which metal atoms pack together. There are no directed forces between the atoms and each atom 'attracts' as many similar atoms as can be accommodated. The ease with which metals conduct electricity indicates that the electrons are only loosely held in this type of structure.

2.1.2 The giant molecule lattice

This is a relatively rare structure, diamond being probably the best known example. Here, the carbon atoms are *not* close-packed. Each carbon is surrounded tetrahedrally by four other carbon atoms (*Figure 2.2*). Clearly, each carbon is exerting a tetrahedrally directed force on its neighbours and such directed forces are operative throughout the whole crystal. Diamond is

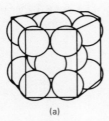   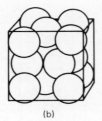

(a)   (b)

Figure 2.1 (a) Hexagonal close packing. (b) Cubic close packing

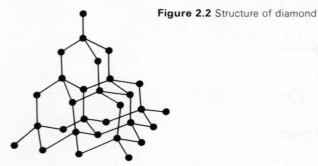

Figure 2.2 Structure of diamond

found to be a refractory solid, i.e. it has an extremely high melting point, indicating that the bonding forces are extremely strong. Boron nitride $(BN)_n$ and silicon carbide $(SiC)_n$ (carborundum) are similar types of solid. These solids are non-conducting, indicating that the electrons are less free and more localized than the electrons in a metal which move easily allowing an electric current to flow through the lattice.

2.1.3   The giant ionic lattice

This is one of the most familiar types of structure in inorganic chemistry; an example is shown in *Figure 2.3*. The crystals can usually be melted in the laboratory although a high temperature is often required. It can be concluded, therefore, that strong forces exist between the particles comprising the crystals, these being usually intermediate in strength between those found in a metal and those found, for example, in diamond. Although the solid crystals do not conduct electricity, the melt does, indicating that the lattice is comprised of charged species, i.e. *ions*. These ions carry the current and are discharged at the oppositely charged electrode where the products can be identified. *X*-Ray diffraction studies indicate that the ions form a regular lattice, each ion being surrounded by a number of ions of the opposite charge; this number depends on the sizes of the ions concerned and is not dictated by directed forces of attraction*. We can correctly assume the non-directional forces of attraction holding the ions together to be electrostatic in nature.

*Many ions can, of course, contain more than one atom (for example NO_3^-, SO_4^{2-}) and directed forces hold together the individual atoms within each of these ionic species.

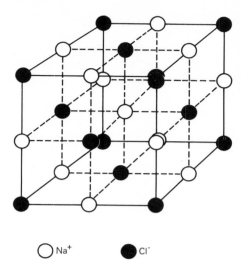

Figure 2.3 The sodium chloride lattice

○ Na$^+$ ● Cl$^-$

2.1.4   Molecular crystals

This is a very large group comprising mainly crystalline organic materials, but a number of inorganic substances, for example iodine (*Figure 2.4*), also come under this heading. These substances melt easily, and may even sublime, indicating the presence of relatively weak forces. They do not conduct electricity in the solid or fused state indicating that the electrons present are localized in strong bonds. These bonds, however, do not

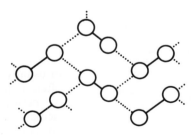

Figure 2.4 The structure of solid iodine. Full lines indicate covalent bonds in I_2 molecules; dotted lines indicate weak intermolecular 'bonds'

permeate the entire structure, as in diamond, and the crystal is comprised of molecules with strong forces between the constituent atoms, but the intermolecular forces are weak.

In substances which are liquid or gaseous at ordinary temperature, the forces of attraction between the particles are so weak that thermal vibration is sufficient for them to be broken. These substances can be converted into solids by cooling to reduce the thermal energy.

The above classification of structures is made primarily for convenience. In fact, the structures of many compounds cannot be precisely described under any of these classes, which represent limiting, or ideal cases. However, we shall use these classes to examine further the limiting types of bonding found in them.

2.2   The electronic theory of valency

After Dalton, in 1807, had put forward the theory that chemical combination
consisted of a union between atoms, chemists began their search for the cause
and mechanism of the unions. Many ideas were put forward during the
following years but, following the discoveries about the structure of the atom,
it was realized that the nuclei of atoms were unaffected by chemical
combination and that union of atoms must result from interaction between
the extranuclear electrons. Kossel and Lewis, working independently in
1916, recognized that the atoms of the different noble gases, with the one
exception of helium, each had an outer quantum level containing eight
electrons; they therefore suggested that this arrangement must be connected
with stability and inactivity, and that interactions occurred between
atoms such that each element attained a noble gas configuration. The
rearrangement of electrons into stable octets could occur in two ways: (a) by
giving or receiving electrons or (b) by sharing electrons.

Since 1916 it has been discovered that some noble gases (originally called
the inert gases) do form compounds and also there are many reactions
known in which elements do not achieve a noble gas configuration.
Nevertheless, the theory was a considerable advance towards modern ideas
and provides a good basis for discussion.

2.3   Electron transfer bonding — electrovalency

The electronic configuration of any element can quickly be deduced from the
periodic table. Consider the reaction, for example, between sodium
$1s^2 2s^2 2p^6 3s^1$ (2,8,1) and chlorine $1s^2 2s^2 2p^6 3s^2 3p^5$ (2,8,7). The theory tells us
that combination will occur by electron transfer from the sodium to the
chlorine to produce the noble gas configurations 2,8 (Ne) and 2,8,8 (Ar)
respectively. Sodium, atomic number 11, becomes the sodium cation Na^+,
and chlorine the chloride anion Cl^-. Electrostatic attraction between these
two ions then holds the compound together. This kind of bonding is found in
'giant ionic lattice' compounds and is an example of *electrovalency*, the bond
being said to be *ionic*. A full discussion of the chemical energetics of such
processes will be found in Chapter 3 but at this point it is desirable to
consider the energy changes involved in the electron transfer process. The
questions to be answered are briefly:
(1)   What energy changes occur when an element achieves a noble gas
       configuration?
(2)   How does the ease of ion formation change as we cross the periodic
       table?
(3)   What changes occur as we descend the groups of the table?

Consider first the formation of cations by electron loss. Here the important
energy quantity is the *ionization energy*. As we have seen (p. 2), the first
ionization energy is the energy required to remove an electron from an atom,
i.e. the energy for the process

$$M(g) \rightarrow M^+(g) + e^-$$
(1 mole)

the second, third and fourth ionization energies being the *additional* energies required to remove subsequent electrons from the increasingly positively charged ion, the element and the ions formed all being in the gaseous state. Ionization energies can be obtained from current–voltage plots for gaseous discharges or more conveniently and completely from spectroscopic measurements. For convenience the transition and typical elements will be treated separately.

2.3.1 Ionization energies: typical elements

Changes down the group

Table 2.1 gives data for Group I elements. The ionization energies are all positive, i.e. energy is absorbed on ionization. Several conclusions can be drawn from this table:

(1) Energy must be supplied if these elements are to attain a noble gas configuration.
(2) Loss of one electron gives the noble gas configuration; the very large difference between the first and second ionization energies implies that an outer electronic configuration of a noble gas is indeed very stable.
(3) Ionization energy falls as the group is descended, i.e. as the size of the atom increases and hence the distance between the nucleus and the outer electron increases.

Table 2.1

				Ionization energies		
				kJ mol^{-1}		
Atomic number	*Element*	*Atomic radius (solid)/nm**	*Radius of M$^+$ ion/nm**	*1st*	*2nd*	*3rd*
3	Li	0.152	0.060	520	7 297	11 800
11	Na	0.186	0.095	496	4 561	6 913
19	K	0.227	0.133	419	3 069	4 400
37	Rb	0.248	0.148	403	2 650	3 900
55	Cs	0.263	0.169	376	2 420	3 300

*Atoms (and ions), unlike ordinary solid spheres, do not have fixed radii; their electron distributions are affected by the other atoms (or ions) to which they are bonded, and by the nature of this bonding. However, approximate values of atomic size are clearly of value. For a metal, the radius quoted is the 'metallic radius', this being half the average internuclear distance in the metal. For gaseous diatomic molecules joined by a single covalent bond (for example Cl–Cl), half the internuclear distance is taken as the covalent radius of the atom. In the solid noble gases, chemical bonds do not exist, and the solids are held together by weak 'van der Waals' forces (p. 41). Half the internuclear distance is then called the van der Waals radius. For solid non metals, the 'atomic radius' may refer to the bulk solid (as for a metal), or to a molecular species such as I_2, P_4, or to the free atoms. Measurements of the internuclear distance in a solid ionic compound MX gives the sum of the ionic radii of M and X. For most purposes, it is sufficient to assume that ionic radii are constant; with this assumption individual ionic radii can be calculated if the radius of one ion can be determined. This can be done by several methods which lie outside the scope of this book. Ionic radii quoted in this book are based on Pauling's value for the O^{2-} ion.

(4)   There is a marked contraction in size on the formation of an ion, the percentage contraction decreasing as the percentage loss in electrons decreases (for example Na → Na$^+$ involves loss of one of eleven electrons, Cs → Cs$^+$ the loss of one of 55 electrons). Some values for Group II and III elements are shown in *Tables 2.2* and *2.3* respectively.

Group II elements can be seen to follow a pattern very like that found in Group I. Note, however, that the energy required to attain a noble gas configuration is considerably higher indicating that the elements will be less 'metallic' or electropositive in their chemistry (Chapter 6).

Table 2.2

Atomic number	Element	Atomic radius (solid)/nm*	Radius of M^{2+} ion/nm*	Ionization energies/kJ mol^{-1} 1st	2nd	3rd	4th
4	Be	0.112	0.031	899	1 758	14 850	21 000
12	Mg	0.160	0.065	738	1 450	7 731	10 540
20	Ca	0.197	0.099	590	1 146	4 942	6 500
38	Sr	0.215	0.113	549	1 064	4 200	5 500
56	Ba	0.221	0.135	502	965		

*See footnote to Table 2.1.

Table 2.3

Atomic number	Element	Atomic radius/nm*	Radius of M^{3+} ion/nm*	Ionization energies/kJ mol^{-1} 1st	2nd	3rd	4th
5	B	0.079	(0.020)	801	2 428	3 660	25 020
13	Al	0.143	0.045	578	1 817	2 745	11 580
31	Ga	0.153	0.062	579	1 979	2962	6 190
49	In	0.167	0.081	558	1 820	2705	5 250
81	Tl	0.171	0.095	589	1 970	2880	4 890

*See footnote to Table 2.1.

The elements in Group III show several irregularities which are of interest. The apparent irregularity in the first ionization energy of gallium, relative to aluminium, can be attributed to the filling of the inner *d* orbitals of the first transition series (atomic numbers 21—31) which causes a contraction in atomic size (*see Table 2.3*). Similarly the filling of inner orbitals in the lanthanide series results in the apparently irregular value given for thallium. Similar tables for elements in other groups can be constructed to show irregularities similar to those of the Group III elements.

Changes in ionization energy across the periods
The number of electrons in the outermost quantum level of an atom increases as we cross a period of typical elements. *Figure 2.5* shows plots of the first ionization energy for Periods 2 and 3.

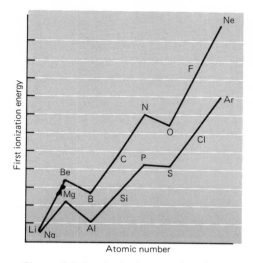

Figure 2.5 First ionization energies of elements of Periods 2 and 3

The discontinuities observed correspond to changes in electronic configuration. Boron and aluminium both have one electron in a *p* orbital (which is less firmly held) whilst oxygen and sulphur have one electron *pair* in a *p* orbital, the second electron being less firmly held. The high values of the first ionization energies of these upper elements in Groups IV, V, VI and VII correctly imply that insufficient energy is liberated in chemical reactions to enable their atoms to achieve noble gas configurations by electron loss.

2.3.2   Transition elements

The first ionization energies of the first transition elements are shown in *Figure 2.6*. The changes across these 10 elements contrast sharply with the changes shown across a period of typical elements and confirms that the *d* block elements need to be treated separately.

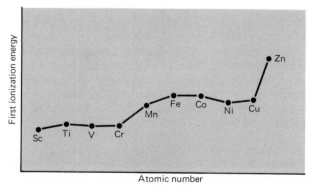

Figure 2.6 First ionization energies of the first series of transition elements

2.3.3 Summary

(1) Ionization energy decreases down a group of elements as the atomic size increases. The elements in consequence become *more* metallic down the group.

(2) With certain irregularities, the ionization energy increases across a period. The elements therefore become *less* metallic across a period.

2.3.4 Electron affinities

Typical elements in Groups V, VI and VII would be expected to achieve a noble gas configuration more easily by gaining electrons rather than losing them. Electron affinity is a measure of the energy change when an atom accepts an extra electron. It is difficult to measure directly and this has only been achieved in a few cases; more often it is obtained from enthalpy cycle calculations (p. 65).

Group trends
Table 2.4 gives the energy values for the reaction

$$X(g) + e^- \rightarrow X^-(g)$$
1 mole

together with atomic and ionic radii.

Table 2.4

Atomic number	Element	Atomic radius (*gas*)/nm*	Radius of X^- ion/nm*	Electron affinity kJ mol^{-1}
9	F	0.064	0.133	-333
17	Cl	0.099	0.181	-364
35	Br	0.111	0.196	-342
53	I	0.130	0.219	-295
85	At	—	—	-256

*See footnote to Table 2.1.

Energy is *evolved* in each case. The table clearly indicates that the electron affinity falls with the increasing size of the atom. The anomalous value for fluorine is explained on the grounds that since the fluorine atom is small, the incoming electron encounters strong repulsion by the nine electrons already closely shielding the nucleus. In each case, the ion produced by electron addition is *larger* than the atom from which it was formed. After the addition of the first electron, subsequent electron addition must take place against the repulsion of a negatively-charged ion. Two-electron affinities are known in only a few cases. The values for oxygen and sulphur are given in *Table 2.5*.

Energy is released on formation of the singly-charged ion but a greater amount of energy is required to add a second electron and the formation of

Table 2.5

| Atomic number | Element | Electron affinity/kJ mol^{-1} | | |
		1st	2nd	Total
8	O	-142	$+844$	$+702$
16	S	-200	$+532$	$+332$

the bivalent ion is an endothermic process in spite of the fact that a noble gas configuration is achieved.

Periodic trends
Table 2.6 shows the electron affinities, for the addition of *one* electron to elements in Periods 2 and 3. Energy is evolved by many atoms when they accept electrons. In the cases in which energy is absorbed it will be noted that the new electron enters either a previously unoccupied orbital or a half-filled orbital; thus in beryllium or magnesium the new electron enters the *p* orbital, and in nitrogen electron-pairing in the *p* orbitals is necessary.

Table 2.6

Period 2								
Atomic number	3	4	5	6	7	8	9	10
Element	Li	Be	B	C	N	O	F	Ne
Electron affinity/kJ mole^{-1}	-57	$+66$	-15	-121	$+31$	$+142$	-333	$+99$

Period 3								
Atomic number	11	12	13	14	15	16	17	18
Element	Na	Mg	Al	Si	P	S	Cl	Ar
Electron affinity/kJ mol^{-1}	-21	$+67$	-26	-135	-60	-200	-364	—

The above discussion indicates that the formation of a noble gas configuration does not necessarily result in an evolution of energy. Indeed, by reference to *Tables 2.1* and *2.4* it can be seen that even for the reaction between caesium and fluorine, the heat energy evolved in the formation of the fluoride ion is less than the heat energy required for the formation of the caesium ion. This implies that the reaction will not proceed spontaneously; in fact it is virtually explosive. Clearly, therefore, energy terms other than ionization energy and electron affinity must be involved, and the most important is the *lattice energy* — the energy evolved when the ions produced arrange themselves into a stable lattice. It can be very large indeed and is a major factor in determining the nature of an ionic compound. We shall discuss this further in Chapter 3.

2.3.5   Arrangement of ions in the crystal lattice

The electrostatic attraction between ions is independent of direction. *X*-Ray diffraction studies show that a crystal lattice can be represented as made up of spherical ions, each ion having a characteristic radius almost independent of the crystal lattice in which it is found. For simple ions the charge on them determines the balance between the numbers of anions and cations whilst the radii determine the way in which the ions pack together in the lattice, this packing always occurring in such a way that, if possible, ions of like charge do not 'touch' each other. *Figure 2.7* shows a cross-section through an octahedral structure (the central ion having six *nearest* neighbours) in the limiting conditions in which the cations and anions are touching. The values of the radius ratio can be obtained by simple geometry.

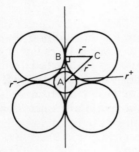

Figure 2.7 Limiting conditions for cation–anion contact (octahedral structure)

If r^+ and r^- are the radii of the cation and anion respectively then by applying Pythagoras's theorem to triangle ABC we find that

$$CA^2 = AB^2 + BC^2$$

i.e.

$$(r^- + r^+)^2 = (r^-)^2 + (r^-)^2 = 2(r^-)^2$$

$$\therefore \quad r^- + r^+ = r^-/\sqrt{2} = 1.414 \, r^-$$

$$\therefore \quad r^+ = 0.414 \, r^-$$

Hence

$$r^+/r^- = 0.414$$

This then is the limiting *radius ratio* for six nearest neighbours — when the anion is said to have a *coordination number* of 6. Similar calculations give the following limiting values:

(1)   For eight nearest neighbours (a coordination number of 8) the radius ratio r^+/r^- must not be less than 0.73.

(2)   For six nearest neighbours (a coordination number of 6) the radius ratio r^+/r^- must not be less than 0.41.

(3)   For four nearest neighbours (a coordination number of 4) the radius ratio r^+/r^- must not be less than 0.225.

These values enable many structures to be correctly predicted; discrepancies arise mainly from the false assumption that ions behave entirely as rigid

Table 2.7 Radius ratios in typical crystal structures

$0.73 > r^+/r^- > 0.41$				$r^+/r^- > 0.73$			
Rock salt		Rutile		Caesium chloride		Fluorite	
Compound	r^+/r^-	Compound	r^+/r^-	Compound	r^+/r^-	Compound	r^+/r^-
NaCl	0.52	TiO_2	0.49	CsCl	0.93	CaF_2	0.73
KBr	0.68	PbO_2	0.60	CsBr	0.87	SrF_2	0.83
MgO	0.46	MnF_2	0.59	CsI	0.78	CeO_2	0.72

spheres. Some examples are given in *Table 2.7*. Examples of two crystal structures* for each coordination number are included in this table.

2.4 Bonding by electron sharing — covalency

There are many compounds which do not conduct electricity when solid or fused, indicating that the bonding is neither metallic nor ionic. Lewis, in 1916, suggested that in such cases bonding resulted from a sharing of electrons. In the formation of methane CH_4 for example, carbon, electronic configuration $1s^2 2s^2 2p^2$, uses the four electrons in the second quantum level to form four equivalent covalent bonds with four hydrogen atoms, each element thus attaining a noble gas configuration:

$$\overset{x}{\underset{x}{x\ C\ x}} \quad + \quad 4H\cdot \quad \longrightarrow \quad H\overset{\bullet x}{\underset{x\bullet}{\overset{H}{\underset{H}{\times\ C\ \times}}}}H$$

Although the electrons from hydrogen and carbon are given • and × signs, these are used only for convenience and there is, of course, no difference between them. Compounds formed by the sharing of electrons are said to be *covalent*. Each pair of electrons $\overset{\bullet}{\times}$ constitutes a single bond (a sigma bond) and is more conveniently represented in graphical formulae by a single line, for example

$$H-\underset{\underset{H}{|}}{\overset{\overset{H}{|}}{C}}-H$$

However, this 'flat' representation does not indicate the shape or *stereochemistry* of the methane molecule, which is tetrahedral and can be represented as in *Figure 2.8*.

*Fluorite, CaF_2, and rutile, TiO_2, are minerals; in CaF_2, each Ca^{2+} is surrounded by eight F^- ions, each F^- by four Ca^{2+} ions, while in TiO_2 the corresponding coordination numbers are 6 and 3. 'Coordination number' is generally referred to the cation.

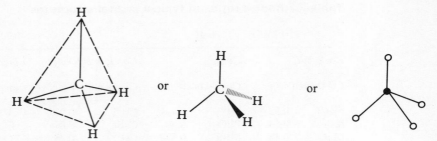

Figure 2.8 Stereochemical representations of the tetrahedral methane molecule

2.4.1 The shape of covalently bonded molecules and ions

Unlike the forces between ions which are electrostatic and without direction, covalent bonds are directed in space. For a simple molecule or covalently bonded ion made up of typical elements the shape is nearly always decided by the *number of bonding electron pairs and the number of lone pairs* (pairs of electrons not involved in bonding) around the central metal atom, which arrange themselves so as to be as far apart as possible because of electrostatic repulsion between the electron pairs. *Table 2.8* and *Figure 2.9* show the essential shape assumed by simple molecules or ions with one central atom X.

Table 2.8 Shapes of molecules and ions

Electron pairs	Essential shape
1	linear
2	linear
3	trigonal planar
4	tetrahedral
5	trigonal bipyramidal
6	octahedral

Carbon is able to form a great many covalently bonded compounds in which there are chains of carbon atoms linked by single covalent bonds. In each case where the carbon atoms are joined to four other atoms the essential orientation around each carbon atom is tetrahedral

The shapes indicated in *Table 2.8* and *Figure 2.9* are only exact in cases in which all the electron pairs are equivalent, i.e. they are all bonding pairs. Methane, CH_4, for example, has a central carbon atom bonded to four hydrogen atoms and the shape is a regular tetrahedron with a H—C—H bond angle of 109°28′, exactly that calculated. Electrons in a 'lone pair', a pair of electrons not used in bonding, occupy a larger fraction of space adjacent to their parent atom since they are under the influence of one nucleus, unlike bonding pairs of electrons which are under the influence of two nuclei. Thus, whenever a lone pair is present some distortion of the essential shape occurs.

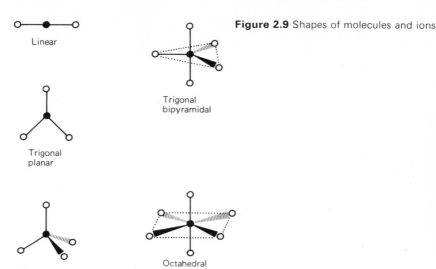

Figure 2.9 Shapes of molecules and ions

Linear

Trigonal bipyramidal

Trigonal planar

Tetrahedral

Octahedral

Consider ammonia, NH_3:

$$\overset{x\,x}{_{x}\!N^{\,x}_{x}} \quad + \quad 3H\bullet \quad \longrightarrow \quad \overset{x\,x}{H\!\overset{}{\underset{x\bullet}{\centerdot}N\centerdot H}} \quad \text{i.e.} \quad H\!\!-\!\!\overset{x\,x}{\underset{|}{N}}\!\!-\!\!H$$
$$\qquad\qquad\qquad\qquad\qquad\qquad\qquad\quad H \qquad\qquad\qquad H$$

In this case we have three bonding pairs and one lone pair. The essential shape is, therefore, tetrahedral but this is distorted owing to the presence of the lone pair of electrons, the H—N—H bond angle being 107 degrees:

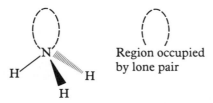

H   H

H

Region occupied by lone pair

When the ammonium ion NH_4^+ is formed the lone pair becomes a bonding pair and the shape becomes a regular tetrahedron.

The distortion due to the presence of lone pairs of electrons is more marked in water:

$$\overset{x\,x}{_{x}\!O^{\,x}_{x}} \quad + \quad 2H\bullet \quad \longrightarrow \quad \overset{x\,x}{H\!\overset{}{\underset{x\bullet}{\centerdot}O^{\,x}_{x}}} \quad \text{i.e.} \quad H\!\!-\!\!\overset{x\,x}{\underset{|}{O}}{}^{\,x}$$
$$\qquad\qquad\qquad\qquad\qquad\qquad\qquad\quad H \qquad\qquad\qquad H$$

The HÔH angle is 105 degrees (*see* p. 34).

If the spatial arrangement of atoms is required this can be deduced from the basic structure by neglecting the positions occupied by lone pairs of electrons. Water, for example, can be described as a **V** shape whilst ammonia is a trigonal pyramid.

2.4.2 Multiple covalent bonds

Double and triple covalent bonds can be formed between elements by the sharing of two or three electron pairs respectively. Consider the formation of ethene (ethylene), C_2H_4:

$$2 \times \overset{x}{\underset{x}{C}} \times \quad + \quad 4H\cdot \quad \longrightarrow \quad \overset{H}{\underset{H}{:}}\overset{x}{\underset{x}{C}}\overset{x}{\underset{x}{:}}\overset{x}{\underset{x}{C}}\overset{H}{\underset{H}{:}} \quad \text{or} \quad \overset{H}{\underset{H}{}}C{=}C\overset{H}{\underset{H}{}}$$

The two kinds of covalent bond are not identical, one being a simple covalent bond, a sigma (σ) bond, the other being a stronger (but more reactive) bond called a π bond (p. 49). As in the formation of methane both elements attain noble gas configurations. We can consider the formation of ethene as the linking of two tetrahedral carbon atoms to form the molecule C_2H_4 represented as:

this approach implying repulsion between the two bonding pairs. Careful consideration of this model correctly indicates that all the atoms lie in one plane. *Spatially* the double bond is found to behave as a single electron pair and reference to *Table 2.8* then (correctly) suggests that each carbon has a trigonal planar arrangement.

The modern quantum-mechanical approach to bonding indicates that these two 'models' for the ethene structure are identical, so that we may use whichever is the more convenient.

Double bonds also occur in other covalent compounds. By considering each double bond to behave spatially as a single bond we are able to use *Table 2.8* to determine the spatial configurations of such compounds.

Triple bonds are formed by the sharing of three pairs of electrons to form a σ and two π bonds. *Spatially* these three bonds behave as a single bond. Consequently acetylene (ethyne) C_2H_2 has the linear configuration often represented as H—C≡C—H.

In each of the examples given so far each element has 'achieved' a noble gas configuration as a result of electron sharing. There are, however, many examples of stable covalent compounds in which noble gas configurations are not achieved, or are exceeded. In the compounds of aluminium, phosphorus and sulphur, shown below, the central atoms have six, 10 and 12 electrons respectively involved in bonding:

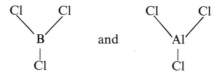

aluminium chloride   phosphorus   sulphur hexafluoride
(vapour)   pentafluoride

(The spatial configurations of each of these compounds can be deduced by reference to *Table 2.8*.)

These apparent anomalies are readily explained. Elements in Group V, for example, have five electrons in their outer quantum level, but with the one exception of nitrogen, they all have unfilled d orbitals in this level. Thus, with the exception of nitrogen, Group V elements are able to use all their five outer electrons to form five covalent bonds. Similarly elements in Group VI, with the exception of oxygen, are able to form six covalent bonds for example in SF_6. The outer quantum level, however, is still incomplete, a situation found for all covalent compounds formed by elements after Period 2, and all have the ability to accept electron pairs from other molecules although the stability of the compounds formed may be low*. This 'donor-acceptor bonding' is very marked in Group III, for when elements in this group form three covalent bonds by sharing, they have only six outer electrons. Consider for example the trichlorides of boron and aluminium:

Cl   Cl   Cl   Cl
 \   /   \   /
  B   and   Al
  | |
  Cl   Cl

Both these molecules exist in the gaseous state and both are trigonal planar as indicated by reference to *Table 2.8*. However, in each, a further covalent bond can be formed, in which both electrons of the shared pair are provided by one atom, not one from each as in normal covalent bonding. For example, monomeric aluminium chloride and ammonia form a stable compound:

*Phosphorus pentafluoride PF_5 will readily accept an electron pair from a fluoride ion F^- to form the stable hexafluorophosphate(V) anion PF_6^-. This ion is isoelectronic with SF_6, and neither SF_6 nor PF_6^- show any notable tendency to accept further electron pairs, though there is some evidence for the existence of an SF_6^- ion.

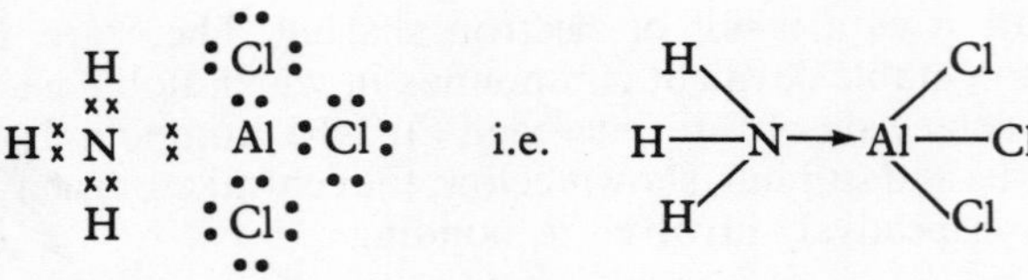

In this molecule, the aluminium receives a pair of electrons from the nitrogen atom. The nitrogen atom is referred to as a *donor* atom and the aluminium as an *acceptor* atom. Once the bond is formed it is identical to the covalent bond of previous examples; it differs only in its origin. It is called a *coordinate* or *dative* bond, and can be expressed either as $H_3N \rightarrow AlCl_3$ or $H_3\overset{+}{N}—\overset{-}{Al}Cl_3$. In the latter formula the positive and negative charges are not ionic charges; they are merely *formal* charges to show that in forming the coordinate link, the nitrogen lost a half share in its original electron pair which is now shared with the aluminium, the latter having gained a half share in the electron pair.

The formation of a fourth covalent bond by the aluminium atom results in spatial rearrangement from the trigonal planar, for three bonding electron pairs, to tetrahedral, for four bonding electron pairs.

Other compounds containing lone pairs of electrons readily form coordinate links and in each case a change in spatial configuration accompanies the bond formation. The oxygen atom in methoxymethane $CH_3—O—CH_3$ has two lone pairs of electrons and is able to donate one pair to, for example, boron trichloride:

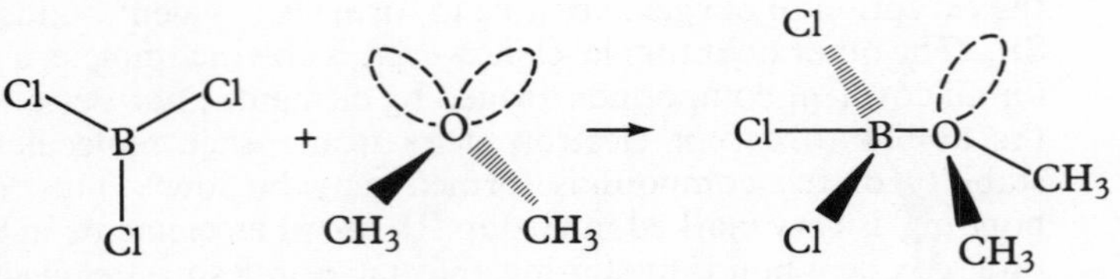

This compound, which contains atoms arranged tetrahedrally around the boron atom, can readily be isolated from a mixture of methoxymethane and boron trichloride. On occasions a chlorine atom, in spite of its high electron affinity, will donate an electron pair, an example being found in the dimerization of gaseous monomeric aluminium chloride to give the more stable Al_2Cl_6 in which each aluminium has a tetrahedral configuration:

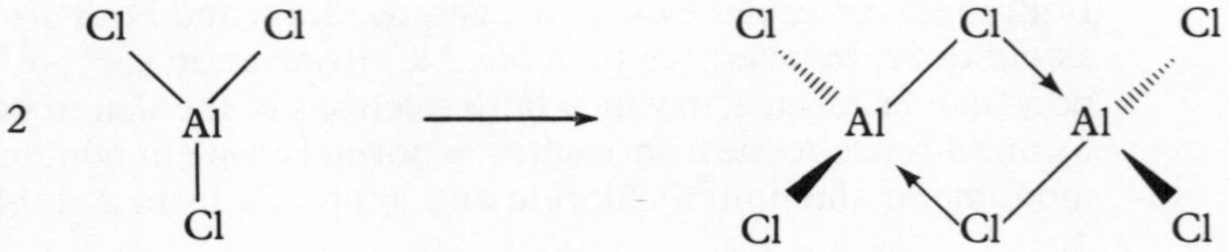

For boron to expland its covalency further it would be necessary to utilize vacant orbitals in the third quantum level since there are no $2d$ orbitals available. The energy required for this exceeds the energy evolved on bond formation. Other Group III elements, however, are able to form more than four covalent bonds, the number depending partly on the nature of the attached atoms or groups.

The ability to act as a lone pair acceptor is not confined to Group III, and can occur wherever a quantum level is incomplete. This ability to accept electrons explains why covalent chlorides, with the exception of tetrachloromethane, are readily hydrolysed, the apparently anomalous behaviour of tetrachloromethane being readily explained by the fact that the carbon has a completed quantum level and is unable to form an 'intermediate complex' with water.

2.4.3 'Covalent ions'

Covalent bonding, in all the cases so far quoted, produces *molecules* not ions, and enables us to explain the inability of the compounds formed to conduct electricity. Covalently bonded groups of atoms can, however, also be ions. When ammonia and hydrogen chloride are brought together in the gaseous state proton transfer occurs as follows:

i.e.

The strongly electronegative (p. 42) chlorine atom becomes a chloride ion, the proton H^+ accepting the electron pair donated by the nitrogen atom. A similar reaction occurs when ammonia is passed into water, but to a much lesser extent as oxygen in water is a poorer donor of the electron pair:

("ammonia hydrate" — weakly associated through hydrogen bonding)

The positive charge resulting from the addition of a proton on to an ammonia molecule is not associated with any particular hydrogen atom, once the bond is formed, and is distributed over the whole ion.

Oxoacid anions

There are many simple examples of common covalently bonded oxo-anions, some being: CO_3^{2-}, NO_3^-, SO_4^{2-} and PO_4^{3-}. The carbonate ion, for example, contains carbon covalently bonded to three oxygen atoms and we can write the structure as:

i.e.

Clearly such bonding would produce two different carbon–oxygen bond distances (p. 41) but in fact all bonds are found to be identical and intermediate in length between the expected $C{=}O$ and $C{-}O$ bond distances. We conclude, therefore, that the true structure of the carbonate ion cannot be accurately represented by any one diagram of the type shown and a number of 'resonance' structures are suggested (p. 44).

As in the case of NH_4^+ the charge is distributed over the whole ion. By considering each multiple bond to behave spatially as a single bond we are again able to use *Table 2.8* to correctly deduce that the carbonate ion has a trigonal planar symmetry. Structures for other covalently-bonded ions can readily be deduced.

2.4.4 Complex ions

The polyatomic ions discussed above are really simple members of a much larger group known collectively as *complex ions*, in which a central atom or ion is surrounded by other atoms, ions or groups of atoms, called *ligands*. Whenever an ion is present in a polar* solvent there is an attraction between the ion and the solvent molecules causing the latter to become attached to the ion, producing a solvated ion. Thus in water the sodium ion is solvated (hydrated) to give $[Na(H_2O)_x]^+$. Here, the forces of attraction are small and the number of attached water molecules — which are ligands — is indefinite; the greater the charge on the central ion and the smaller its size, the greater the force of attraction between the ion and the ligand, and the more covalent the link between them becomes; as in the case of simple covalent-ionic

*A polar substance is one in which the molecules have an electrical dipole moment (p. 44).

bonding (p. 43) there is no sharp dividing line. Salts of Groups I and II clearly show the changes which accompany increases in ionic size. For example, for a given anion, the number of water molecules crystallizing in the salt is found to *increase* as the size of the ion *decreases*

There are many ligands in addition to water, for example Cl^-, NH_3, CN^-, NO_2^-, and transition metal ions, in particular, form a large number of complex ions with different ligands. The number of ligands surrounding the central atom, or ion, is called the *coordination number*. The numerical value of the coordination number depends on a number of factors, but one important factor is the sizes of both the ligands and central atom, or ion. A number of complex ions are given below in *Table 2.9*. The shape of complex ions or

Table 2.9 Characteristics of some complex ions and molecules

Central unit	Ligand	Coordination number	Ligand type	Complex ion	Shape
Be^{2+}	H_2O	4	Molecule	$[Be(H_2O)_4]^{2+}$	Tetrahedral
Co^{3+}	NH_3	6	Molecule	$[Co(NH_3)_6]^{3+}$	Octahedral
Al^{3+}	F^-	6	Ion	$[AlF_6]^{3-}$	Octahedral
Ni^0	CO	4	Molecule	$Ni(CO)_4$	Tetrahedral
Fe^{2+}	CN^-	6	Ion	$[Fe(CN)_6]^{4-}$	Octahedral
Co^{3+}	NO_2^-	6	Ion	$[Co(NO_2)_6]^{3-}$	Octahedral

molecules formed by many elements can be determined by assuming each ligand to be covalently bonded to the central ion and applying the theory of electron pair repulsion which gives the structures summarized in *Table 2.9*. The shape of transition metal complexes, however, cannot always be deduced by this method. The development of the theory of bonding in transition metal complexes is beyond the scope of this book but a brief outline of the main features is given at the end of this chapter.

2.4.5   Hydrolysis of complex aquo-ions

Smaller and more highly charged ions such as magnesium and aluminium attract water strongly, and in these cases the attractive forces between the water and the ions are so great that salts containing water of crystallization decompose when attempts are made to dehydrate them by heating — the process being called *hydrolysis*. For example

$$[Mg(H_2O)_2]^{2+}2Cl^- \xrightarrow{\text{heat}} [Mg(OH)]^+Cl^- + HCl + H_2O$$

or, as more commonly written,

$$MgCl_2.2H_2O \rightarrow Mg(OH)Cl + HCl + H_2O$$

The aluminium ion, charge $+3$, ionic radius 0.045 nm, found in aluminium trifluoride, undergoes a similar reaction when a soluble aluminium salt is placed in water at room temperature. Initially the aluminium ion is surrounded by six water molecules and the complex ion has the predicted octahedral symmetry (*see Table 2.8*):

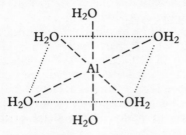

This complex ion behaves as an acid in water, losing protons, and a series of equilibria are established (H^+ is used, rather than H_3O^+, for simplicity):

$$[Al(H_2O)_6]^{3+} \rightleftharpoons [Al(OH)(H_2O)_5]^{2+} + H^+$$
$$\updownarrow$$
$$[Al(OH)_2(H_2O)_4]^+ + H^+$$
$$\updownarrow$$
$$[Al(OH)_3(H_2O)_3] + H^+$$
$$\updownarrow$$
$$[Al(OH)_4(H_2O)_2]^- + H^+$$
$$\updownarrow$$
$$[Al(OH)_5(H_2O)]^{2-} + H^+$$
$$\updownarrow$$
$$[Al(OH)_6]^{3-} + H^+$$
$$\downarrow \text{ heat}$$
$$AlO_2^- + 2H_2O + 2OH^-$$

Addition of acid

Addition of base

These equilibria give rise to an acidic solution in water, to the hexahydroxoaluminate ion $[Al(OH)_6]^{3-}$ in a strongly alkaline solution, and only in strongly acidic solutions is the hexaaqua-ion $[Al(H_2O)_6]^{3+}$ found. The solid hydrate, often written $AlCl_3.6H_2O$ and more correctly $[Al(H_2O)_6]Cl_3$ can, therefore, only be obtained from a strongly acidic solution. The reaction with water resulting in the liberation of a proton is again known as *hydrolysis* and occurs whenever the central metal ion is small and highly charged (i.e. having a high surface density of charge), for example in salts of iron(III), chromium (III)*.

2.4.6   Nomenclature for complex ions

When naming complex ions the number and type of ligands is written first, followed by the name of the central metal ion. If the complex as a whole has a positive charge (i.e. is a cation) or is a neutral molecule the name of the central

*The species resulting from the 'hydrolysis' of hydrated cations such as those mentioned here are often highly complex, containing more than one metal atom (i.e. they may be *polynuclear*). The description here is simplified to show the essentials of the processes.

metal is written unchanged and followed by the oxidation state of the metal in brackets, for example $[Cu(NH_3)_4]^{2+}$ becomes tetraamminecopper(II). A similar procedure is followed for anions but the suffix '-ate' is added to the central metal ion; some examples are:

$[Fe(CN)_6]^{3-}$ hexacyanoferrate(III)
$[HgI_4]^{2-}$ tetraiodomercurate(II)
$[Co(NO_2)_6]^{3-}$ hexanitrocobaltate(III)
$Ni(CO)_4$ tetracarbonylnickel(0)

2.5   The strength of covalent bonds: bond energies

The energy required to break the bond between two covalently bonded atoms is called the 'bond dissociation energy'. In polyatomic molecules this quantity varies with environment. For example, ammonia has three N—H bond dissociation energies:

$NH_3(g) \rightarrow NH_2(g) + H(g)$ 448 kJ mol^{-1}
$NH_2(g) \rightarrow NH(g) + H(g)$ 368 kJ mol^{-1}
$NH(g) \rightarrow N(g) + H(g)$ 356 kJ mol^{-1}

For many purposes, for example the estimation of approximate heats of formation (p. 57), it is sufficient to have an average value. This average of the bond dissociation energies is called the *average thermochemical bond energy* or (more commonly) simply the *bond energy**.

Bond energy values can be obtained from thermochemical calculations (p. 65) and a number are included in *Table 2.10* together with the compound used in the calculation.

In most covalent compounds, the strong covalent bonds link the atoms together into molecules, but the molecules themselves are held to each other by much weaker forces, hence the low melting points of molecular crystals and their inability to conduct electricity. These weak intermolecular forces are called *van der Waals* forces; in general, they increase with increase in size of the molecule. Only in a few cases does the covalent bonding extend throughout the whole structure and in these cases a 'giant molecule' is produced as in diamond (p. 22) where each carbon atom has four covalent links tetrahedrally arranged. Since the bonds are strong the molecule is very stable and extremely hard. Carborundum (Si—C) and boron nitride have similar structures and properties. The high melting points of these solids correctly indicate that the covalent bonds are usually together than ionic bonds.

2.6   Covalent bond lengths

As in the case of ions we can assign values to covalent bond lengths and covalent bond radii. Interatomic distances can be measured by, for example,

*Strictly, these values are bond *enthalpies,* but the term energies is commonly used. Other descriptions are: 'average standard bond energies', 'mean bond energies'.

Table 2.10 Bond energies

Bond	In compound	Average thermochemical bond energy/kJ mol^{-1}
C—H	CH_4	416
N—H	NH_3	391
O—H	H_2O	467
F—H	HF	566
Cl—H	HCl	431
C—Cl	CCl_4	327
N—Cl	NCl_3	193
Si—Cl	$SiCl_4$	391
C—C	C_2H_6	346
C=C	C_2H_4	598
C≡C	C_2H_2	813
N—N	N_2H_4	160
N≡N	N_2	946
O—O	H_2O_2	146
O=O	O_2	498

X-ray and electron diffraction methods. By halving the interatomic distances obtained for diatomic elements, covalent bond radii can be obtained. Other covalent bond radii can be determined by measurements of bond lengths in other covalently bonded compounds. By this method, tables of multiple as well as single covalent bond radii can be determined. A number of *single* covalent bond radii* in nm are in *Table 2.11*.

Table 2.11 Single covalent bond radii/nm

H	C	N	O	F
0.037	0.078	0.070	0.066	0.064
	Si	P	S	Cl
	0.117	0.110	0.104	0.099

Deductions of bond lengths for any unknown can be made by adding bond radii, but these theoretical values often differ from the experimental values; the greatest deviations occur when elements of widely different *electronegativities* are joined together.

2.7   Electronegativity

If two *like* atoms form a covalent bond by sharing an electron pair, for example

$$\overset{xx}{\underset{xx}{\overset{x}{}\text{F}\overset{x}{}}}\overset{xx}{\underset{xx}{\overset{x}{}\text{F}\overset{x}{}}}$$

*While bond energies *increase* in, for example, the sequence C—C, C=C, C≡C (*Table 2.10*), bond radii *decrease*: C=C gives C = 0.067, C≡C gives C = 0.060 nm.

it is clear that the pair will be shared equally. For any two *unlike* atoms, the sharing is always unequal and depending on the nature of the two atoms (A and B say) we can have two extreme possibilities

$$A + B \rightarrow A : B \begin{cases} \text{or} \quad A \; :B \quad \text{i.e.} \quad A^+B^- \\ \text{equal} \\ \text{sharing} \quad \text{or} \quad A: \; B \quad \text{i.e.} \quad A^-B^+ \end{cases}$$

and an ionic bond is formed. There are many compounds which lie between truly covalent (equal sharing) and truly ionic. The bond between two atoms A and B is likely to be ionic rather than covalent (with A forming a positive ion and B a negative ion) if:
(1)   A and B have small charges,
(2)   A is large,
(3)   B is small.

Tables 2.1, 2.2, 2.3 and *2.4* give data for atomic radii, ionization energies and electron affinities which allow these rough rules to be justified.
    Pauling and others have attempted to define an 'electronegativity scale' by which the inequality of sharing might be assessed. Some of Pauling's electronegativity values are shown in *Table 2.12*. The greater the differences

Table 2.12 Some electronegativity values (Pauling)

H	Li	Be	B	C	N	O	F
2.1	1.0	1.5	2.0	2.5	3.0	3.5	4.0
	Na	Mg	Al	Si	P	S	Cl
	0.9	1.2	1.5	1.8	2.1	2.5	3.0

in the electronegativities of the two elements jointed by a covalent bond, the less equally the electrons are shared; a partial polarity (p. 44) of the covalent bond results and the two atoms exert an electrostatic attraction for each other. The results of this attraction are a decrease in the bond length and an increase in the bond strength from those values expected for a 'pure' covalent bond*. There is in fact no sharp distinction between ionic and covalent bonds and all 'degrees' of ionicity and covalency are possible.

   *Pauling's electronegativity values are derived from the differences between 'pure covalent' and actual bond energies. Another simple measure of electronegativity is the sum of the ionization energy I and electron affinity E. The more electronegative elements have high values of $I + E$. Consider the alternative ionic forms of the diatomic species AB:, i.e. A^+B^- or A^-B^+. To form the first in the gas phase requires an energy $I_A - E_B$; to form the second requires an energy $I_B - E_A$. Whichever energy is the lesser will indicate the direction of electron transfer; if A is more electronegative than B then we require that A^-B^+ is favoured and thus that $I_A - I_B > I_B - E_A$ or
$I_A + E_A > I_B + E_B$ and on this basis the order of values of $I + E$ indicates an electronegativity scale.

2.7.1   Resonance

Bonds with characteristics intermediate between ionic and covalent can also
be represented by, for example, two *imaginary* structures, (I) and (II), both of
which 'contribute' to the true structure (III). Consider gaseous hydrogen
chloride:

H^+Cl^- H—Cl $\overset{(+)\ (-)}{\text{H—Cl}}$
electrovalent   equal sharing   unequal sharing
                             covalent   covalent
(I)   (II)   (III)

The strength of the bonding found in the actual structure (III) is greater than
that calculated for either of the *imaginary* structures (I) and (II). This has been
explained on the *theory of resonance* based on wave mechanics. In this theory,
it is supposed that the true structure of the molecule is a *resonance hybrid* of
two or more structures which can be written in a conventional way (i.e. as
H—Cl or H^+Cl^-). We can say that just as a hybrid plant is better than the
individual true-breeding plants from which it was produced, so a resonance
hybrid is a 'better' molecule than any of the structures that we can write for it.
It must be realized that, for example, hydrogen chloride does *not* consist of a
mixture of the forms (I) and (II) nor does the molecule of hydrogen chloride
exist for part of the time in form (I) and for part in form (II). Forms (I) and (II)
are purely imaginary structures which contribute to structure (III).

The resonance concept is of great value in organic chemistry. For example,
the carbon–carbon bond lengths found in benzene are all 0.139 nm in length.
This compares with a carbon–carbon single bond length of 0.154 nm and a
carbon–carbon double bond length of 0.134 nm. The heat of formation of
benzene is found to be greater than that calculated and the chemical
properties indicate the absence of a normal carbon–carbon double bond.
Resonance theory explains these facts by suggesting a number of structures,
each contributing to the true structure in which all six carbon atoms are
equivalent, and all the carbon–carbon bonds are of equal length.

2.7.2   Dipole moments

The unequal distribution of charge produced when elements of different
electronegativities combine causes a *polarity* of the covalent bond joining
them and, unless this polarity is balanced by an equal and opposite polarity,
the molecule will be a dipole and have a dipole moment (for example, a
hydrogen halide). Tetrachloromethane is one of a relatively few examples in
which a strong polarity does not result in a molecular dipole. It has a
tetrahedral configuration and the effect of each chlorine is exactly balanced
by the others so that there is no residual dipole

$\overset{\delta+}{\text{H}}\text{———}\overset{\delta^-}{\text{Cl}}$

However, chloromethane (methyl chloride, CH_3Cl) has a pronounced dipole moment although the shape of the molecule is also tetrahedral. Because of the dipole, chloromethane molecules are attracted to each other by *dipole–dipole* forces — the negative end of one molecule attracting the positive end of another. As a result of these attractive forces, chloromethane (relative molecular mass 50.5) has a melting point of 174.5 K, well above that of methane (relative molecular mass 16, m.p. 89 K) and also well above the hydrocarbon butane which has a relative molecular mass comparable with it (relative molecular mass 58, m.p. 138 K). In solid chloromethane, unlike solid methane, there is also evidence of orientation of the molecules packed together in the crystal.

2.8   Hydrogen bonding

Figure 2.10 shows the boiling points of the hydrides in elements of Groups IV, V, VI and VII. Clearly there is an attractive force between the molecules of the hydrides of fluorine, oxygen and nitrogen in addition to the expected

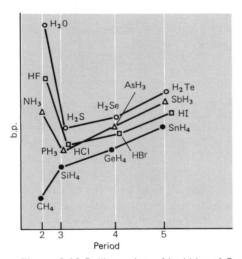

Figure 2.10 Boiling points of hydrides of Groups IV to VII

van der Waals forces. This force, whatever its origin, is virtually absent in the hydrides of all but the three elements named. The absence of the force in methane indicates that the presence of at least one pair of electrons is essential, but this attractive force is not found in the hydrides of larger elements in the same group, which do have lone pairs of electrons.

The attractive force is called *hydrogen bonding* and is normally represented by a dotted line, for example

A—H· · ·A—H

It is this force which explains the abnormally high boiling points of hydrogen fluoride, water and ammonia. The hydrogen bonding in hydrogen fluoride is so strong that salts of a hypothetical acid H_2F_2 can be isolated, for example, KHF_2 with the structure $K^+[F\cdots H\cdots F]^-$. Again, ice is known to have a structure similar to that of diamond with four bonds tetrahedrally arranged. Two hydrogen bonds bind the lone pairs of electrons on a given oxygen atom to the positively charged hydrogen atoms of two adjacent water molecules, these hydrogen bonds being slightly longer than the hydrogen–oxygen covalent bonds of the water molecule (*Figure 2.11*). The whole

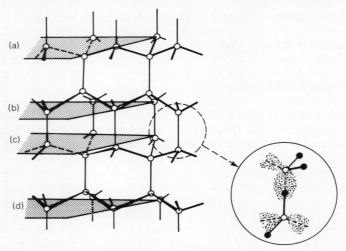

Figure 2.11 The tetrahedral structure of ice: (a) and (b) are planes through sheets of selected oxygen nuclei (open circles); hydrogen nuclei (shown in the inset as solid circles) are not shown in the main drawing. The inset shows the overlap of oxygen lone pairs and the hydrogen nuclei, thus forming the hydrogen bonds (broken lines)

structure is rigid but open, giving ice a low density. The structure of liquid water is similar but less rigid; this explains the fact that water has a high melting point and dielectric constant (relative permittivity). Hydrogen bonding has been suggested as one reason why both H^+ and OH^- ions have very high ionic mobilities.

Hydrogen bonding is found between most compounds containing hydrogen attached to nitrogen, oxygen or fluorine; it explains why, for example, ethanol C_2H_5OH (C_2H_6O) has a boiling point of 351 K whilst the isomeric methoxymethane (dimethyl ether) CH_3—O—CH_3 boils at 249.4 K, and why some carboxylic acids associate into dimers, for example ethanoic acid in benzene dimerizes to form

$$H_3C-C \overset{\displaystyle O-H\cdots O}{\underset{\displaystyle O\cdots H-O}{\Big\langle}} C-CH_3$$

Hydrogen bonding is not restricted, however, to bonding between like molecules; it can exist between two different molecules (for example water and ethanol) or between a molecule and an ion (for example the species [H $\cdots$ F $\cdots$ H]$^-$ already mentioned). Hydrogen bonding also plays a vital role by providing cross linkage in proteins. It is, therefore, a very important bond; although it is usually weak, having a strength of approximately 20 kJ compared with a normal covalent bond strength of 200—400 kJ, certain hydrogen bonds can have strengths up to 80 kJ (*see* p. 49).

2.9   The modern theory of the covalent bond

The idea that a shared electron pair constitutes a covalent bond ignores any difficulty about the actual position and nature of the electrons in the combining atoms or in the resulting molecule. The idea that electrons are particles revolving in 'orbits' or situated in 'shells' is inadequate when we desire to picture electrons in covalent bonds. It is, however, known that a beam of electrons can undergo diffraction, and that they therefore possess a wave-like nature like light waves. It has also been found that there is a simple relationship between the momentum of an electron (characteristic of its particle-nature) and the wavelength (characteristic of its wave-nature). But if we give a definite wavelength or amplitude to an electron, then its position in space becomes uncertain, i.e. it cannot be pin-pointed. Instead, the wave amplitude (strictly, the square of the amplitude) can be used to represent the *probability* of finding the electron at a given point in an atom or molecule. This amplitude is usually given the symbol ψ (psi) and is called a *wave function*. For hydrogen (or helium), with one (or two) electron in the K 'shell', ψ is found to depend only on the distance from the nucleus, diminishing as this distance increases; hence our picture of the hydrogen atom is that shown in *Figure 2.12*.

Figure 2.12 Charge-cloud of hydrogen atom

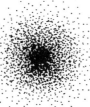

The intensity of shading at any point represents the magnitude of ψ^2, i.e. the probability of finding the electron at that point. This may also be called a spherical 'charge-cloud'. In helium, with two electrons, the picture is the same, but the two electrons must have opposite spins. These two electrons in helium are in a definite energy level and occupy an *orbital*, in this case an *atomic orbital*. Now the combination of two hydrogen atoms to give a hydrogen molecule can be visualized as in *Figure 2.13*.

In elements of Periods 2 and 3 the four orbitals are of two kinds; the first two electrons go into a spherically symmetrical orbital — an *s* orbital with a shape like that shown in *Figure 2.12* — and the next six electrons into three *p*

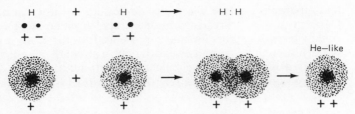

Figure 2.13 The two atomic orbitals overlap giving a covalent bond and the two electrons are now in a molecular orbital. (If the two nuclei could be pushed together completely, the result would be analogous to a helium atom, but with no neutrons in the nucleus)

orbitals each of which has a roughly 'double-pear' shape, like those shown unshaded in each half of *Figure 2.15*.

When elements in Period 2 form covalent bonds, the $2s$ and $2p$ orbitals can be mixed or *hybridized* to form new, *hybrid* orbitals each of which has, effectively, a 'single-pear' shape, well suited for overlap with the orbital of another atom. Carbon being taken as an example, the four orbitals $2s,2p,2p,2p$ can all the mixed to form four new hybrid orbitals (called sp^3 because they are formed from one s and three p); these new orbitals appear as in *Figure 2.14*, i.e. they project to the corners of a tetrahedron. The four

Figure 2.14 Hybrid orbitals of carbon in methane

Figure 2.15 Formation of the ethene molecule

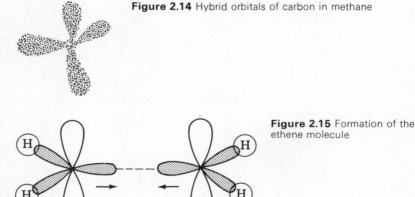

valency electrons of carbon go one into each orbital, and overlap of these singly-occupied orbitals with the four spherical $1s$ orbitals of four hydrogen atoms gives the tetrahedral methane molecule, with four covalent bonds.

In ethene the situation is rather different; here, each carbon atom has one $2s$ and *two* $2p$ orbitals hybridized to form three sp^2 'single-pear' orbitals which are trigonal planar (shown shaded in each half of *Figure 2.15*). The remaining $2p$ orbital is not hybridized, and remains as a 'double-pear' (unshaded). The three hybrid orbitals of each carbon are used thus: two to overlap with the orbitals of hydrogen atoms to form two C—H covalent bonds, and one to overlap with the corresponding orbital of the other carbon atom, along the C...C axis, giving a C—C bond, as the two halves of the molecule come together as indicated in *Figure 2.15*. The unhybridized $2p$ orbitals now overlap 'sideways-on', and we get the molecule as shown in *Figure 2.16*.

Hence we have two *molecular* orbitals, one along the line of centres, the other as two sausage-like clouds, called the π orbital or π *bond* (and the two electrons in it, the π electrons). The double bond is shorter than a single C—C

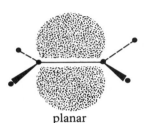

Figure 2.16 The ethene molecule

planar

bond because of the 'double' overlap; but the π electron cloud is easily attacked by other atoms, hence the reactivity of ethene compared with methane or ethane.

This representation of the double bond applies to other double bonds also, for example C=O, S=O, P=O, and so on.

The element before carbon in Period 2, boron, has one electron less than carbon, and forms many covalent compounds of type BX_3 where X is a univalent atom or group. In these, the boron 'uses' three sp^2 hybrid orbitals to form three trigonal planar bonds, like carbon in ethene, but the unhybridized $2p$ orbital is *vacant*, i.e. it contains no electrons. In the nitrogen atom (one more electron than carbon) one orbital must contain two electrons — the lone pair; hence sp^3 hybridization will give four tetrahedral orbitals, one containing this lone pair. Oxygen similarly hybridized will have two orbitals occupied by lone pairs, and fluorine, three. Hence the hydrides of the elements from carbon to fluorine have the structures shown in *Figure 2.17*,

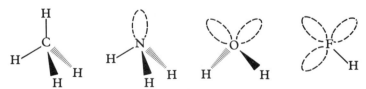

Figure 2.17 Lone-pair orbitals

with the lone-pair orbitals indicated by broken lines. The coordinate link is formed by overlap of a doubly-occupied (lone pair) orbital with an unoccupied orbital. The projecting charge-clouds of molecules like water or ammonia also impart other properties. The concentration of negative charge on one side of the molecule makes the molecule electrically *polar*, i.e. one end is positive, the other (lone pair) end is negative; the molecule is then a *dipole* and the magnitude of the polarity is expressed as the *dipole moment**. In molecules such as NH_3 and H_2O the positive end of the dipole is 'concentrated' at the small hydrogen atoms and there is consequently a strong electrostatic attraction between these and the negative charge-clouds of neighbouring molecules; this particularly strong attraction is the origin of *hydrogen bonding* (p. 46). The projecting charge-clouds can also be attracted by ions so that positive ions, for example, become hydrated (or solvated) by attraction of the lone pair charge-clouds to the ion, as, for example, the hydrated Al^{3+} ion (pp. 40, 138).

The elements of Period 2(Li—F) cannot have a covalency greater than 4, because not more than four orbitals are available for bonding. In Period 3 (Na—Cl) similar behaviour would be expected, and indeed the molecule SiH_4 is tetrahedral like that of CH_4, and PH_3 is like NH_3 with a lone pair occupying one tetrahedral position. But it is found that certain very electronegative atoms or groups, notably fluorine, can cause expansion of the valency shell, and further orbitals of higher energy — the *d* orbitals — can be hybridized with the *s* and *p* orbitals. Consider phosphorus, with five valency electrons; these can be placed either in four tetrahedral sp^3 hybrid orbitals (with one orbital doubly occupied) or singly in five orbitals formed by hybridization of one $3s$, and three $3p$ and one $3d$ (sp^3d) to give a trigonal bipyramidal shape (*Table 2.8*). sp^3 mixing is found in the phosphine molecule PH_3 while sp^3d is found in the phosphorus pentafluoride molecule PF_5. Similarly with sulphur, sp^3 mixing with two lone pairs is found in the H_2S molecule while sp^3d^2 mixing gives six octahedral orbitals as found in the SF_6 molecule. It will now become apparent that *all the common molecular shapes given in Table 2.8 can be accounted for by assuming appropriate hybridization of the orbitals of the central atom* — sp, linear: sp^2, trigonal planar: sp^3, tetrahedral: sp^3d, trigonal bipyramidal and sp^3d^2, octahedral.

2.10   The bonding in metals

We have seen that in a metal the atoms are close-packed, i.e. each metal atom is surrounded by a large number of similar atoms (*Figure 2.1*, p. 22). The heat required to break up 1 mole of a metal into its constituent atoms is the *heat of atomization* or *heat of sublimation*. Values of this enthalpy vary between about 80 and 800 kJ mol^{-1}, for metals in their standard states; these values indicate that the bonds between metal atoms can vary from weak to very strong. There is a rough proportionality between the m.p. of a metal and its heat of atomization, so that the m.p. gives an approximate measure of bond strength.

Here we can discuss the nature of metallic bonding only in a qualitative way. The bulk metal may be pictured as consisting of positively charged atoms embedded in a 'sea' of free valency electrons. There are, therefore, no localized bonds, as in a giant covalent crystal like diamond. The freedom of the electrons is shown by their ability to move in an electrical field, so bestowing electrical conductance on the metal. The strength of the metal

*Note that a dipole moment can arise from bond polarity (p. 44) also.

bonding (as measured by the heat of atomization) is determined essentially by (a) the size of the atoms, increase in size decreasing the heat of atomization and (b) the number of valency electrons, increase in the number of valency electrons increasing the heat of atomization. In the close-packed metal structure of, for example, sodium, each metal atom of sodium is surrounded by (and therefore bonded to) eight other atoms, and each atom contributes one valency electron; clearly the number of electrons per 'bond' is $\frac{1}{8}$. For a larger atom with the same coordination number and the same number of valency electrons, for example, caesium, the electron/bond ratio is still $\frac{1}{8}$, but the interatomic distance is necessarily larger and the 'bond strength' would be expected to be weaker. In fact, the heats of atomization at 298 K for solid sodium and caesium are 109 and 79 kJ mol^{-1} respectively. The atoms of sodium in metallic sodium, and calcium in metallic calcium, have almost identical sizes (calculated for the same coordination number); but since calcium has two valency electrons, the heat of atomization is increased to 177 kJ mol^{-1}. Many transition metals have high heats of atomization; these elements have d electrons and a larger number of electrons is available for interatomic bonds in the metals; examples of heats of atomization are: iron, 416 kJ mol^{-1}, tungsten, 837 kJ mol^{-1}. The stronger bonds in transition metals give rise not only to higher m.p. but also to greater tensile strength and hardness — hence the many uses of these metals for practical purposes.

2.11   Bonding in transition metal complexes

We have already noted that transition metals can readily form complexes with a variety of ligands. We have also noted that, in complexes of the main group metals, the metal–ligand bonds can be electrostatic (i.e. ion–ion or ion–dipole), or covalent, or intermediate between these two extremes. In transition metal complexes, the bonding can be *described* on the basis of either an 'electrostatic' or a 'covalent' model; again, the *actual* bonding may well be intermediate in character. But an important feature of either description must be to take account of the d orbitals. When a transition metal ion forms a complex with ligands, two important changes often occur; a change of *colour*, and a change in *magnetic properties*; any theory of bonding must account for these changes. Briefly, this is done by postulating a split in the d orbital energy levels. In the free atom or ion of a first series transition metal, there are five d orbitals all having the same energy. If the metal ion is surrounded by ligands, all the d orbital energies are raised; when there are six ligands arranged octahedrally (or six ions of opposite change in an ionic lattice) the d orbitals undergo an energy split as shown in *Figure 2.18*. The magnitude of the energy split, ΔE, determines how the electrons will be distributed between the d orbitals (and hence the magnetic properties, p. 204). Moreover, electrons can be promoted from the lower to the higher energy level by absorption of light; the frequency of the absorbed light is directly related to ΔE; and hence this latter quantity greatly influences the colour of the complex.

The detailed theory of bonding in transition metal complexes is beyond

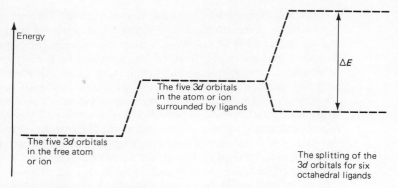

Figure 2.18 Energy level splitting in *d* orbitals

the scope of this book, but further references will be made to the effects of the energy splitting in the *d* orbitals in Chapter 13.

2.12   The colour of inorganic compounds

Many transition metal compounds owe their colour to absorption of light which causes electrons to move between *d* orbitals of different energy, these orbitals being essentially those of the central metal atom or ion. However, colour is also seen in some main-group elements (for example, iodine), some main-group compounds [e.g. lead(II) oxide, yellow], and some transition metal complexes where there are *either* no electrons initially in *d* orbitals [e.g. the manganate(VII) ion, MnO_4^-], *or* the *d* orbitals are completely filled (and hence electrons cannot move between them) [for example, copper(I) oxide, yellow-red; mercury(II) oxide, red]. A detailed discussion of the causes of colour in these compounds is out of place in this book, but essentially the colour is due to electrons moving between *different* atoms or ions. In most compounds, the energy required for movement of electrons (sometimes referred to as charge-transfer) is large, and the frequency of light required is consequently in the ultraviolet region of the spectrum. But in the coloured compounds already mentioned, the energy is sufficiently low to cause absorption of light in the visible part of the spectrum. Thus, for example, in the MnO_4^- ion, we have manganese in a high oxidation state $(+7)$ and oxygen in state -2; movement of electrons from oxygen to manganese requires relatively little energy, and the intense purple colour results.

Summary

The four limiting kinds of structure are the *metallic, giant molecule* and *giant ionic* lattices and *molecular crystals*. In ionic or electrovalent bonding, the energy changes involved are (*a*) for loss of electron(s) to form cations, *ionization energies* and (*b*) for gain of electron(s) to form anions, *electron affinities*. Cations and anions form *ionic lattices*; the structures depend on the cation/anion *radius ratios*. When atoms are bound *covalently*, the shapes of the resulting structures are determined by *repulsions between electron pairs*. The electron pair of a covalent bond can result from *electron sharing* between two atoms or *electron donation* of a pair from one atom to the other.

A covalent bond is characterized by a *bond energy* and a bond length. Bonds intermediate in character between ionic and covalent are formed when the two atoms concerned differ in *electronegativity*; the bond formed is *polar* and the resulting molecule may have a *dipole moment*. In molecular crystals, the intermolecular forces can be *van der Waals* or *dipole–dipole*; strong forces between some hydrogen-containing molecules are called *hydrogen bonds*.

When a central metal ion M is surrounded by a definite number x of molecules or oppositely-charged ions, L, the resulting species ML_x is called a *complex*, with a *coordination number* x; the ions or molecules L are called ligands and ML_x may be neutral or a cation or an anion. A small, highly charged metal ion surrounded by water molecules undergoes *hydrolysis*. The forces between the central metal ion and the ligands may be relatively weak (*ion–dipole attraction*) or may be effectively those of covalent bonding; in the latter case, changes in the d electron levels in the central metal ion may result in a colour change as well as changes in magnetic properties. Colour in inorganic compounds can also result from *charge transfer* between different atoms or ions.

In the modern theory of the covalent bond, the latter is formed by *overlap of atomic orbitals* to form a *molecular orbital*. Atomic orbitals can be *hybridized* to form 'mixed' or *hybrid* orbitals which have directional properties, and these can be used to explain the shapes of covalent molecules.

In a metal, the atoms are close-packed and the bonding can be considered to consist of positively charged atoms embedded in a 'sea' of free valency electrons; in general, the greater the atom/free electron ratio, the harder is the metal.

Questions

1   Discuss the types of bonding that hold atoms and ions together in molecules and crystals. Include in your answer evidence for the existence of the bonds that you describe, and some indication of their relative strength.

N,A

2   Describe, with a brief explanation, the shapes of the following molecules and ions: (*a*) $SnCl_2$, (*b*) BCl_3, (*c*) PCl_3, (*d*) $SbCl_5$, (*e*) PCl_4^+ and (*f*) ICl_4^-. Indicate, giving a reason, which of the molecules (*a*), (*b*), (*c*) and (*d*) you would expect to possess a dipole moment.

JMB,S

3   State the type of chemical binding in each of the chlorides represented by the empirical formulae

NH_4Cl, $BeCl_2$, $MgCl_2$

and show how these binding forces, and other factors, determine the
behaviour of these chlorides when acted upon by (i) heat, (ii) electricity, (iii)
water.

C,A

4   (a) Describe the spatial arrangement of the atoms in a molecule of
           ammonia.
       (b) How is your answer to (a) explained in terms of the electronic structure of
           ammonia?
       (c) Describe the spatial arrangement of the atoms in a molecule of water.
       (d) How is your answer to (c) explained in terms of the electronic structure of
           water?
       (e) Describe the spatial arrangement of the atoms in the positive ion formed
           when ammonia reacts with water.
       (f) How is your answer to (e) explained in terms of the electronic structure of
           the positive ion?
       (g) How is the positive charge distributed in the positive ion?

JMB,A

5   How can the shapes of simple molecules be explained in terms of electron
       pair repulsions? Your answer should include at least one example from each
       of four different shapes.
       What effect does the presence of a lone pair of electrons on the nitrogen atom
       have on:
       (a) the H—N—H angle in ammonia,
       (b) the properties of the ammonia molecule?

JMB,A

6   (a) The circles in the diagram represent the positions of the ions in a single
           layer of a crystal of sodium chloride.

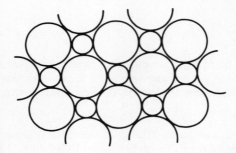

       (i)   Which ion is the smaller of the two types present in the structure?
       (ii) On a diagram mark with a cross the positions of the centres of the
             positive ions in the layer immediately above that shown.
       (iii) Explain briefly the magnitude of the melting point of sodium
             chloride in terms of its crystalline structure.
       (iv) What is the coordination number of the chloride ion?

(b) (i) What is the fundamental difference between the structures of graphite and diamond?

   (ii) Explain briefly how your answer to (b)(i) accounts for the hardness of diamond and the lubricating properties of graphite.

   (iii) How does the structure of graphite account for its electrical conductance?

JMB,A

Chapter 3
Energetics

A full treatment of this important — and indeed exciting — area of chemistry belongs to physical chemistry. Here, we are chiefly concerned with two fundamental questions about a chemical reaction — why does it proceed, and why does it give one product rather than another? There are many processes, both physical and chemical, which proceed spontaneously. Consider first two flasks, one containing only oxygen and the other only nitrogen, which are connected by opening a tap. The two gases mix spontaneously and the mixture is eventually uniform in both flasks — there has been no chemical reaction but spontaneous mixing has occurred. When anhydrous aluminium chloride is added to water the reaction described on p. 39 occurs with the evolution of a great deal of heat — a strongly *exothermic* spontaneous reaction. Addition of solid ammonium nitrate to water leads to solution with the absorption of heat — a spontaneous *endothermic* reaction. These reactions are all spontaneous, but clearly there are wide differences in the apparent energy changes involved.

3.1 Chemical stability

Before we proceed to discuss energy changes in detail it is first necessary to be clear that two factors determine the stability of a chemical system — stability here meaning *not* undergoing any chemical change. These two factors are the *energy* factor and the *kinetic* factor.

3.1.1 The energy factor

A change can only take place if the energy factor is favourable. Most simple laboratory reactions are carried out in vessels open to the atmosphere and are therefore at constant pressure. Consequently the most commonly met energy factor is the *enthalpy*, H; the *enthalpy change*, ΔH, is a measure of the *heat* gained from, or lost to, the surroundings during a chemical process, such that, at the end of the reaction, the temperature and pressure of the system are the same as before the reaction occurred. In an *exothermic* process, the total enthalpy of the products H_2 is less than that of the reactants, H_1, and the enthalpy change, ΔH, is *negative* (*Figure 3.1*). For an *endothermic* process the enthalpy change is positive.

The enthalpy (strictly, the enthalpy change) for a reaction can readily be

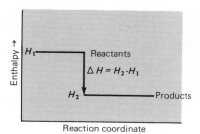

Figure 3.1 Enthalpy change

calculated from enthalpies of formation ΔH_f which can often be obtained from tables of data.

ΔH values relate to defined conditions, usually to the standard state of the substance at 298 K and 1 atm pressure, indicated by $\Delta H_{298}^{\ominus}$.* That is,

$$\Delta H_{\text{reaction}} = \Sigma \Delta H_f \text{ products} - \Sigma \Delta H_f \text{ reactants}$$

For example, for the reaction

$$C_2H_6(g) + 3\tfrac{1}{2}O_2(g) \rightarrow 2CO_2(g) + 3H_2O(l)$$

$$\Delta H_{\text{reaction}} = [2 \times \Delta H_f CO_2(g) + 3 \times \Delta H_f H_2O(l)] - [\Delta H_f C_2H_6(g)]$$

(Note that ΔH_f for an element in its standard state is zero by definition.) Hence $\Delta H_{\text{reaction}} = -1560 \text{ kJ mol}^{-1}$. (This is in fact an enthalpy of combustion.)

3.1.2 The kinetic factor

Even given a favourable energy factor, a change may still not take place or occur at a negligible rate if the kinetic factor is unfavourable. The situation is somewhat analogous to an object on the ground. First, the object can only move spontaneously if the ground slopes downwards — it will not move spontaneously on level ground or up a slope. If the object is, say, a smooth sphere, it will, given a downward gradient, move spontaneously. However, if the object is less regular in shape, say a lump of rock, it may be at rest on an incline. This rock is energetically unstable but kinetically stable. The rock can be made kinetically unstable by giving it a push to get it over its *energy barrier* — adding initial energy (the energy of activation). Similarly, many chemical systems are energetically unstable but kinetically stable and need a 'push', usually in the form of heat, to make them go (*Figure 3.2*). We should note that not all the molecules in a given system need to be given the additional 'activation energy' for the reaction to proceed. Each molecule that reacts produces energy, in an exothermic reaction, and this can activate more molecules. Hence, once a sufficiently large proportion of the molecules reaches the activated state, the reaction proceeds spontaneously. The burning of coal and wood are familiar examples of this type of process.

*The temperature subscript 298 will be assumed in this book unless otherwise stated.

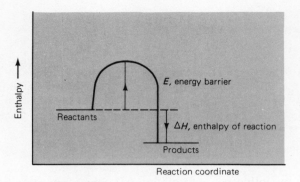

Figure 3.2 Activation energy

3.2 Free energy and equilibria

Let us now consider two simple representative reactions:

1     $Na(s) + \frac{1}{2}Cl_2(g) \rightarrow NaCl(s)$
2     $\frac{1}{2}H_2(g) + \frac{1}{2}Cl_2(g) \rightarrow HCl(g)$

In *both* reactions 1 and 2 the energy factors are favourable; pure sodium and chlorine do react at room temperature but hydrogen and chlorine are (kinetically) stable in the absence of light; in the presence of light (to give the reaction additional energy) they react explosively to form hydrogen chloride. Since we have seen on p. 56 that a spontaneous reaction can be endothermic (although the vast majority are exothermic), we must now consider the energy factor in more detail.

When we say that reactions 1 and 2 'go' we actually mean that the equilibrium between reactants and products is displaced from the reactants towards the products. We represent this strictly by the equation (for reaction 2)

$$\frac{1}{2}H_2(g) + \frac{1}{2}Cl_2(g) \rightleftharpoons HCl(g)$$

By application of the Equilibrium Law, the equilibrium constants are

$$K_c = \frac{[HCl]}{[H_2]^{1/2}[Cl_2]^{1/2}} \qquad K_p = \frac{[P_{HCl}]^2}{[P_{H_2}]^{1/2}[P_{Cl_2}]^{1/2}}$$

Here, the reaction proceeds effectively to completion; $[HCl]$ is very large relative to $[H_2]$ and $[Cl_2]$ and hence K_c (and K_p) are also large. In these circumstances the reverse arrow is usually omitted.

The equilibrium constant at constant temperature is directly related to the maximum energy, called the *free energy* ΔG, which is obtainable from a reaction, the relationship being

$$\Delta G = -RT \ln K_p$$

Here G is the free energy and ΔG the change in free energy during the reaction, R the gas constant and T the absolute temperature.

At 298 K, under standard conditions ($G = G^\ominus$)

$$\log_{10}K_p = -0.000733\Delta G^\ominus$$

where $\Delta G^\ominus$ is the change in free energy under standard conditions.

The above equation enables us to calculate the equilibrium constant for any value of ΔG or *vice versa*, and we readily see that for a reaction to 'go to completion', i.e. for K to be large, ΔG needs to be large and negative (*see Figure 3.3*).

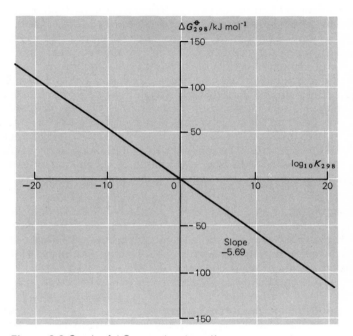

Figure 3.3 Graph of ΔG_{298} against $\log_{10}K_{298}$

When $\Delta G = 0$, the equilibrium constant K is unity. A large positive value of ΔG indicates that the reaction will not 'go', being energetically unfavourable under the specific conditions to which ΔG refers.

3.3   Free energy and entropy

Free energy is related to two other energy quantities, the enthalpy (the heat of reaction measured at constant pressure) and the entropy, S, an energy term most simply visualized as a measure of the disorder of the system, the relationship for a reaction taking place under standard conditions being

$$\Delta G^\ominus = \Delta H^\ominus - T\Delta S^\ominus$$

where $\Delta G^\ominus$ is the change in free energy, $\Delta H^\ominus$ *the change in enthalpy*, $\Delta S^\ominus$

the change in entropy (all measured under standard conditions), and T is the absolute temperature.

If overall disorder increases during a reaction, ΔS is positive; where overall disorder decreases, ΔS is negative.

3.3.1   Spontaneous reactions

We have seen above that for a reaction to 'go to completion' ΔG must be negative. Enthalpies of reaction often amount to several hundred kJ mol^{-1} but values of entropy changes are rarely greater than a few hundred J and often much smaller when no gas is absorbed (or evolved). Hence at room temperature the term $T\Delta S^{\ominus}$ can often be disregarded and the sign of $\Delta H^{\ominus}$ determines the sign of $\Delta G^{\ominus}$. However, when ΔH is small, less than approximately 40 kJ mol^{-1}, then $T\Delta S$ is important and can result in a negative value for ΔG even when ΔH is positive — i.e. for an endothermic reaction. In the endothermic dissolution of ammonium nitrate in water, quoted in the introduction on p. 56, it is the entropy contribution which produces the spontaneous reaction since the $T\Delta S^{\ominus}$ is greater than $\Delta H^{\ominus}$ and produces a negative value for $\Delta G^{\ominus}$. Also in the introduction the mixing of two gases was mentioned. In this case the enthalpy of 'reaction' is very small but clearly disorder is increased by the mixing of the two gases. Thus ΔS is positive and the terms $-T\Delta S$ and ΔG are negative.

3.3.2   The extraction of metals

From the above discussion, we might expect that endothermic reactions for which the enthalpy change is large cannot take place. However, a further consideration of the equation

$$\Delta G^{\ominus} = \Delta H^{\ominus} - T\Delta S^{\ominus}$$

clearly indicates that an increase in temperature could result in a negative value of the free energy, but only if the entropy change for the reaction is positive; if the entropy change is negative then there is no possibility of the reaction occurring. (Note that ΔH varies only slightly with temperature.) Most metals react exothermically with oxygen to form an oxide; clearly the reverse reaction, oxide to metal, is then endothermic. *Figure 3.4* shows how the value of $\Delta G^{\ominus}$ for the forward reaction varies with temperature for some metals (and for carbon); it can be seen that $\Delta G^{\ominus}$ is negative, becoming less negative with increase of temperature, but never positive within the temperature range shown. Hence, within this range, decomposition of any of the metal oxides is not possible.

Let us now consider the reduction of a metal oxide by carbon which is itself oxidized to carbon monoxide. The reaction will become energetically feasible when the free energy change for the combined process is negative (*see also Figure 3.4*). Free energies, like enthalpies, are additive, and the minimum temperature for energetic feasibility can readily be found.

As an example, consider the reduction of zinc oxide to zinc by the reaction:

$$ZnO + C \rightarrow Zn + CO$$

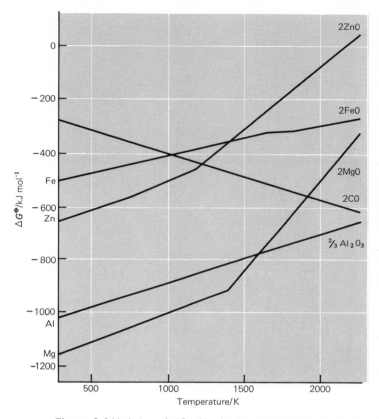

Figure 3.4 Variation of ΔG with absolute temperature for the reactions

$$2Zn + O_2 \rightarrow 2ZnO$$
$$2Fe + O_2 \rightarrow 2FeO$$
$$2Mg + O_2 \rightarrow 2MgO$$
$$2C + O_2 \rightarrow 2CO$$
$$\tfrac{4}{3}Al + O_2 \rightarrow \tfrac{2}{3}Al_2O_3$$

Reference to *Figure 3.4* shows that the reduction is not feasible at 800 K, but is feasible at 1300 K. However, we must remember that energetic feasibility does not necessarily mean a reaction will 'go'; kinetic stability must also be considered. Several metals are indeed extracted by reduction with carbon, but in some cases the reduction is brought about by carbon monoxide formed when air, or air–oxygen mixtures, are blown into the furnace. Carbon monoxide is the most effective reducing agent below about 980 K, and carbon is most effective above this temperature.

3.3.3   An alternative approach

Since

$$\Delta G^{\ominus} = \Delta H^{\ominus} - T\Delta S^{\ominus}$$

and

$$\Delta G^{\ominus} = -RT \ln K$$

then

$$\ln K = -\frac{\Delta H^{\ominus}}{R} \cdot \frac{1}{T} + \frac{\Delta S^{\ominus}}{R}$$

or

$$\log_{10} K = -\frac{\Delta H^{\ominus}}{2.303 R} \cdot \frac{1}{T} + \text{constant}$$

Hence an alternative to *Figure 3.4* is to plot $\log_{10} K$ against $1/T$(*Figure 3.5*);

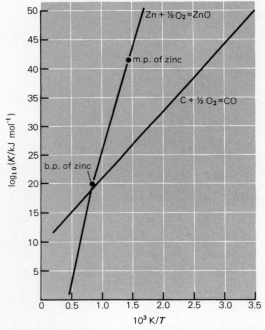

Figure 3.5 Graphs of $\log_{10} K$ against reciprocal absolute temperature for the reactions

$$Zn + \tfrac{1}{2}O_2 \rightleftharpoons ZnO$$
$$CO + \tfrac{1}{2}O_2 \rightleftharpoons CO_2$$

the slope of each line is equal to $-\Delta H^{\ominus}/2.303R$. A discontinuity in the line for a given metal–metal oxide system corresponds to a change in *phase* (solid, liquid, gas) of the metal or its oxide (usually the metal). The change in slope is related to the enthalpy change involved in the change. Thus for magnesium–magnesium oxide

$$2Mg(l) + O_2(g) \rightarrow 2MgO(s) \qquad \Delta H_1^{\ominus} = -1220 \text{ kJ mol}^{-1}$$
$$2Mg(g) + O_2(g) \rightarrow 2MgO(s) \qquad \Delta H_2^{\ominus} = -1480 \text{ kJ mol}^{-1}$$

and hence

$$2Mg(l) \rightarrow 2Mg(g) \qquad\qquad \Delta H^{\ominus} = 260 \text{ kJ mol}^{-1}$$

which is twice the enthalpy of vaporization of one mole of magnesium.

We have seen from the plots of $\Delta G^{\ominus}$ against T that the extraction of a metal from its compound by a reducing agent becomes energetically feasible when the free energy change for the combined process is negative.

When using $\log_{10}K$ against $1/T$ graphs, in order to find the temperature at which reduction becomes energetically feasible it is necessary to determine the temperature at which the equilibrium constant for the reduction indicates a displacement of the reaction in favour of the metal.

Consider the reduction of zinc oxide by carbon monoxide. The equations are:

1 $\qquad Zn + \tfrac{1}{2}O_2 \underset{\longleftarrow}{\overset{K_1}{\longrightarrow}} ZnO$

2 $\qquad CO + \tfrac{1}{2}O_2 \underset{\longleftarrow}{\overset{K_2}{\longrightarrow}} CO_2$

Hence for the reduction of zinc oxide by carbon monoxide we have,

$$ZnO + CO \underset{\longleftarrow}{\overset{K}{\longrightarrow}} Zn + CO_2$$

Here

$K = K_1/K_2$

Hence

$$\log_{10}K = \log_{10}K_1 - \log_{10}K_2$$

The 'complete' reduction of zinc oxide is favoured by a small value of K, i.e. when $\log_{10}K_2 \gg \log_{10}K_1$. Figure 3.5 shows plots of $\log_{10}K_1$ and $\log_{10}K_2$ against $1/T$; where the two graphs intersect $\log_{10}K$ for the reduction process is zero and hence $K = 1$.

At higher temperatures $\log_{10}K$ has a positive value and K becomes large. Thus complete reduction of the oxide is energetically feasible.

Similar graphs can be plotted for the reduction of any metal oxide and also for the reduction of chloride and sulphide ores.

3.4   Factors contributing to the enthalpy of reaction

In the preceding sections we have considered the overall change in a chemical reaction. Factors contributing to this change will now be considered for simple covalent and ionic systems.

3.4.1   Covalent compounds: the hydrogen halides

Let us consider again the reaction between hydrogen and chlorine:

$H_2(g) + Cl_2(g) \rightarrow 2HCl(g)$

An energy diagram for this reaction is given below (*Figure 3.6*). (Note that this is *not* a representation of the actual reaction path but, since the overall change is, by Hess's law, independent of the path of the reaction, this is still valid as an energy diagram.)

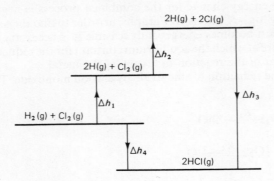

Figure 3.6 Energy diagram for the gaseous reaction of hydrogen with chlorine

The enthalpy changes in the reaction are:

Δh_1 the dissociation or bond energy of hydrogen (it is also, by definition, twice the enthalpy of atomization — two gram atoms being produced).

Δh_2 the dissociation or bond energy of chlorine, again twice the enthalpy of atomization.

Δh_3 twice the bond energy of hydrogen chloride (twice since two moles of hydrogen chloride are produced).

Δh_4 the enthalpy of reaction, which is in this case twice the enthalpy of formation of hydrogen chloride. Clearly Δh_4 is the difference between the total bond energies of the products and the total bond energies of the reactants. That is

$\Delta H_{\text{reaction}} = \Sigma$ bond energies of products $- \Sigma$ bond energies of reactants

For a reaction to be exothermic the sum of the bond energies of the products must exceed those of the reactants.

For the formation of the hydrogen halides by the direct combination of the elements, the enthalpies of formation are:

	HF	HCl	HBr	HI
$\Delta H_f^{\ominus}/\text{kJ mol}^{-1}$	-269	-92.3	-36.2	$+26$

These values indicate a rapid fall in thermal stability of the halide from fluorine to iodine, and hydrogen iodide is an endothermic compound. If we now examine the various enthalpy changes involved, we find the values (in kJ) shown in *Table 3.1*. Note that the term 2 is included; it is the enthalpy required to convert the element in its standard state at 298 K into a gas at 298 K — and it does not apply to fluorine and chlorine which are both gases at this temperature.

The heats of formation of the gaseous atoms, term 4, are not very different;

Table 3.1 Enthalpy changes in hydrogen halides

Term	Reaction	HF	HCl	HBr	HI
1	$\frac{1}{2}H_2(g) \rightarrow H(g)$	$+218$	$+218$	$+218$	$+218$
2	$\frac{1}{2}X_2(l,s) \rightarrow \frac{1}{2}X_2(g)$	0	0	$+15$	$+31$
3	$\frac{1}{2}X_2(g) \rightarrow X(g)$	$+79$	$+121$	$+96$	$+76$
4	$\frac{1}{2}H_2(g) + \frac{1}{2}X_2(l,s) \rightarrow H(g) + X(g)$	$+297$	$+339$	$+330$	$+325$
5	$H(g) + X(g) \rightarrow HX(g)$	-566	-431	-366	-299
6	$\frac{1}{2}H_2(g) + \frac{1}{2}X_2(s,l,g) \rightarrow HX(g)$: ΔH_f	-269	-92	-36	$+26$

clearly, it is the change in the bond dissociation energy of HX, which falls steadily from HF to HI, which is mainly responsible for the changes in the heats of formation, term 6. We shall see later that it is the very high H—F bond energy and thus the less easy dissociation of H—F into ions in water which makes HF in water a weak acid in comparison with other hydrogen halides.

3.4.2 Covalent compounds: other systems

We have just seen that a knowledge of bond energies enables enthalpies of reaction to be calculated. This is certainly true for simple diatomic systems. When polyatomic molecules are considered, however, the position can be more complicated and there are a number of different dissociation energies for even a two-element polyatomic molecule. Consider, for example, ammonia. There are three N—H bond dissociation energies (p. 41) and the bond dissociation energy is different for each N—H bond and depends on the environment of the atoms concerned. The same conditions apply to any polyatomic molecule. However, average values, called *average thermochemical bond energies* (or average standard bond enthalpies) have been determined from a wide variety of compounds, and tables can be found in most data books. In spite of the known limitations of these bond energies, they are useful in estimating enthalpies of reactions, as indicated on p. 57, and the likely stabilities of covalent compounds. However, special care is needed when small positive or negative values for enthalpies are obtained (often as the difference between two larger values), since the predictions may then be unreliable because of the lack of precision in the original data.

3.4.3 Ionic compounds: lattice energy

Let us consider the formation of sodium chloride from its elements. An energy (enthalpy) diagram (called a Born–Haber cycle) for the reaction of sodium and chlorine is given in *Figure 3.7*. (As in the energy diagram for the formation of hydrogen chloride, an upward arrow represents an endothermic process and a downward arrow an exothermic process.)

The enthalpy changes involved are:

Δh_1 the enthalpy of atomization (or sublimation) of sodium.

Δh_2 the first ionization energy of sodium.

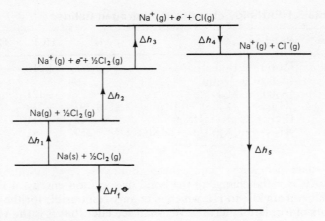

Figure 3.7 Born-Haber cycle for sodium chloride

Δh_3 the enthalpy of atomization of chlorine, which is also half the bond
   dissociation enthalpy.

Δh_4 the electron affinity of chlorine.

Δh_5 the lattice energy of sodium chloride; this is the heat liberated when
   one mole of crystalline sodium chloride is formed from one mole of
   gaseous sodium ions and one mole of chloride ions.

$\Delta H_f^{\ominus}$ the enthalpy of formation of sodium chloride.

Hence

$$\Delta H_f^{\ominus} = \Delta h_1 + \Delta h_2 + \Delta h_3 + \Delta h_4 + \Delta h_5$$

Of these enthalpies, all can be determined experimentally except the lattice
energy. Ionization energies, electron affinities, bond dissociation energies
and heats of atomization have all received some discussion previously. The
lattice energy can be determined by using the Born–Haber cycle as shown
above, or by calculation, summing the attractive and repulsive energies
between all the ions in 1 mole of crystal. Details of this calculation are outside
the scope of this book. However, it may be noted that the calculation is based
on the assumption that ionic crystals are made up of discrete spherical ions
which exert non-directional electrostatic attractive or repulsive forces on
their neighbours in the crystal. The calculation gives a result which is most
simply represented as follows:

$$\text{Lattice energy } (\Delta h_5) = A\frac{z^+ z^-}{r^+ + r^-} - B$$

where A is a constant for a particular crystal type, z^+ and z^- are the charges
on the ions, r^+ and r^- are the ionic radii (*see* p. 25) and B is a small constant of
repulsion. The important quantities which determine the magnitude of the
lattice energy are, therefore, ionic charges z, and the ionic radii r. Since z
increases and r decreases across a period it is not surprising to find that a
Group II halide has a much higher lattice energy than the corresponding
Group I halide. Calculated lattice energies for the alkali metal halides are in

good agreement with values determined from Born–Haber cycle measurements; e.g. for sodium chloride, the cycle gives -787 and the calculation -772 kJ mol^{-1}.

For other compounds, the agreement is not always so good. The assumption that the lattice is always wholly ionic is not always true; there may be some degree of covalent bonding or (where the ions are very large and easily distorted) some appreciable van der Waals forces between the ions (p. 41).

3.4.4   Ionic compounds: stoichiometry

To date there is no evidence that sodium forms any chloride other than NaCl; indeed the electronic theory of valency predicts that Na$^+$ and Cl$^-$, with their noble gas configurations, are likely to be the most stable ionic species. However, since some noble gas atoms *can* lose electrons to form cations (p. 310) we cannot rely fully on this theory. We therefore need to examine the evidence provided by energetic data. Let us consider the formation of a number of possible ionic compounds; first, the formation of 'sodium dichloride', NaCl$_2$. The energy diagram for the formation of this hypothetical compound follows the pattern of that for NaCl but an additional endothermic step is added for the second ionization energy of sodium. The lattice energy is calculated on the assumption that the compound is ionic and that Na^{2+} is comparable in size with Mg^{2+}. The data are summarized below (standard enthalpies in kJ):

Δh_1 enthalpy of atomization for sodium (unchanged)	$+108$
Δh_2 first ionization energy for sodium (unchanged)	$+496$
$\Delta h_2'$ second ionization energy for sodium (additional)	$+4561$
Δh_3 enthalpy of atomization of chlorine, $\times 2$ (since two atoms are needed)	$+242$
Δh_4 electron affinity of chlorine, $\times 2$ (two ions are formed)	-728
Δh_5 calculated lattice energy	-2539

Hence

$$\Delta H_f^{\ominus} = \Delta h_1 + \Delta h_2 + \Delta h_2' + \Delta h_3 + \Delta h_4 + \Delta h_5 = 2140 \text{ kJ mol}^{-1}$$

The positive enthalpy of formation of NaCl$_2$ is so large that the possibility of the reaction Na(s) + Cl$_2$(g) $\rightarrow$ NaCl$_2$(s) occurring under any conditions is extremely remote.

The main factor responsible for the large positive value of $\Delta H_f^{\ominus}$ for NaCl$_2$ is the high second ionization energy of sodium. Since for any element, the second ionization energy is much larger than the first, we might ask the question:

Why do elements from Group II form ionic dichlorides? The standard enthalpy changes for the formation of MgCl, MgCl$_2$ and MgCl$_3$ are given in *Table 3.2*.

The values of $\Delta H_f^{\ominus}$ indicate that it is extremely unlikely that MgCl$_3$(s) can be prepared under any conditions, but both MgCl(s) and MgCl$_2$(s) appear to be energetically stable with respect to magnesium and chlorine.

Table 3.2 Enthalpies of formation/kJ mol^{-1} of magnesium chlorides

Term	Reaction	MgCl	MgCl$_2$	MgCl$_3$
Δh_1	$Mg(s) \rightarrow Mg(g)$	+146	+146	+146
Δh_2	$Mg(g) \rightarrow Mg^{n+}(g) + ne^-$	+736	+2184	+9924
Δh_3	$\frac{1}{2}nCl_2(g) \rightarrow nCl(g)$	+121	+242	+363
Δh_4	$nCl(g) + ne^- \rightarrow nCl^-(g)$	−364	−728	−1092
Δh_5	$Mg^{n+}(g) + nCl^-(g) \rightarrow MgCl_n$	−753	−2502	−5440
ΔH_f =	$\Delta h_1 + \Delta h_2 + \Delta h_3 + \Delta h_4 + \Delta h_5$			
		−114	−658	+3901

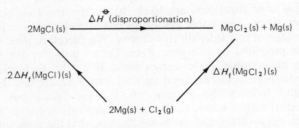

$2\Delta H_f(MgCl)(s) + \Delta H(disproportionation) - \Delta H_f(MgCl_2)(s) = 0$

Hence

$\Delta H(disproportionation) = -427$ kJ

Figure 3.8 Energy cycle for disproportionation of MgCl(s)

MgCl(s), however, is *not* energetically stable with respect to disproportionation. The energy cycle in *Figure 3.8* enables the enthalpy of disproportionation to be calculated, i.e.

$$2\Delta H_f^{\ominus}(MgCl)(s) + \Delta H(\text{disproportionation}) - \Delta H_f^{\ominus}(MgCl_2) = 0$$

We see, therefore, that magnesium normally forms a dichloride and not a mono- or tri-chloride. Similar calculations can be made for many systems, but greater uncertainties arise, especially when covalent bonds are involved. Moreover, we must not assume that magnesium trichloride *cannot* exist.

Early calculations of a similar kind indicated that the compound AlCl is unlikely to exist; but at temperatures above about 1100 K aluminium oxide Al_2O_3 and the trichloride $AlCl_3$ react to form the compound AlCl; on cooling this disproportionates to give the trichloride and aluminium metal

$$3AlCl \rightarrow AlCl_3 + 2Al \quad (p.\ 132)$$

There are many compounds in existence which have a considerable positive enthalpy of formation. They are not made by direct union of the constituent elements in their standard states, but by some process in which the necessary energy is provided indirectly. Many known covalent hydrides (Chapter 5) are made by indirect methods (for example from other hydrides) or by supplying energy (in the form of heat or an electric discharge) to the direct reaction to dissociate the hydrogen molecules and also possibly vaporize the other element. Other known endothermic compounds include nitrogen oxide and ethyne (acetylene); all these compounds have considerable *kinetic* stability.

3.4.5   Reactions in aqueous solution: ionic substances

Let us examine the enthalpy terms involved when an ionic crystal MX is dissolved in water. The energy diagram for a Group I halide is as shown in *Figure 3.9*.

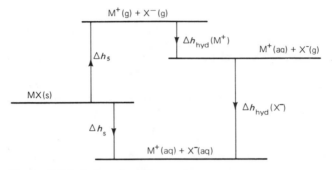

Figure 3.9 Enthalpy of solution cycle

In *Figure 3.9* Δh_s represents the heat (enthalpy) of solution, which can be measured experimentally, and Δh_5 is the lattice energy. $\Delta h_{hyd}(M^+)$ and $\Delta h_{hyd}(X^-)$ are the *hydration* enthalpies of the ions M^+ and X^-. These require further consideration.

Hydration enthalpies
When an ion is solvated the resulting solvated ion is more stable than the original free ion. Consequently all hydration enthalpies are negative; hydration is an exothermic process. Since we can measure the enthalpy of solution and calculate the lattice energy, we can determine the total hydration enthalpy of the ions. However, since we are unable to measure hydration enthalpies for isolated ions, it is necessary to divide this enthalpy to give individual values. This problem can be resolved by giving an arbitrary value to the hydration enthalpy of one ionic species so that the others can be obtained by difference. There are good grounds for using the proton as the standard giving $\Delta h_{hyd}(H^+)$ the value of -1091 kJ mol^{-1}. On this basis some hydration enthalpies are given in *Table 3.3*. It will be noted that hydration enthalpy decreases with increasing ionic radius and increases very sharply with increase in ionic charge, these results being what we should expect for an electrostatic interaction between a charged ion and the dipole of a water molecule (p. 57).

Table 3.3 Hydration enthalpies/kJ mol⁻¹ at 298 K

H^+	-1091	Fe^{2+}	-1946	Tl^+	-326	Pb^{2+}	-1481
Li^+	-519	Co^{2+}	-1996	Be^{2+}	-2494	Al^{3+}	-4665
Na^+	-406	Ni^{2+}	-2105	Mg^{2+}	-1921	Fe^{3+}	-4430
K^+	-322	Cu^{2+}	-2100	Ca^{2+}	-1577	F^-	-515
Rb^+	-293	Zn^{2+}	-2046	Sr^{2+}	-1443	Cl^-	-381
Cs^+	-264	Hg^{2+}	-1824	Ba^{2+}	-1305	Br^-	-347
Ag^+	-473	Sn^{2+}	-1552	Cr^{2+}	-1904	I^-	-305

Enthalpies of solution

The enthalpy of solution is quite small for many simple ionic compounds and can be either positive or negative. It is the difference between two large quantities, the sum of the hydration enthalpies and the lattice energy.

Let us consider the halides of sodium and silver. The details of the enthalpy changes involved in dissolving them in water are in *Table 3.4*. Although the data for the silver halides suggest that silver(I) fluoride is likely to be more soluble than the other silver halides (which is in fact the case), the hydration enthalpies for the sodium halides almost exactly balance the lattice energies. What then is the driving force which makes these salts soluble, and which indeed must be responsible for the solution process where this is endothermic? We have seen on p. 59 that $\Delta G^\ominus = \Delta H^\ominus - T\Delta S^\ominus$ and noted that for a reaction to be spontaneous $\Delta G^\ominus$ must be negative. The driving force, then, is to be found in the entropy term $T\Delta S^\ominus$. When a crystal dissolves the orderly arrangement of ions in the lattice is destroyed, but since each ion becomes solvated order is brought into the areas of solvent around each ion. Generally, however, despite this 'ordering of the solvent' there is an overall increase in entropy and $\Delta S^\ominus$ is positive. Hence, negative values of

Table 3.4 Enthalpies of solution of sodium and silver halides

Term	*Reaction*	*Enthalpy/kJ mol⁻¹*			
		NaF	NaCl	NaBr	NaI
Δh_s	$NaX(s) \rightarrow Na^+(g) + X^-(g)$	$+919$	$+787$	$+752$	$+703$
$\Sigma\Delta h_{hyd}$	$Na^+(g) + X^-(g) \rightarrow Na^+(aq) + X^-(aq)$	-921	-787	-753	-711
Δh_s	$NaX(s) \rightarrow Na^+(aq) + X^-(aq)$	-2	0	-1	-8
		AgF	AgCl	AgBr	AgI
Δh_s	$AgX(s) \rightarrow Ag^+(g) + X^-(g)$	$+966$	$+917$	$+905$	$+891$
$\Sigma\Delta h_{hyd}$	$Ag^+(g) + X^-(g) \rightarrow Ag^+(aq) + X^-(aq)$	-986	-851	-820	-778
Δh_s	$AgX(s) \rightarrow Ag^+(aq) + X^-(aq)$	-20	$+66$	$+85$	$+113$

$\Delta G^{\ominus}$ can be produced even for endothermic reactions, and since $T\Delta S^{\ominus}$ increases with temperature, it is not surprising to find that the solubility of nearly all simple ionic substances increases as the temperature is increased.

Prediction of solublity for simple ionic compounds is difficult since we need to know not only values of hydration and lattice enthalpies but also entropy changes on solution before any informed prediction can be given. Even the kinetic factors must be considered.

This problem does not become easier when considering ionic compounds of Group II elements since with the increase in ionic charge and decrease in ionic radius of the Group II ions not only does hydration energy increase but also the lattice energy of the compound itself, and again the value of the enthalpy of solution is the difference between two large (indeed, in the case of Group II, very large) quantities.

3.4.6   Reactions in aqueous solution: covalent substances

Metals in higher oxidation states form halides which are essentially covalent, for example $AlCl_3$, $SnCl_4$, $FeCl_3$; when these compounds dissolve in water they do so by a strongly exothermic process. Indeed it is perhaps incorrect to think of this only as a dissolution process, since it is more like a chemical reaction — but to differentiate for a particular substance is not easy, as we shall see. The steps involved in the case of aluminium chloride can be represented as

$AlCl_3(s) \rightarrow AlCl_3(g)$
$AlCl_3(g) \rightarrow Al(g) + 3Cl(g)$
$Al(g) + 3Cl(g) \rightarrow Al^{3+}(g) + 3Cl^{-}(g)$
$Al^{3+}(g) + 3Cl^{-}(g) \rightarrow Al^{3+}(aq) + 3Cl^{-}(aq)$

Obviously sufficient energy is available to break the Al—Cl covalent bonds and to remove three electrons from the aluminium atom. Most of this energy comes from the very high hydration enthalpy of the $Al^{3+}(g)$ ion (p. 70). Indeed it is the very high hydration energy of the highly charged cation which is responsible for the reaction of other essentially covalent chlorides with water (for example, $SnCl_4$).

Essentially the same processes occur when chlorides (for example) of non-metallic elements 'dissolve' in water. Thus, the enthalpy changes for hydrogen chloride can be represented:

$HCl(g) \rightarrow H(g) + Cl(g)$
$H(g) + Cl(g) \rightarrow H^{+}(g) + Cl^{-}(g)$
$H^{+}(g) + Cl^{-}(g) \rightarrow H^{+}(aq) + Cl^{-}(aq)$

This process is exothermic owing largely to the large hydration enthalpy of the proton. However, unlike the metallic elements, non-metallic elements do not usually form hydrated cations when their compounds 'dissolve' in water; the process of *hydrolysis* occurs instead. The reason is probably to be found in the difference in ionization energies. Compare boron and aluminium in Group III (*Table 3.5*). Clearly the hydration of the 'B^{3+}' ion would have to

Table 3.5 Ionization energies/kJ mol⁻¹ of boron and aluminium

Element	1st	2nd	3rd	Total
Boron	801	2428	3660	6889
Aluminium	578	1817	2745	5140

produce an enormous amount of energy to compensate for that necessary to produce $B^{3+}(g)$, and in fact this ion is not found as such. In fact, there is no sharp division between hydration and hydrolysis, since hydrated multicharged cations such as $Al^{3+}(aq)$ and $Fe^{3+}(aq)$ do undergo a loss of protons which is also a 'hydrolysis' (p. 40).

Questions

1   (a) Describe how the use of Ellingham diagrams such as shown below helps to explain why metal oxides can be reduced by the use of
       (i)   other metals,
       (ii) carbon,
       (iii) carbon monoxide.

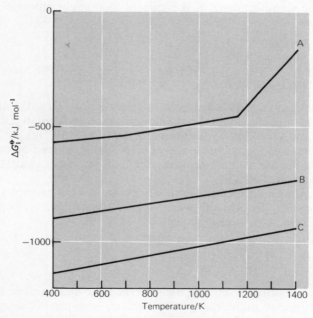

Ellingham diagrams for the reactions

A $2Zn + O_2 \rightarrow 2ZnO$
B $\frac{4}{3}Al + O_2 \rightarrow \frac{2}{3}Al_2O_3$
C $2Ca + O_2 \rightarrow 2CaO$

(b) Why is it necessary to use electrolysis for the extraction of some metals?
(c) Why is it that the slope of the graph of free energy of formation of zinc oxide against temperature is as shown in the diagram, whereas the slope of the graph of free energy of formation of carbon monoxide against temperature has the opposite sign?

N,A

2   The Born–Haber cycle below represents the enthalpy changes in the formation of an alkali metal halide MX from an alkaline metal (Li, Na, K, Rb, Cs) and a halogen (F_2, Cl_2, Br_2 or I_2).

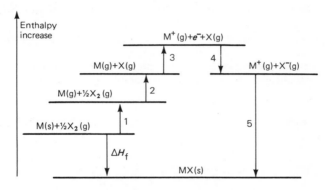

Born–Haber cycle for MX

(a) Name the halogen for which the enthalpy change 2 has the largest value.
(b) Name the alkali metal for which the enthalpy change 3 has the largest value.
(c) Name the halogen for which the enthalpy change 4 has the smallest value.
(d) Name the alkali metal halide for which the enthalpy change 5 has the smallest value.
(e) The following is a list of the enthalpy changes for potassium bromide (in kJ mol^{-1}):

$K(s)$	$\rightarrow K(g)$	$\Delta H =$	$+92$
$K(g)$	$\rightarrow K^+(g) + e^-$	$\Delta H =$	$+418$
$\frac{1}{2}Br_2(g)$	$\rightarrow Br(g)$	$\Delta H =$	$+96$
$Br(g) + e^-$	$\rightarrow Br^-(g)$	$\Delta H =$	-326
$K^+(g) + Br^-(g)$	$\rightarrow KBr(s)$	$\Delta H =$	-677

Calculate the standard enthalpy of formation, $\Delta H_f^{\ominus}$ of potassium bromide.

JMB,A

3   Comment on the following:
(a) Despite the thermochemical data contained in the following equations, sodium metal reacts vigorously and exothermically with chlorine gas.

$$Na(s) \rightarrow Na^+(g) \qquad \Delta H = 605 \text{ kJ mol}^{-1}$$
$$\tfrac{1}{2}Cl_2(g) \rightarrow Cl^-(g) \qquad \Delta H = -260 \text{ kJ mol}^{-1}$$

In view of your comments, discuss why sodium chloride is soluble in water.

(b) The ionization energies [expressed in electron volts (eV)] of the elements in the first short period are: Li, 5.4; Be, 9.3; C, 11.3; N, 14.5; O, 13.6; F, 17.4; Ne, 21.6.

C,A

4 Comment on the following:
   (a) KBr is a stable compound although the process $K(g) + Br(g) \rightarrow K^+(g) + Br^-(g)$ is endothermic.
   (b) Silver fluoride is the only silver halide that is appreciably soluble in water.
   (c) Nitrogen forms one endothermic chloride NCl_3 but phosphorus reacts with chlorine to give two chlorides PCl_3 and PCl_5.

O, Schol.

5 The Ellingham diagram for a number of metallic sulphides is reproduced below.

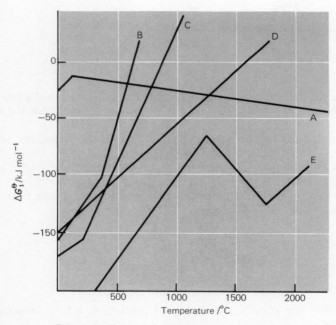

Ellingham diagrams for the reactions

A $\tfrac{1}{2}C + S \rightarrow \tfrac{1}{2}CS_2$
B $Hg + S \rightarrow HgS$
C $\tfrac{2}{3}Bi + S \rightarrow \tfrac{1}{3}Bi_2S_3$
D $H_2 + S \rightarrow H_2S$
E $Pb + S \rightarrow PbS$

Explain the shape of the graphs and show how possible reducing agents and conditions of temperature for the production of metals from sulphides can be deduced from the diagram.

In cases where a choice of reagent and conditions is possible for producing a metal from its sulphide what practical considerations might influence the actual choice made by industry?

Chapter 4
Acids and bases: oxidation and reduction

These topics, which are more fully treated in texts on physical chemistry, require some consideration here, because the terms 'acid', 'base', 'oxidation' and 'reduction' are used so widely in inorganic chemistry.

4.1 Protonic acids and bases

An acid was once defined simply as a substance which produces hydrogen ions, or protons. However, the simple proton, H^+, is never found under ordinary conditions, and this definition required amendment. Brønsted and, independently, Lowry, therefore redefined an acid as a substance able to *donate* protons to other molecules or ions, and a base as a substance capable of *accepting* such protons. If we consider hydrogen chloride, HCl, as an example, the HCl molecule is essentially covalent, and hydrogen chloride (gas or liquid) contains no protons. But anhydrous hydrogen chloride in benzene will react with anhydrous ammonia:

$$HCl + NH_3 \rightarrow NH_4^+Cl^-$$

Here, clearly, a proton is donated to the ammonia, which is the base, and hydrogen chloride is the acid. In water, the reaction of hydrogen chloride is essentially

$$HCl + H_2O \rightarrow H_3O^+ + Cl^-$$

and clearly here water is a base, but giving a *new acid* H_3O^+ and a new *base*, Cl^-. The concept of Cl^- as a base may at first seem strange but if an ionic chloride is added to concentrated sulphuric acid the following reaction occurs:

$$H_2SO_4 + Cl^- \rightarrow HCl + HSO_4^-$$
$$\text{acid} \qquad \text{base} \qquad \text{acid} \qquad \text{base}$$

Product acids and bases such as those formed in this process are termed *conjugate acids* and *conjugate bases*. Thus, all acid–base reactions can be written as

$$HA + B \rightarrow BH^+ + A^-$$
$$\text{acid} + \text{base} = \text{conjugate} + \text{conjugate}$$
$$\text{acid of} \qquad \text{base of}$$
$$\text{base B} \qquad \text{acid HA}$$

and this equation is the prototype for acid–base reactions whether or not B is a solvent. To quote an example, HCl in ethanol reacts as follows:

1        $HCl + C_2H_5OH \rightleftharpoons C_2H_5OH_2^+ + Cl^-$

but in ethanol the reaction is by no means complete, hence the equilibrium sign. If benzene is the solvent there is virtually no ionization and no reaction because benzene is a very weak base and HCl is not a strong enough acid to protonate it significantly. Let us consider a series of acids in water:

2             $HCl + H_2O \rightarrow H_3O^+ + Cl^-$
3          $H_2SO_4 + H_2O \rightarrow H_3O^+ + HSO_4^-$
4           $HSO_4^- + H_2O \rightleftharpoons H_3O^+ + SO_4^{2-}$
5           $HNO_3 + H_2O \rightarrow H_3O^+ + NO_3^-$
6   $CH_3CO_2H + H_2O \rightleftharpoons H_3O^+ + CH_3CO_2^-$

Ionizations 2, 3 and 5 are complete ionizations so that in water HCl and HNO_3 are completely ionized and H_2SO_4 is completely ionized as a monobasic acid. Since this is so, all these acids in water really exist as the solvated proton (the 'hydrogen ion')*, and as far as their acid properties are concerned they are the same conjugate acid species (with different conjugate bases). Such acids are termed *strong acids* or more correctly strong acids in water. (In ethanol as solvent, equilibria such as 1 would be the result for all the acids quoted above.) Ionizations 4 and 6 do not proceed to completion and thus the conjugate acid H_3O^+ is not completely formed — such acids are termed *weak acids*. (Again, more correctly, weak acids in the solvent specified; HCl is a weak acid in ethanol.) The *strength* of an acid is measured by the position of equilibrium. For example, for a weak acid in water

$HA + H_2O \rightleftharpoons H_3O^+ + A^-$

the equilibrium constant is given by

$$K_c = \frac{[H_3O^+][A^-]}{[H_2O][HA]}$$

However, in dilute solution $[H_2O]$ is virtually constant ($[H_2O] = 55.5$ mol l^{-1} since 1 litre of water contains $1000/18$ mol of H_2O) and taking this into the above expression for the equilibrium constant we obtain a second constant

$$K_a = \frac{[H_3O^+][A^-]}{[HA]} \text{mol } l^{-1}$$

K_a is known as the *acid dissociation constant*; it is a measure of the strength of an acid in a particular solvent, which should be specified.

Values of K_a are small for weak acids and they range very widely (*Table 4.1*). It is common practice to quote values as the negative logarithm to the base ten, i.e. $-\log_{10} K_a$, since such numbers are less cumbersome and positive when $K_a < 1$. The symbol for $-\log_{10}$ is by convention 'p', thus $-\log_{10} K_a$ becomes pK_a. *Table 4.1* shows some typical pK_a values.

*Solvated proton species $[H(H_2O)_x]^+$ are conveniently represented as H_3O^+, the oxonium or hydroxonium ion (more briefly still as the hydrogen ion H^+).

Table 4.1 Some values of pK_a for acids in water at 298 K

Acid	K_a/mol l^{-1}	pK_a
Ethanoic (acetic)	1.75×10^{-5}	4.756
Methanoic (formic)	1.77×10^{-4}	3.752
Hydrocyanic	7.9×10^{-10}	9.1
Hydrofluoric	6.61×10^{-4}	3.18
Hydrogen sulphide*	10^{-7}	7.00
Phenol	1.05×10^{-10}	9.98

*For the reaction $H_2S + H_2O \rightleftharpoons HS^- + H_3O^+$.

For strong acids, K_a values are large and pK_a values are negative, for example pK_a for hydrochloric acid is -7.

4.1.1 The effect of the solvent

If, for a given acid, we wish to increase the acid strength, then we choose a solvent which has a greater affinity for protons than has water. If we add ammonia to a solution of hydrogen chloride in water, the essential equilibrium is

$$H_3O^+ + NH_3 \rightleftharpoons H_2O + NH_4^+$$

and clearly here ammonia has a stronger affinity for protons than water — it is a stronger base. Hence if we dissolve an acid which is weak in water in *liquid* ammonia, the strength of the acid is increased, i.e. pK_a decreases. Thus methanoic (formic) acid is a weak acid in water but a strong acid in liquid ammonia.

When we use *any* substance as a solvent for a protonic acid, the acidic and basic species produced by dissociation of the solvent molecules determine the limits of acidity or basicity in that solvent. Thus, in water, we cannot have any substance or species more basic than OH^- or more acidic than H_3O^+; in liquid ammonia, the limiting basic entity is NH_2^-, the acidic is NH_4^+. Many common inorganic acids, for example HCl, HNO_3, H_2SO_4 are all equally strong in water because their strengths are '*levelled*' to that of the solvent species H_3O^+. Only by putting them into a more acidic solvent do they become weak acids, with determinate pK_a values which differentiate their strengths. Thus in pure ethanoic (acetic) acid as solvent, the order of strength of some common strong acids is

$$H_2SO_4 > HCl > HNO_3$$

As we shall see later, the limitations imposed by most solvents may prevent us from being able to utilize the very strong *basic* characteristics of some anions. However, at this point it is more useful to consider other factors affecting the strengths of acids.

4.1.2 The effect of structure: acid strength in water

Consider first two substances which have very similar molecules, HF, hydrogen fluoride and HCl, hydrogen chloride; the first is a weak acid in

Table 4.2 Acid strengths of hydrofluoric and hydrochloric acids

Term	Reaction	$\Delta H^{\ominus}/kJ\ mol^{-1}$	
		HF	HCl
1	$HX(aq) \rightarrow HX(g)$	48	18
2	$HX(g) \rightarrow H(g) + X(g)$	566	431
3	$H(g) \rightarrow H^+(g) + e^-$	1318	1318
4	$X(g) + e^- \rightarrow X^-(g)$	−333	−364
5	$H^+(g) \rightarrow H^+(aq)$	−1091	−1091
6	$X^-(g) \rightarrow X^-(aq)$	−515	−381
7	$HX(aq) \rightarrow H^+(aq) + X^-(aq)$	−7	−69

water, the second is a strong acid. To see the reason consider the enthalpy changes involved when each substance in water dissociates to form an acid, as shown in *Table 4.2*. Clearly, the higher enthalpy of solution 1 and bond dissociation energy 2 of hydrogen fluoride outweigh the greater hydration enthalpy of $F^-(g)$ 6 and $\Delta H^{\ominus}_{298}$ for HF, 7 is quite small; this means a smaller pK_a value than for HCl. Clearly, one important factor in determining acid strength is the strength of the X—H bond; in many inorganic substances, this is in fact an O—H bond, for example in water (a weak acid) and in HNO_3, H_2SO_4 (strong acids). For water, the strength of the O—H bond is decreased (and the acid strength increased) by coordination of the water to a small highly charged cation. This means that species such as $[Al(H_2O)_6]^{3+}$ are quite strongly acidic; the relevant equilibria have already been discussed in some detail (p. 40).

Many of the inorganic oxoacids are strong (i.e. have negative pK_a vaalues) in aqueous solution. But, as we have seen, use of a solvent with a lower proton affinity than water [for example pure ethanoic (acetic) acid] makes it possible to differentiate between the strengths of these acids and measure pK_a values. The order of strength of some typical oxoacids is then found to be (for $H_nX \rightarrow H_{n-1}X^- + H^+$) as shown in *Table 4.3*. If the formulae of the acids are written as shown on the right, it becomes apparent that *acid strength increases as the number of oxygen atoms not involved in* O—H *bonding increases*.

Table 4.3 Strengths of some oxoacids

	Formula	Acid	Hydroxide formula
Increasing strength	H_2CO_3	Carbonic	$OC(OH)_2$
	H_3PO_4	Phosphoric(V)	$OP(OH)_3$
	H_2SO_4	Sulphuric	$O_2S(OH)_2$
	$HClO_4$	Chloric(VII) (Perchloric)	$O_3Cl(OH)$

4.1.3 The effect of structure: base strength

A base must be capable of accepting protons; for this, at least one lone pair of electrons is a prerequisite, since an electron pair is needed to attach a proton. In general, base strength (a) decreases as the *number of lone pairs* increases, (b) increases as the *size of the base molecule or ion* decreases, and (c) increases as the *negative charge on the base* increases. As an example of the effect of lone pairs, consider the sequence NH_3, H_2O, HF. All are neutral molecules and are of similar size; but the marked decrease of base strength from NH_3 to HF occurs as the number of electron pairs increases from one to three. The effect of size has already been observed; both ions F^- and Cl^-, with four lone pairs each, are weak bases, but F^- is a stronger base (loses its proton less readily) than is Cl^- because F^- is smaller. The effect of charge can be considerable: of the two species H_2O and OH^-, the latter is by far the stronger base, even though it has three lone pairs as against two in H_2O. If we consider O^{2-} (for example, in K_2O), with four lone pairs, but a double negative charge, this is so strongly basic that it reacts with water thus:

$$O^{2-} + H_2O \rightarrow 2OH^-$$

As an example of a really strong base, the hydride ion H^- (for example in NaH) is unique; it has one lone pair, a negative charge and a very small size. Like O^{2-}, it is too strong a base to exist in water:

$$H^- + H_2O \rightarrow H_2 + OH^-$$

Since, generally, *any* base stronger than OH^- will react with water to produce OH^- we must use another solvent to 'observe' very strong bases. The high base strengths of the hydride ion and the oxide ion can best be observed in *molten salts* as solvents*, since hydrides and ionic oxides are either insoluble in ordinary solvents or attack them.

For very strong acids, it is usually possible to use a solvent of a more conventional kind; thus, for example, the acid HBF_4, tetrafluoroboric acid, is extremely strong, because attachement of the hydrogen to the tetrafluoroborate group BF_4 is essentially ionic, $H^+BF_4^-$, and hence dissociation to an acid is very easy. Hence HBF_4 behaves as a strong acid in, for example, an organic solvent, in which it can be used.

4.2 Other concepts of acids and bases

Liquid ammonia (p. 197), like water, is very slightly dissociated, and shows a very small electrical conductance:

$$2NH_3 \rightleftharpoons NH_4^+ + NH_2^-$$
cf.
$$2H_2O \rightleftharpoons H_3O^+ + OH^-$$

By analogy, ammonium salts should behave as acids in liquid ammonia,

---

*Thus, the strongly basic oxide ion O^{2-} attacks the weakly acidic SiO_2 in a molten salt as solvent (p. 169):

$$SiO_2 + O^{2-} \rightarrow SiO_3^{2-}$$

since they produce the cation NH_4^+ (the 'solvo-cation'), and soluble inorganic amides (for example KNH_2, ionic) should act as bases. This idea is borne out by experiment; ammonium salts in liquid ammonia react with certain metals and hydrogen is given off. The neutralization of an ionic amide solution by a solution of an ammonium salt in liquid ammonia can be carried out and followed by an indicator or by the change in the potential of an electrode, just like the reaction of sodium hydroxide with hydrochloric acid in water. The only *notable* difference is that the salt formed in liquid ammonia is usually insoluble and therefore precipitates.

Other liquid inorganic compounds show the 'autodissociation' characteristic of water and liquid ammonia; for example, dinitrogen tetroxide (p. 207), as well as undergoing the more familiar *homolytic* dissociation

$$N_2O_4 \xrightleftharpoons[\text{cool}]{\text{heat}} 2NO_2$$

can also dissociate thus:

$$N_2O_4 \rightleftharpoons NO^+ + NO_3^-$$

i.e. a *heterolytic* dissociation, giving ions, and therefore producing a slight electrical conductance. By analogy, compounds containing the ion NO^+ (the *nitrosyl* cation) should behave as acids and nitrates as bases in liquid dinitrogen tetroxide. The neutralization reaction

$$\begin{array}{llll} NOCl & + \ KNO_3 & \rightarrow \ KCl \ + & N_2O_4 \\ \text{nitrosyl chloride} & \text{potassium} & \text{salt} & \text{solvent} \\ \text{(acid)} & \text{nitrate} & & \\ & \text{(base)} & & \end{array}$$

does in fact occur in liquid dinitrogen tetroxide. Just as some metals dissolve in water or alkali to give off hydrogen and yield hydroxides, metals can dissolve in dinitrogen tetroxide to give off nitrogen monoxide and yield nitrates; this type of reaction has been used to produce an anhydrous nitrate of copper(II) which has unexpected properties (p. 360).

Hence, acids can be defined as substances producing cations characteristic of the solvent (solvo-cations, for example H_3O^+, NH_4^+, NO^+), and bases as substances producing anions characteristic of the solvent (solvo-anions, for example OH^-, NH_2^-, NO_3^-). This concept has been applied to solvents such as liquid sulphur dioxide, liquid hydrogen chloride and pure sulphuric acid.

We have seen that a base can be defined as combining with a proton and, therefore, requires at least one lone pair of electrons. A more general definition of acids and bases, due to G. N. Lewis, describes a base as *any* species (atom, ion or molecule) which can donate an electron pair, and an acid as any species which can accept an electron pair — more simply, *a base is an electron-pair donor, an acid an electron-pair acceptor*. Some examples of Lewis acids and bases are shown in *Table 4.4*.

These other concepts of acids and bases are not so easily applied quantitatively as the Lowry–Brønsted concept. Nevertheless they have proved to be very useful as ways of classifying chemical substances and —

Table 4.4 Lewis acids and bases

Acid	Base	Neutralization reaction			
$AlCl_3$	NH_3	$AlCl_3$	$+$	NH_3	$\rightarrow H_3N{:}AlCl_3$
SO_3	$N(CH_3)_3$	SO_3	$+$	$N(CH_3)_3$	$\rightarrow (CH_3)_3N{:}SO_3$
Ag^+	NH_3	Ag^+	$+$	$2NH_3$	$\rightarrow [Ag(NH_3)_2]^+$
CO_2	O^{2-}	CO_2	$+$	O^{2-}	$\rightarrow CO_3^{2-}$
H^+	OH^-	H^+	$+$	OH^-	$\rightarrow H_2O$
BF_3	$(C_2H_5)_2O$	BF_3	$+$	$(C_2H_5)_2O$	$\rightarrow (C_2H_5)_2O{:}BF_3$
Ni^{2+}	H_2O	Ni^{2+}	$+$	$6H_2O$	$\rightarrow [Ni(H_2O)_6]^{2+}$

more importantly — these ideas have been a stimulus to many advances in inorganic chemistry.

4.3   Reduction–oxidation processes

The term *oxidation* was originally applied to the formation of a metal oxide by the direct combination of the metal and oxygen. For example,

$$2Mg + O_2 \rightarrow 2MgO$$

The reverse of this process was termed *reduction* and reagents which removed oxygen were termed *reducing agents*. Consider the reactions

1        $CuO + H_2 \rightarrow Cu + H_2O$
2        $ZnO + C \rightarrow Zn + CO$

In reaction 1 hydrogen is the reducing agent, as it removes oxygen, but we should also note that the hydrogen, in accepting oxygen, to form water, is itself oxidized. Carbon, in example 2, is the reducing agent, being itself oxidized by accepting oxygen. Here we see immediately that both processes, oxidation and reduction, *must* occur simultaneously.

Reduction was then defined as the removal of oxygen or the addition of hydrogen, whilst oxidation was the addition of oxygen or the removal of hydrogen.

These definitions are still valuable, especially in organic chemistry; for inorganic reactions they require extension. It was soon recognized that substances other than oxygen can behave as oxidizing agents. The conversion of aqueous sulphur dioxide solution to sulphuric acid, for example, can be accomplished using mercury(II) oxide or chlorine water, the equations being most simply represented as

$$SO_2 + H_2O + HgO \rightarrow H_2SO_4 + Hg$$
$$SO_2 + 2H_2O + Cl_2 \rightarrow H_2SO_4 + 2HCl$$

and the oxidation being from sulphur(IV) to sulphur(VI). It follows that the reaction simply represented as

$$2FeCl_2 + Cl_2 \rightarrow 2FeCl_3$$

can be described as an oxidation of iron(II) to iron(III). Since like many other inorganic compounds the iron(II) and iron(III) chlorides form ions in solution, this oxidation could be represented by the ionic equation

$$Fe^{2+}(aq) \rightarrow Fe^{3+}(aq) + e^-$$

Thus an oxidizing agent is identified as an electron acceptor and the oxidation of iron(II) by chlorine can be written as two 'half' equations, viz.

$$2Fe^{2+}(aq) \rightarrow 2Fe^{3+}(aq) + 2e^-$$
$$Cl_2 + 2e^- \rightarrow 2Cl^-$$

$$2Fe^{2+}(aq) + Cl_2 \rightarrow 2Fe^{3+}(aq) + 2Cl^-$$

Reduction can now be defined as a process in which electrons are acquired and oxidation a process in which electrons are released. These definitions are often difficult to remember and the following simplification may be helpful:

$$X^{3+} \rightarrow X^{2+} \rightarrow X^{+1} \rightarrow X^0 \rightarrow X^{-1} \rightarrow X^{-2}$$
$$\text{reduction} \longrightarrow$$

Thus, the *reducing* agent causes *reduction* to take place, i.e. causes a *reduction* in the positive charge; it must therefore *supply* electrons. It follows immediately that the *oxidizing* agent must accept electrons.

4.3.1   Electron transfer

Using the electron transfer definition, we can identify many more reactions as redox (reduction–oxidation) reactions. An example is the displacement of a metal from its salt by a more reactive metal. Consider the reaction between zinc and a solution of copper(II) sulphate, which can be represented by the equation

$$CuSO_4 + Zn \rightarrow ZnSO_4 + Cu$$

This can be written as two simple ionic 'half' equations

1    $Cu^{2+}(aq) + 2e^- \rightarrow Cu(s)$
2    $Zn(s) \rightarrow Zn^{2+}(aq) + 2e^-$

$$Cu^{2+}(aq) + Zn(s) \rightarrow Zn^{2+}(aq) + Cu(s)$$

In reaction 1 the copper ions are being reduced; zinc is responsible and is therefore the reducing agent. In reaction 2 which occurs simultaneously, the zinc is being oxidized and the copper(II) ions are responsible and must therefore be the oxidizing agent. Electron transfer in this case can easily be established using the apparatus shown in *Figure 4.1*. When M is a field-effect transistor voltmeter taking no current it gives an indication of the differing energy of the two systems (p. 88); when M is an ammeter, electron flow is from the zinc (the negative), which is being oxidized, to the copper (the positive) and hence to the copper(II) ions, which are being discharged and therefore reduced. The salt bridge is filled with an electrolyte, usually potassium chloride solution, to complete the circuit. This cell is more commonly encountered as the Daniell cell in the form shown diagrammatically in *Figure 4.2*. A series of experiments using different metals and their salts enables an

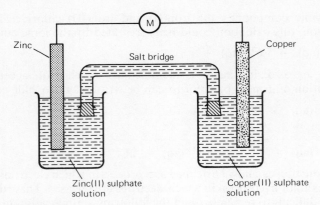

Figure 4.1 Apparatus to show electron transfer between copper and zinc

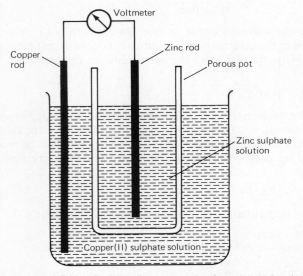

Figure 4.2 The Daniell cell, an example of an electrochemical cell

approximate order of reducing power, or of reactivity, to be established for metals — this is known as the reactivity or electrochemical series.

Electron transfer can be established experimentally in reactions involving only ions in solution. Inert electrodes, made from platinum, are used to transfer electrons to and from the ions. The apparatus used is shown in *Figure 4.3*. The redox reaction being considered can be represented as

$$2Fe^{2+}(aq) + Br_2(aq) \rightarrow 2Fe^{3+}(aq) + 2Br^-(aq)$$

When M is a voltmeter an indication of the energy difference between the reactants and products is obtained (*see* below). A current passes when M is an ammeter, and if a little potassium thiocyanate is added to the $Fe^{2+}(aq)$ a red colour is produced around the electrode, indicating the formation of iron(III)

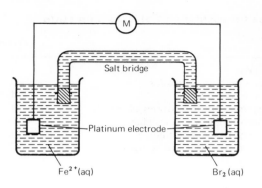

Figure 4.3 Apparatus to show electron transfer between ions in solution

ions in solution; the typical bromine colour is slowly discharged as it is converted into colourless bromide Br^-.

A series of experiments can be performed and an order of reducing power established.

4.3.2   Stoichiometry of redox reactions

Since electrical neutrality must be maintained in a redox reaction, the total number of electrons lost by the reducing agent must equal the total number of electrons gained by the oxidizing agent. For example, if each atom of the reducing agent gives three electrons, and each atom of the oxidizing agent accepts two electrons, i.e.

(i) $A \rightarrow A^{3+} + 3e^-$
(ii) $B + 2e^- \rightarrow B^{2-}$

then the stoichiometry is (i) $\times$ 2, and (ii) $\times$ 3 so that electrical neutrality is maintained, i.e.

$$2A + 3B \rightarrow 2A^{3+} + 3B^{2-}$$

We have discussed the simple ionic reaction

$$2Fe^{2+}(aq) + Br_2(aq) \rightarrow 2Fe^{3+}(aq) + 2Br^-(aq)$$

but when complex ions are involved the use of oxidation states proves useful. The oxidation state for a simple ion is the charge on the ion; for the central atom of a complex ion it is the charge the element in question would have it it was a simple ion, i.e. not co-ordinated or bonded to other species. Oxidation states can be deduced from the definitions and assumptions shown in *Table 4.5*.

The sum of all the oxidation numbers in a molecule in zero. Several examples are shown in *Table 4.6*.

Oxidation states can be used to establish the stoichiometry for an equation. Consider the reaction between the manganate(VII) (permanganate) and ethanedioate (oxalate) ions in acidic solution. Under these conditions the $MnO_4^-(aq)$ ion acts as an oxidizing agent and it is reduced to $Mn^{2+}(aq)$, i.e.

Table 4.5 Rules for assignment of oxidation state

Species	Oxidation state
Uncombined element	0
Combined oxygen except in peroxides	-2
Combined oxygen in peroxides	-1
Combined hydrogen except in hydrides of metals	$+1$
Combined hydrogen in hydrides of metals	-1
Alkali metals (Group I) in compounds	$+1$
Alkaline earth metals (Group II) in compounds	$+2$

Table 4.6 Calculation of the oxidation state of some central atoms in oxo-ions

Ion	Number of oxygen atoms (x)	Total oxidation number due to oxygen $(2x)$	Charge on ion (y)	Oxidation state of central atom $[=-(2x-y)]$	Name of ion
MnO_4^-	4	-8	-1	$+7$	manganate(VII)
ClO_3^-	3	-6	-1	$+5$	chlorate(V)
NO_3^-	3	-6	-1	$+5$	nitrate(V)
PO_4^{3-}	4	-8	-3	$+5$	phosphate(V)
SO_4^{2-}	4	-8	-2	$+6$	sulphate(VI)
SO_3^{2-}	3	-6	-2	$+4$	sulphate(IV)
$Cr_2O_7^{2-}$	7	-14	-2	$+12/2$	dichromate(VI)

*In the case of the dichromate(VI) ion, the two chromium atoms are equivalent, and each is assigned the oxidation state $+6$. A knowledge of the structure of the ion is necessary because simplistic treatments can lead to incorrect results (*see* p. 258).

$$Mn^{VII} + 5e^- \rightarrow Mn^{2+}$$

The full half equation is

(i) $MnO_4^-(aq) + 8H_3O^+ + 5e^- \rightarrow Mn^{2+}(aq) + 12H_2O$

The ethanedioate (oxalate) ion $C_2O_4^{2-}(aq)$ is oxidized to carbon dioxide, i.e.

(ii) $C_2O_4^{2-}(aq) \rightarrow 2CO_2 + 2e^-$

To maintain electrical neutrality in the reaction we need to multiply (i) by 2 and (ii) by 5, ten electrons being transferred. The overall reaction then becomes

$$2MnO_4^-(aq) + 16H_3O^+ + 10e^- \rightarrow 2Mn^{2+}(aq) + 24H_2O$$
$$5C_2O_4^{2-}(aq) \rightarrow 10CO_2 + 10e^-$$

$$2MnO_4^-(aq) + 16H_3O + 5C_2O_4^{2-} \rightarrow 2Mn^{2+}(aq) + 24H_2O + 10CO_2$$

Consider also the oxidation of iron(II) ions by dichromate(VI) ions in acidic solution. The $Cr_2O_7^{2-}$ is reduced to $Cr^{3+}(aq)$

$$Cr_2O_7^{2-}(aq) + 6e^- \rightarrow 2Cr^{3+}(aq)$$

The full half equation is

(i) $Cr_2O_7^{2-}(aq) + 6e^- + 14H_3O^+ \rightarrow 2Cr^{3+}(aq) + 21H_2O$

The $Fe^{2+}(aq)$ is oxidized to $Fe^{3+}(aq)$, i.e.

(ii) $Fe^{2+}(aq) \rightarrow Fe^{3+}(aq) + e^-$

Thus the equation for the reaction is:

$$Cr_2O_7^{2-}(aq) + 6Fe^{2+}(aq) + 14H_3O^+ \rightarrow 2Cr^{3+}(aq) + 6Fe^{3+}(aq) + 21H_2O$$

4.3.3   Standard redox potentials

When the reaction between zinc and copper(II) sulphate was carried out in the form of an electrochemical cell (p. 84), a potential difference between the copper and zinc electrodes was noted. This potential resulted from the differing tendencies of the two metals to form ions. An equilibrium is established when any metal is placed in a solution of its ions.

The enthalpy changes involved are shown in *Figure 4.4* for the equilibrium

$$M(s) \rightleftharpoons M^{2+}(aq) + 2e^-$$

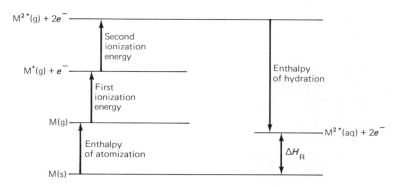

Figure 4.4 Enthalpy changes for the reaction
$M(s) \rightleftharpoons M^{2+}(aq) + 2e^-$

and values for copper and zinc are given in *Table 4.7*. It can then be deduced that the equilibrium for copper is further to the left than for zinc, i.e. copper has less tendency to form ions in solution than has zinc. The position of equilibrium (which depends also on temperature and concentration) is related to the relative reducing powers of the metals when two different metals in solutions of their ions are connected (as shown in *Figure 4.1* for the copper–zinc cell); a potential difference is noted because of the differing equilibrium positions.

Since it is not possible to measure a single electrode potential, one electrode system must be taken as a standard and all others measured relative to it. By international agreement the hydrogen electrode has been

Table 4.7 Energy values/kJ mol⁻¹ for zinc and copper in the process shown in *Figure 4.4*

Metal	Enthalpy of atomization	Sum of both ionization energies	Enthalpy of hydration	ΔH_R
Cu	339	2703	−2100	+942
Zn	126	2640	−2046	+720

chosen as the reference:

$$H_2(g) \rightleftharpoons 2H^+(aq) + 2e^-$$

This electrode, shown diagrammatically in *Figure 4.5*, is assigned zero potential when hydrogen gas at one atmosphere pressure bubbles over platinized platinum in a solution of hydrogen ions of concentration $1 \text{ mol } l^{-1}$ (strictly, at unit activity).

Figure 4.5 The hydrogen electrode

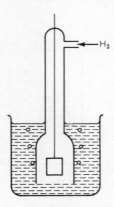

H₂

Standard redox potentials for metals (usually called electrode potentials), $E^{\ominus}$, are measured at 298 K relative to a standard hydrogen electrode for the pure metal in a solution containing $1 \text{ mol } l^{-1}$ of its ions and at pH = 0 (i.e. containing $1 \text{ mol } l^{-1}$ hydrogen ions). (The importance of pH is stressed later, p. 92). If the metal is a better reducing agent than hydrogen the metal will lose electrons more readily than hydrogen and, therefore, be negative with respect to the hydrogen electrode. *Table 4.8* gives the standard redox potentials of some common metals. By convention the oxidized state is always written on the left-hand side.

Redox half-reactions are often written for brevity as, for example, $Li^+ + e^- \rightarrow Li$, with the state symbols omitted. The electrode system represented by the half-reaction may also be written as Li^+/Li. The standard redox potentials for ion–ion redox systems can be determined by setting up the relevant half-cell and measuring the potential at 298 K relative to a standard hydrogen electrode.

Table 4.8 Standard redox potentials of some common ions

Reaction		$E^{\ominus}/V$
$Li^+(aq) + e^- \rightarrow Li(s)$		-3.04
$K^+(aq) + e^- \rightarrow K(s)$		-2.92
$Ba^{2+}(aq) + 2e^- \rightarrow Ba(s)$		-2.90
$Ca^{2+}(aq) + 2e^- \rightarrow Ca(s)$		-2.87
$Na^+(aq) + e^- \rightarrow Na(s)$		-2.71
$Mg^{2+}(aq) + 2e^- \rightarrow Mg(s)$		-2.37
$Al^{3+}(aq) + 3e^- \rightarrow Al(s)$		-1.66
$Zn^{2+}(aq) + 2e \rightarrow Zn(s)$		-0.76
$Fe^{2+}(aq) + 2e^- \rightarrow Fe(s)$	Increasing	-0.44
$Ni^{2+}(aq) + 2e^- \rightarrow Ni(s)$	reducing	-0.25
$Sn^{2+}(aq) + 2e^- \rightarrow Sn(s)$	power	-0.14
$Pb^{2+}(aq) + 2e^- \rightarrow Pb(s)$	of metal	-0.13
$Fe^{3+}(aq) + 3e^- \rightarrow Fe(s)$		-0.04
$H_3O^+ + e^- \rightarrow \frac{1}{2}H_2(g) + H_2O(l)$		0.00
$Cu^{2+}(aq) + 2e^- \rightarrow Cu(s)$		$+0.34$
$Ag^+(aq) + e^- \rightarrow Ag(s)$		$+0.80$
$Hg^{2+}(aq) + 2e^- \rightarrow Hg(s)$		$+0.86$
$Au^{3+}(aq) + 3e^- \rightarrow Au(s)$		$+1.50$

For example, the standard redox potential for the half-reactions

$$Fe^{3+}(aq) + e^- \rightarrow Fe^{2+}(aq)$$

can be determined by measuring the potential of a half-cell, made 1 molar with respect to both iron(II) and iron(III) ions, and in which a platinized platinum electrode is placed, relative to a standard hydrogen electrode at 298 K.

For many purposes the hydrogen electrode is not convenient and it can be replaced by another electrode of known standard electrode potential. A well-known example is the calomel electrode, one form of which is shown in *Figure 4.6.*

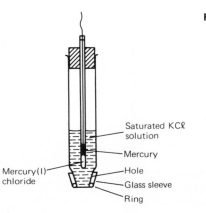

Figure 4.6 The saturated calomel electrode

Saturated KCℓ solution

Mercury

Mercury(I) chloride

Hole

Glass sleeve

Ring

Table 4.9 Redox potentials for ion–ion systems in acid solutions

	Reaction		$E^{\ominus}/V$
	$Sn^{4+}(aq) + 2e^- \rightarrow Sn^{2+}(aq)$		$+0.15$
	$\frac{1}{2}I_2(s) + e^- \rightarrow I^-(aq)$		$+0.54$
	$Fe^{3+}(aq) + e^- \rightarrow Fe^{2+}(aq)$		$+0.76$
Increasing	$\frac{1}{2}Br_2(l) + e^- \rightarrow Br^-(aq)$	Increasing	$+1.07$
oxidizing	$IO_3^-(aq) + 6H_3O^+ + 5e^- \rightarrow \frac{1}{2}I_2(s) + 9H_2O$	reducing	$+1.19$
power	$O_2(g) + 4H_3O^+ + 4e^- \rightarrow 6H_2O$	power	$+1.23$
of left-hand	$Cr_2O_7^{2-} + 14H_3O^+ + 6e^- \rightarrow 2Cr^{3+} + 21H_2O$	of right-hand	$+1.33$
reagent	$\frac{1}{2}Cl_2(g) + e^- \rightarrow Cl^-(aq)$	reagent	$+1.36$
	$MnO_4^- + 8H_3O^+ + 5e^- \rightarrow Mn^{2+}(aq) + 12H_2O$		$+1.52$
	$\frac{1}{2}F_2(g) + e^- \rightarrow F^-(aq)$		$+2.80$

A number of redox potentials for ion–ion systems are given in *Table 4.9*; here again, state symbols are often omitted.

4.3.4   Calculation of standard cell potentials

Values of standard cell potentials and cell polarity can readily be obtained by writing the data, relative to a standard hydrogen electrode $E^{\ominus} = 0.00$, in a diagram as shown below.

For the cell shown in *Figure 4.1* (p. 84) but with both solutions molar, the data are

$Zn^{2+} + 2e^- \rightleftharpoons Zn \qquad E^{\ominus} = -0.76$ V
$Cu^{2+} + 2e^- \rightleftharpoons Cu \qquad E^{\ominus} = +0.34$ V

giving the diagram shown in *Figure 4.7*.

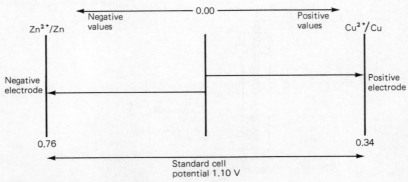

Figure 4.7 Cell diagram for zinc and copper

By convention this cell is written

$$Zn|Zn^{2+}||Cu^{2+}|Cu \qquad E^{\ominus}_{cell} = +1.10 \text{ volts}$$

representing zinc metal | in a solution of zinc ions connected by a salt bridge || to a solution of copper ions | with a copper electrode.

The positive electrode, the oxidizing agent is, again by convention, written on the right hand side and determines the sign of the cell potential E_{cell}, in this case 1.10 V.

Similarly for the cell

$$Pt|2I^-(aq),I_2(aq)||MnO_4^-(aq),Mn^{2+}(aq)|Pt$$

the data are

$$\tfrac{1}{2}I_2 + e^- \rightleftharpoons I^- \qquad\qquad\qquad\qquad\qquad\qquad E^{\ominus} = +0.54 \text{ V}$$
$$MnO_4^- + 8H_3O^+ + 5e^- \rightleftharpoons Mn^{2+} + 12H_2O \qquad E^{\ominus} = +1.52 \text{ V}$$

and, from *Figure 4.8*, we obtain

$$Pt|2I^-(aq),I_2(aq)||MnO_4^-(aq),Mn^{2+}(aq)|Pt \qquad\qquad E^{\ominus} = +0.98 \text{ V}$$

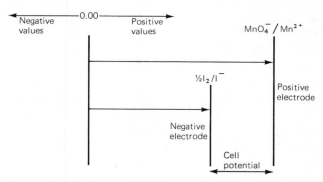

Figure 4.8 Cell diagram for the oxidation of iodine by manganate(VII) ion

4.3.5 The effect of concentration and temperature on potentials

Changes in ion concentration and temperature influence redox potentials by affecting the equilibrium

$$M(s) \rightleftharpoons M^{n+}(aq) + ne^-$$

The change in the redox potential is given quantitatively by the Nernst equation:

$$E = E^{\ominus} + \frac{RT}{nF}\log_e[(M^{n+}(aq)]$$

where E is the actual electrode potential, $E^{\ominus}$ is the standard electrode potential, R the gas constant, T the temperature in K, F the Faraday constant and n the number of electrons.

Substituting for R and F and for a temperature of 298 K this equation approximates to:

$$E = E^\ominus + \frac{0.06}{n}\log_{10}[M^{n+}(aq)]$$

The redox (electrode) potential for ion–ion redox systems at any concentration and temperature is given by the Nernst equation in the form

$$E = E^\ominus + \frac{RT}{nF}\log_e\left[\frac{\text{Oxidized state}}{\text{Reduced state}}\right]$$

(Note that the equation for metal–metal ion systems is a special case of this general equation since the reduced state is the metal itself and the concentration of a solid is a constant and omitted from the equation.)

4.3.6 The effect of change of ligand and pH on redox potentials

The data in *Tables 4.8* and *4.9* refer to ions in aqueous *acid* solution; for cations, this means effectively $[M(H_2O)_x]^{n+}$ species. However, we have already seen that the hydrated cations of elements such as aluminium or iron undergo 'hydrolysis' when the pH is increased (p. 40). We may then assume (correctly), that the redox potential of the system

$$Fe^{3+}(aq) + e^- \rightarrow Fe^{2+}(aq)$$

will change with change of pH. In fact, in this example, change of pH here means a change of ligand since, as the solution becomes more alkaline, the iron(III) species in solution changes from $[Fe(H_2O)_6]^{3+}$ to $[Fe(OH)_3(H_2O)_3]$ [i.e. iron(III) hydroxide]. The iron(II) species changes similarly. The redox half-reaction then becomes

$$[Fe(OH)_3(H_2O)_3] + e^- + H_2O \rightarrow [Fe(OH)_2(H_2O)_4] + OH^- \qquad E^\ominus = -0.56 \text{ V}$$

This may be compared with $E^\ominus = +0.76$ V in acid solution; thus in alkaline conditions, iron(II) becomes a good reducing agent, i.e. is easily oxidized.

When the water ligands around a cation are replaced by other ligands which are more strongly attached, the redox potential can change dramatically, for example for the cobalt(II)–cobalt(III) system we have

(i) $[Co^{III}(H_2O)_6]^{3+} + e^- \rightarrow [Co^{II}(H_2O)_6]^{2+}$ $E^\ominus = +1.81$ V

(ii) $[Co^{III}(NH_3)_6]^{3+}(aq) + e^- \rightarrow [Co^{II}(NH_3)_6]^{2+}(aq)$ $E^\ominus = +0.1$ V

(iii) $[Co^{III}(CN)_6]^{3-}(aq) + e^- \rightarrow [Co^{II}(CN)_5(H_2O)]^{3-}(aq) + CN^-$ $E^\ominus = -0.83$ V

Half-reaction (i) means that Co(II) in aqueous solution cannot be oxidized to Co(III); by adding ammonia to obtain the complexes in (ii), oxidation is readily achieved by, for example, air. Similarly, by adding cyanide, the hexacyanocobaltate(II) complex becomes a sufficiently strong reducing agent to produce hydrogen from water!

When either hydrogen ions or hydroxide ions participate in a redox half-reaction, then clearly the redox potential is affected by change of pH. Manganate(VII) ions are usually used in well-acidified solution, where (as we shall see in detail later) they oxidize chloride ions. If the pH is increased to make the solution only mildly acidic (pH = 3–6), the redox potential changes from 1.52 V to about 1.1 V, and chloride is not oxidized. This fact is of practical use; in a mixture of iodide and chloride ions in mildly acid solution, manganate(VII) oxidizes only iodide; addition of acid causes oxidation of chloride to proceed.

Other important effects of ligand and pH changes on redox potentials will be given under the appropriate element.

4.3.7   Uses of redox potentials

Reaction feasibility predictions
When the e.m.f. of a cell is measured by balancing it against an external voltage, so that no current flows, the maximum e.m.f. is obtained since the cell is at equilibrium. The maximum work obtainable from the cell is then nFE J, where n is the number of electrons transferred, F is the Faraday unit and E is the maximum cell e.m.f. We saw in Chapter 3 that the maximum amount of work obtainable from a reaction is given by the free energy change, i.e. $-\Delta G$. Hence

$$-\Delta G = nFE$$

or

$$\Delta G = -nFE$$

For a half-cell under standard conditions this becomes

$$\Delta G^{\ominus} = -nFE^{\ominus}$$

where $\Delta G^{\ominus}$ and $E^{\ominus}$ are the free energy and redox potential under standard conditions. In Chapter 3 we also noted that for a reaction to be energetically feasible the total free energy must fall, i.e. ΔG must be negative. An increase in free energy indicates that the reaction cannot proceed under the stated conditions The relationship $\Delta G = -nFE$ can now be used to determine reaction feasibility. Let us consider first the oxidation of iron(II) to iron(III) by bromine in aqueous solution, i.e.

$$2Fe^{2+}(aq) + Br_2(aq) \rightarrow 2Fe^{3+}(aq) + 2Br^-(aq)$$

We can determine the energetic feasibility for this reaction from the two half reactions

(i) $2Fe^{2+}(aq) \rightarrow 2Fe^{3+}(aq) + 2e^-$
(ii) $Br^2(aq) + 2e^- \rightarrow 2Br^-(aq)$

Data tables give the following standard electrode potentials

$$Fe^{3+}(aq) + e^- \rightarrow Fe^{2+}(aq) \qquad\qquad E^{\ominus} = +0.76 \text{ V}$$

Hence for the reverse reaction

$$Fe^{2+}(aq)^{\cdot} \rightarrow Fe^{3+}(aq) + e^- \qquad\qquad E^{\ominus} = -0.76 \text{ V}$$

Remembering that e.m.f. is an intensive, not an extensive property, we obtain

(i) $2Fe^{2+}(aq) \rightarrow 2Fe^{3+}(aq) + 2e^-$ $E^{\ominus} = -0.76$ V

From this

$$\Delta G^{\ominus}_{(i)} = -nFE^{\ominus} = -[2 \times 96\,487 \times (-0.76)]$$
$$= +146.7 \text{ kJ mol}^{-1}$$

Similarly

$\frac{1}{2}Br_2(aq) + e^- \rightarrow Br^-(aq)$ $E^{\ominus} = +1.07$ V
(ii) $Br_2(aq) + 2e^- \rightarrow 2Br^-(aq)$ $E^{\ominus} = +1.07$ V

and

$$\Delta G^{\ominus}_{(ii)} = -nFE^{\ominus} = -[2 \times 96\,487 \times (+1.07)]$$
$$= -206.5 \text{ kJ mol}^{-1}$$

By addition

(i) $2Fe^{2+}(aq) \rightarrow 2Fe^{3+}(aq) + 2e^-$ $\Delta G^{\ominus} = +146.7$ kJ mol^{-1}
(ii) $Br_2(aq) + 2e^- \rightarrow 2Br^-(aq)$ $\Delta G^{\ominus} = -206.5$ kJ mol^{-1}

$2Fe^{2+}(aq) + Br_2(aq) \rightarrow 2Fe^{3+}(aq) + 2Br^-$ $\Delta G^{\ominus} = -59.8$ kJ mol^{-1}

Therefore, since $\Delta G^{\ominus}$ is negative, the reaction is energetically feasible and does indeed take place.

It is interesting at this point to investigate the reasons why iron(II) ions in aqueous solutions are quantitatively estimated by titration using potassium manganate(VII) (permanganate) when chloride ions are absent but by potassium dichromate(VI) when chloride ions are present. The data for the oxidation of chloride ions to chlorine by (a) manganate(VII) and (b) dichromate(VI) ions under standard conditions are given in *Table 4.10*.

Table 4.10 Data for the oxidation of chloride ion by manganate(VII) and by dichromate(VI) in acid solution

Reaction	$E^{\ominus}$/V	$\Delta G^{\ominus} = -nFE^{\ominus}$
$MnO_4^-(aq) + 5e^- + 8H_3O^+$ $\rightarrow Mn^{2+}(aq) + 12H_2O$	+1.52	
(i) $2MnO_4^-(aq) + 10e^- + 16H_3O^+$ $\rightarrow 2Mn^{2+}(aq) + 24H_2O$	+1.52	$-10 \times 96\,487 \times (+1.52)$ $= -1467$ kJ mol^{-1}
$\frac{1}{2}Cl_2(aq) + e^- \rightarrow Cl^-(aq)$	+1.36	
$Cl^-(aq) \rightarrow \frac{1}{2}Cl_2(aq) + e^-$	-1.36	
(ii) $10Cl^-(aq) \rightarrow 5Cl_2(aq) + 10e^-$	-1.36	$-10 \times 96\,487 \times (-1.36)$ $= +1312$ kJ mol^{-1}
(iii) $Cr_2O_7^{2-}(aq) + 6e^- + 14H_3O^+$ $\rightarrow 2Cr^{3+}(aq) + 21H_2O$	+1.33	$-6 \times 96\,487 \times (+1.33)$ $= -769$ kJ mol^{-1}
(iv) $6Cl^-(aq) \rightarrow 3Cl_2(aq) + 6e^-$	-1.36	$-6 \times 96\,487 \times (-1.36)$ $= +787$ kJ mol^{-1}

Addition of reactions (i) and (ii) (*see Table 4.10*) leads to

(a) $2MnO_4^-(aq) + 10Cl^-(aq) + 16H_3O^+ \rightarrow$
   $\qquad 2Mn^{2+}(aq) + 24H_2O + 5Cl_2(aq) \qquad \Delta G = -155 \text{ kJ mol}^{-1}$

showing that chloride ions are oxidized by manganate(VII) ions under standard conditions.

Addition of reactions (iii) and (iv) leads to

(b) $Cr_2O_7^{2-}(aq) + 6Cl^-(aq) + 14H_3O^+ \rightarrow$
   $\qquad 2Cr^{3+}(aq) + 21H_2O + 3Cl_2(aq) \qquad \Delta G = +18 \text{ kJ mol}^{-1}$

Thus under *standard conditions* chloride ions are *not* oxidized to chlorine by dichromate(VI) ions. However, it is necessary to emphasize that changes in the concentration of the dichromate(VI) and chloride ions alters their redox potentials as indicated by the Nernst equation. Hence, when concentrated hydrochloric acid is added to *solid* potassium dichromate and the mixture warmed, chlorine is liberated.

Equilibrium constants from electrode potentials

We have seen that the energetic feasibility of a reaction can be deduced from redox potential data. It is also possible to deduce the theoretical equilibrium position for a reaction. In Chapter 3 we saw that when $\Delta G = 0$ the system is at equilibrium. Since $\Delta G = -nFE$, this means that the potential of the cell must be zero. Consider once again the reaction

$$Cu^{2+}(aq) + Zn(s) \rightarrow Cu(s) + Zn^{2+}(aq)$$

Referring to the Nernst equation (section 4.3.5), we see that, at equilibrium at 298 K, the electrode potential of the half-reaction for copper, given approximately by

$$E_{Cu} = E_{Cu}^{\ominus} + \frac{0.06}{2}\log_{10}[Cu^{2+}(aq)]$$

must equal the electrode potential for the half-reaction for zinc, given approximately by

$$E_{Zn} = E_{Zn}^{\ominus} + \frac{0.06}{2}\log_{10}[Zn^{2+}(aq)]$$

Thus,

$$E_{Zn}^{\ominus} + \frac{0.06}{2}\log_{10}[Zn^{2+}(aq)] = E_{Cu}^{\ominus} + \frac{0.06}{2}\log_{10}[Cu^{2+}(aq)]$$

Hence,

$$\log_{10}[Zn^{2+}(aq)] - \log_{10}[Cu^{2+}(aq)] = (E_{Cu}^{\ominus} - E_{Zn}^{\ominus}) \times \frac{2}{0.06}$$

Substituting for $E_{Cu}^{\ominus} = +0.34$, and $E_{Zn}^{\ominus} = -0.76$ we have:

$$\log_{10}\frac{[Zn^{2+}(aq)]}{[Cu^{2+}(aq)]} = [+0.34 - (-0.76)] \times \frac{2}{0.06} = \frac{1.10 \times 2}{0.06} = 36.7$$

Hence

$$\frac{[\text{Zn}^{2+}(\text{aq})]}{[\text{Cu}^{2+}(\text{aq})]} = 10^{36.7}$$

This is in fact the equilibrium constant for the reaction

$$\text{Cu}^{2+}(\text{aq}) + \text{Zn}(\text{s}) \rightarrow \text{Cu}(\text{s}) + \text{Zn}^{2+}(\text{aq})$$

and its high value indicates that the reaction goes effectively to completion.

Similar calculations enable the equilibrium constants for other reactions to be calculated.

Potentiometric titrations

The problem in any quantitative volumetric analysis for ions in solution is to determine accurately the equivalence point. This is often found by using an indicator, but in redox reactions it can often be more satisfactorily found by potential measurements of a cell incorporating the redox reaction.

Consider the estimation of iron(II) ions by cerium(IV) ions in aqueous solution:

$$\text{Fe}^{2+}(\text{aq}) + \text{Ce}^{4+}(\text{aq}) \rightarrow \text{Ce}^{3+}(\text{aq}) + \text{Fe}^{3+}(\text{aq})$$

The electrode potential for the iron(II)–iron(III) system is given by

$$E_1 = E_1^{\ominus} + \frac{RT}{F}\log_e\frac{[\text{Fe}^{3+}(\text{aq})]}{[\text{Fe}^{2+}(\text{aq})]}$$

and for the cerium(IV)–cerium(III) system by

$$E_2 = E_2^{\ominus} + \frac{RT}{F}\log_e\frac{[\text{Ce}^{4+}(\text{aq})]}{[\text{Ce}^{3+}(\text{aq})]}$$

Experimentally, the aqueous iron(II) is titrated with cerium(IV) in aqueous solution in a burette. The arrangement is shown in *Figure 4.9*; the platinum

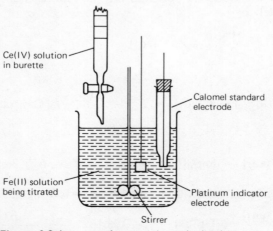

Ce(IV) solution in burette

Calomel standard electrode

Fe(II) solution being titrated

Platinum indicator electrode

Stirrer

Figure 4.9 Apparatus for potentiometric titration

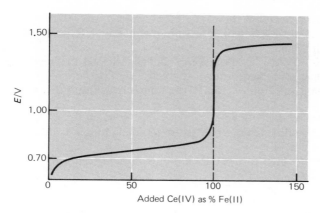

Figure 4.10 Potentiometric titration of iron(II) with cerium(V)

indicator electrode changes its potential (with reference to a calomel half-cell
as standard) as the solution is titrated. *Figure 4.10* shows the graph of the cell
e.m.f. against added cerium(IV). At the equivalence point the amount of the
added Ce^{4+}(aq) is equal to the original amount of Fe^{2+}(aq); hence the
amounts of Ce^{3+}(aq) and Fe^{3+}(aq) are also equal. Under these conditions
the potential of the electrode in the mixture is

$$\frac{E_1^{\ominus} + E_2^{\ominus}}{2}$$

This, the equivalent point, occurs at the point indicated.

Potentiometric methods can be used for the study of a large number of
redox reactions; quantitatively they have several advantages over ordinary
indicator methods.

Thus, for example, an analysis using coloured solutions can be carried out,
where an indicator cannot be used. Moreover, it is not easy to find a redox
indicator which will change colour at the right point. Potentiometric
methods can fairly readily be made automatic.

4.4   Tests for reducing and oxidizing agents

The redox properties of all reagents are relative and a given reagent may be
both a reducing and an oxidizing agent depending upon the reaction in
which it is involved. Thus, for example, sulphur dioxide in aqueous solution
is an oxidizing agent with respect to hydrogen sulphide, but a reducing agent
with respect to acidified potassium dichromate(VI) solution. Similarly
hydrogen peroxide in acidic solution is an oxidizing agent relative to iron(II)
ions but a reducing agent relative to manganate(VII) ions in aqueous
solution. However, it is convenient to establish approximate 'reference
points' for laboratory reagents, which can then be loosely classified as
follows:

Reagents are *reducing* if they:

(1) Decolorize a solution of potassium manganate(VII) acidified with dilute sulphuric acid.

(2) Turn a solution of potassium dichromate(VI) acidified with dilute sulphuric acid from orange to green.

(3) Change a solution of iron(III) in aqueous solution to iron(II).

Reagents are *oxidizing* if they:

(1) Liberate iodine from a potassium iodide solution acidified with dilute sulphuric acid.

(2) Convert iron(II) to iron(III) in aqueous acid solution.

Summary

1   Lowry and Brønsted define (protonic) acids as *proton-donors*, bases as *proton-acceptors*; the acid dissociation constant K_a (or $pK_a = -\log_{10}K_a$) measures the acid strength; pK_a is negative for a strong acid. Acid and base strengths are determined by structure and by the solvent.

An acid can be defined in other ways, either (a) as giving a cation characteristic of the solvent or (b) as an electron-pair acceptor ('Lewis acid'); a base correspondingly is defined either as (a) a solvo-anion or (b) as an electron-pair donor.

2   When an atom or ion or molecule is *reduced*, electrons are *added* to it; when it is *oxidized*, electrons are *removed*. In an oxidation–reduction reaction, the number of electrons lost by the *reducing agent* must equal the number gained by the *oxidizing agent*; if a redox reaction in aqueous solution is rapid and quantitative, it can be used in a *redox titration*. The reducing or oxidizing power of a substance is measured by its *redox potential*; this may be affected by concentration, temperature, complex formation and pH. Redox titrations can be followed by using an electrode to determine the equivalence point — a *potentiometric titration*.

Questions

1   (a) The following are standard redox potentials in volts in acid 1N solution for the reactions

$$M^{n+} + xe^- \rightarrow M^{(n-x)+} \text{ (symbolized as } M^{n+}/M^{(n-x)+}),$$

where, for example, the process

$$Na^+ + e^- \rightarrow Na \text{ (symbolized as } Na^+/Na)$$

is defined as having a large negative potential:

Reaction	Cr^{2+}/Cr	Mn^{2+}/Mn	Cr^{3+}/Cr^{2+}	Mn^{3+}/Mn^{2+}	Fe^{2+}/Fe	Fe^{3+}/Fe^{2+}
$E^{\ominus}$/V	-0.9	-1.2	-0.4	$+1.5$	-0.4	$+0.8$

Use these data to comment upon:
(i)   the stability in acid solution of Fe^{3+} towards reducing agents as compared with that of either Cr^{3+} or Mn^{3+};
(ii) the ease with which metallic iron can be oxidized to iron(II) (ferrous) ions compared with the similar process for either metallic chromium or metallic manganese;
(iii) the result of treating a solution containing either chromium(II) (chromous) or manganese(II) (manganous) ions with a solution containing iron(III) (ferric) ions.

(b) The following equations represent four chemical reactions involving redox processes:
(i) $3N_2H_4 + 2BrO_3^- \rightarrow 3N_2 + 2Br^- + 6H_2O$
(ii) $5As_2O_3 + 4MnO_4^- + 12H^+ \rightarrow 5As_2O_5 + 4Mn^{2+} + 6H_2O$
(iii) $SO_2 + I_2 + 2H_2O \rightarrow H_2SO_4 + 2HI$
(iv) $VO_4^{3-} + Fe^{2+} + 6H^+ \rightarrow VO^{2+} + Fe^{3+} + 3H_2O$
Identify the oxidizing agent and the reducing agent in each reaction and write 'half-equations' showing the donation or acceptance of electrons by each of these eight reagents.

C,S

2   Discuss (a) the acidity and (b) the substitution reactions of metal hexa-aquo cations, $[M(H_2O)_6]^{n+}$ (where $n=2$ or 3), giving two examples of each type of reaction. Discuss the effect upon the stabilities of the $+2$ and $+3$ oxidation states of
(i)   increasing the pH in iron chemistry, and
(ii) complex formation (with ligands other than water) in cobalt chemistry.

JMB,A

3   Liquid ammonia, which boils at 240 K, is an ionizing solvent. Salts are less ionized in liquid ammonia than they are in water but, owing to the lower viscosity, the movement of ions through liquid ammonia is much more rapid for a given potential gradient. The ionization of liquid ammonia

$$2NH_3 \rightleftharpoons NH_4^+ + NH_2^-$$

is very slight. The ionic product $[NH_4^+][NH_2^-] = 10^{-28} \text{ mol}^2 \text{ dm}^{-6}$ at the boiling point. Definitions of an acid and a base similar to those used for aqueous solvents can be used for solutes in liquid ammonia. This question is mainly about acid–base reactions in liquid ammonia as solvent.
(a) Write the formula of the solvated proton in the ammonia system.
(b) In the ammonia system state, what are the bases corresponding to each of the following species in the water system?
(i) H_2O, (ii) OH^-, (iii) O^{2-}.
(c) Write equations for the reactions in liquid ammonia of:
(i)   sodium to give a base and hydrogen,
(ii) the neutralization reaction corresponding to:

$$HCl(aq) + NaOH(aq) \rightarrow NaCl(aq) + H_2O(l)$$

(d) What would the concentration be of NH_2^- (in mol dm^{-3}) in a solution of liquid ammonia containing 0.01 mol dm^{-3} of ammonium ions?

(e) The dissociation constant of ethanoic (acetic) acid in liquid ammonia is greater than it is in water. Suggest a reason for the difference.

N,A

4 (a) Outline the principles of the method you would use to measure the standard redox potential for the reaction

$$MnO_4^- + 8H^+ + 5e^- \rightarrow Mn^{2+} + 4H_2O$$

(b) The standard redox potentials for Ce^{4+}/Ce^{3+} (Ce=cerium) and Fe^{3+}/Fe^{2+} are $+1.610$ V and $+0.771$ V respectively. Deduce the direction of the reaction

$$Ce^{3+} + Fe^{3+} = Ce^{4+} + Fe^{2+}$$

and outline an experiment you could use to find the end point when the reaction is carried out as a titration. (N.B. Both Ce^{4+} and Fe^{3+} ions are yellow in aqueous solution.)

(c) What explanation can you offer for the fact that the standard electrode potentials of copper and zinc are $+0.34$ V and -0.76 V respectively, although the sums of the first two ionization energies for both metals are approximately 2640 kJ mol^{-1}?

C,A

5 The following redox potentials are given for the oxidation of manganese(II) to manganese(III) in acid and alkaline solution.

Reaction	Conditions	$E^{\ominus}/V$
$Mn^{3+} + e^- \rightarrow Mn^{2+}$	Acid	$+1.51$
$O_2 + 4H^+ + 4e^- \rightarrow 2H_2O$	Acid	$+1.23$
$Mn(OH)_3 + e^- \rightarrow Mn(OH)_2 + OH^-$	Alkaline	-0.40
$O_2 + 2H_2O + 4e^- \rightarrow 4OH^-$	Alkaline	$+0.40$

(a) Would manganese(II) be oxidized to manganese(III) by atmospheric oxygen under
(i) acid
(ii) alkaline, conditions?

(b) What would you expect to happen if anhydrous MnF_3 were dissolved in water?

N, Phys. Sci., Part I

6 Discuss the factors which influence the redox potential of a half-reaction, illustrating your answer by as many examples as possible.

Liverpool B.Sc., Part I

7 (a) Describe, with the aid of a labelled diagram, an experiment to measure

the standard electrode potential of silver and write an equation representing the cell reaction.

(b) Construct a cycle of the Born–Haber type for the formation of silver ions in aqueous solution from solid silver. Name the enthalpy change in each step and indicate its sign.

(c) By reference to the following data, discuss possible methods of preparation of fluorine and chlorine.

$$\tfrac{1}{2}F_2(g) + e^- \rightarrow F^-(aq) \qquad\qquad E^\ominus = +2.87 \text{ V}$$
$$\tfrac{1}{2}Cl(g) + e^- \rightarrow Cl^-(aq) \qquad\qquad E^\ominus = +1.36 \text{ V}$$
$$MnO_4^-(aq) + 8H^+(aq) + 5e^- \rightarrow Mn^{2+}(aq) + 4H_2O(l) \qquad E^\ominus = +1.51 \text{ V}$$
$$MnO_2(s) + 4H^+(aq) + 2e^- \rightarrow Mn^{2+}(aq) + 2H_2O(l) \qquad E^\ominus = +1.23 \text{ V}$$

Chapter 5
Hydrogen

One of the most readily observed reactions in chemistry is the familiar production of bubbles of a colourless gas when certain metals (for example, iron, zinc) react with dilute acids. Cavendish investigated these reactions rather more than 200 years ago, and found the gas evolved to be the same in each case; the gas, later named *hydrogen*, was much ligher than air and when burned in air produced water. The gas is composed of dihydrogen molecules, H_2.

Hydrogen in the combined state, mainly as water, hydrocarbons and other inorganic compounds, constitutes about 11 per cent of the Earth's crust by weight*. Hydrogen gas is not very reactive; it reacts spontaneously with very electropositive elements (some of the metals of Groups I and II) and with the very electronegative element fluorine; with other elements, reactions usually require a catalyst, or heat or light, and even then may be incomplete. If hydrogen gas is passed through a solution containing a strongly oxidizing ion, for example manganate(VII) MnO_4^- or iron(III) $Fe_{(aq)}^{3+}$, reduction does not take place unless a catalyst is present, and even then it is often slow and incomplete, despite the fact that for the redox system

$$H_3O^+ + e^- \rightarrow \tfrac{1}{2}H_2(g) + H_2O \qquad E^\ominus = 0\ V$$

i.e. hydrogen is a mild reducing agent. This absence of reactivity does not usually arise because the hydrogen molecule is energetically stable, but rather because it is kinetically stable (p. 57); almost any process in which the hydrogen molecule is to participate must involve the breaking of the H—H bond, which is relatively strong (p. 65). This kinetic stability can be removed by a catalyst (for example, a metal surface), or heat or light, to break up the hydrogen molecule and allow reaction to proceed. The reactions of hydrogen will now be examined in more detail.

5.1 Reactions with electropositive metals

These give *ionic* or *salt-like* hydrides, for example

$$2Na + H_2 \rightarrow 2NaH$$

These solid ionic hydrides (having an ionic lattice and containing the hydride

*Large-scale methods of producing hydrogen are considered in a later chapter (p. 107).

ion H^-) react with water, for example

$$CaH_2 + 2H_2O \rightarrow Ca(OH)_2 + 2H_2$$

i.e.

$$H^- + H_2O \rightarrow OH^- + H_2$$

We can see that the hydride ion H^- functions as a very strong base (p. 80) withdrawing a proton from the water molecule and uniting with it to give H_2, i.e. $H^- + H^+ \rightarrow H_2$, a highly exothermic process. It follows that we cannot use these ionic hydrides in aqueous solutions; however, some of them (notably lithium hydride, LiH) can be used in suspension in organic solvents as reducing agents, and others can be converted into complex hydrides which can be used in solution (*see* below).

The existence of the hydride ion is shown by electrolysis of the fused salt when hydrogen is evolved at the *anode*. If calcium hydride is dissolved in another fused salt as solvent, the amount of hydrogen evolved at the anode on electrolysis is 1 g for each faraday of charge (mole of electrons) passed, as required by the laws of electrolysis.

5.2 Reactions with transition metals

Most of these metals only react with hydrogen on heating; the first stage of reaction is the taking of hydrogen on to the metal surface, whereby the hydrogen molecules become attached as hydrogen atoms — a process known as *chemisorption*. With some metals reaction can proceed further, and hydrogen atoms penetrate into the metal lattice and occupy positions between the metal atoms — *interstitial* positions, as shown in *Figure 5.1*.

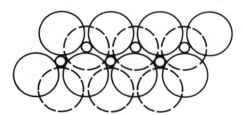

Figure 5.1 Interstitial positions between layers of metal atoms

If all these 'holes' were filled, the hydrogen–metal ratio would be a definite and fixed number; in practice, this rarely happens, and these *metal hydrides* or *interstitial hydrides* may have variable composition (for example $TiH_{1.7}$), depending on the uptake of hydrogen, i.e. they are non-stoichiometric. One further property in particular distinguishes these metal hydrides from the ionic hydrides; in the latter, uptake of hydrogen is not only quantitative but causes a contraction, i.e. the centres of the metal atoms (which become cations) move closer together — the metal lattice is, as it were, drawn together. In the metal hydrides, there is no such contraction, and, indeed, the metal atoms may move apart slightly. Hence formation of an ionic hydride leads to an increase in density, but formation of a metal hydride causes a decrease in density.

5.3 Reactions with non-metals and weakly electropositive metals

Most of the elements of Groups III to VII form hydrides which are essentially covalent. Some examples are Group IV, methane CH_4; Group V, phosphine PH_3; Group VI, hydrogen sulphide H_2S; Group VII, hydrogen chloride, HCl. There are several points to notice about these covalent hydrides. First, they are nearly all volatile liquids or gases; but the simple hydrides NH_3, H_2O and HF, formed from the head elements of Groups V–VII, show hydrogen bonding characteristics which make them less volatile than we should expect from the small size of their molecules (p. 45).

Secondly, the ability to form more than one hydride falls off as we go across a period. Thus, in Period 1, boron and carbon both form whole families of hydrides, nitrogen forms three (ammonia, NH_3; hydrazine, N_2H_4; hydrogen azide, N_3H), oxygen two (H_2O, H_2O_2) and fluorine one (HF). Again, as we descend a group, the energetic stability of the hydrides decreases — indeed, many hydrides are endothermic, and need indirect methods to supply the necessary energy for their preparation. In Group IV, methane is exothermic, the others are endothermic and plumbane PbH_4, the last hydride in the group, is almost too unstable to exist at all. (We shall note some of the methods needed to prepare these less stable hydrides in later chapters.) Since the stability of the typical hydride (i.e. that in which the element shows its group valency) falls off, it is hardly surprising to find that the lower elements in a group do not form families of hydrides [for example, in Group IV carbon and silicon form numerous hydrides, germanium forms a few, tin forms one (stannane, SnH_4) and lead just manages to form PbH_4].

The most important trend to be noted in the covalent hydrides is the change in acid–base behaviour as we cross a period from Group IV to Group VII. In Period 1, we have

CH_4	NH_3	H_2O	HF
no acidic or	basic	basic	acidic
basic properties	(very weakly acidic)	and acidic	(weakly basic)

This change in properties cannot be simply accounted for in terms of bond energies; the mean X—H bond energy increases from nitrogen to fluorine, and hydrogen fluoride has a large bond-dissociation energy (566 kJ mol^{-1}). But we note that in the CH_4 molecule there are no lone pairs of electrons — all four valency electrons are involved in bonding. In ammonia, there is one lone pair, which as we have seen can be donated either to a proton, making ammonia a Lowry–Brønsted base,

$$NH_3 + H^+ \rightleftharpoons NH_4^+$$

or to another acceptor molecule (making ammonia a Lewis base, p. 80). The molecules H_2O and HF have two and three lone pairs respectively; falling-off of base strength implies that the presence of more than one lone pair reduces the donor power of the molecule. But, obviously, the appearance of acidic behaviour implies that the bond X—H is more readily broken *heterolytically*, i.e. to give X^- + H^+. We may ascribe this to *polarity* of the bond, i.e. by saying that the pair of electrons in the covalent H—F bond is closer to the fluorine than to the hydrogen. Unfortunately, there is no very sure method of ascertaining this *bond* polarity (the fact that hydrogen fluoride HF has a dipole moment means that the molecule *as a whole* is polar in, presumably, the sense $\overset{+}{H}$—$\overset{-}{F}$, but this does not necessarily tell us about the *bond* polarity). Another way of describing this trend towards acidity is to say that the electronegativity of the element increases from carbon to fluorine. We may simply note that this trend to acidity is also apparent in other periods, for example, in Period 3, silane SiH_4 is non-acidic and non-basic; phosphine PH_3 is weakly basic, hydrogen sulphide H_2S is weakly acidic and hydrogen chloride HCl markedly acidic. We should note that these descriptions 'basic' and 'acidic' *refer to solutions in water*; a gaseous hydrogen halide does not display acidity (p. 78).

5.4   Complex hydrides

A non-metal or weakly electropositive metal X in Group III of the periodic table would be expected to form a covalent volatile hydride XH_3. In fact, the simplest hydride of boron is B_2H_6 and aluminium hydride is a polymer $(AlH_3)_n$.

The structure of diborane B_2H_6 is considered later (p. 133). Here we may note that 'BH_3' and 'AlH_3' will be acceptor molecules since there are only six valency electrons around the B or Al atoms and a vacant orbital exists. Both in fact can accept the electron pair from a hydride ion thus:

BH_3 + H^- → BH_4^-
'borane'   tetrahydridoborate or
                                        borohydride

AlH_3 + H^- → AlH_4^-
'alane'   tetrahydridoaluminate or
                                        aluminohydride

Salts containing these ions can be prepared, for example, by the reaction

$$4LiH + AlCl_3 \xrightarrow{\text{ether}} LiAlH_4 + 3LiCl$$

$LiAlH_4$, lithium tetrahydridoaluminate ('lithium aluminium hydride', so-called) is an excellent reducing agent in ether solution for both organic and inorganic compounds; it may be used to prepare covalent hydrides SiH_4, PH_3 from the corresponding chlorides in ether*, for example

$$SiCl_4 + LiAlH_4 → LiCl + AlCl_3 + SiH_4$$
silicon   silane
tetrachloride

*This method produces an endothermic hydride by indirect means.

The tetrahydridoborate ion, as 'sodium borohydride' $NaBH_4$ is soluble in water and is similarly an excellent reducing agent in this solvent. (Lithium tetrahydridoaluminate cannot be used in water, with which it reacts violently to give hydrogen.)

5.5 Atomic hydrogen

If a high voltage electric discharge is passed through hydrogen at low pressure, a small fraction of the hydrogen molecules are dissociated into atoms, which are highly reactive and unite with many elements to give hydrides*. If a metal such as zinc is dissolved in acid, hydrogen gas is evolved, and thus the dissolving metal is a good reducing agent:

$$Zn^{2+}(aq) + 2e^- \rightarrow Zn(s) \qquad E^{\ominus} = 0.76 \text{ V}$$

Here, therefore, hydrogen is being formed as a reduction product of the proton

$$H_3O^+ + e^- \rightarrow \tfrac{1}{2}H_2 \qquad E^{\ominus} = 0.00 \text{ V}$$

and it is not itself the reducing agent. (As we have seen, the kinetic stability of the hydrogen molecule makes it a poor reducing agent in practice.) However, it is probable that hydrogen atoms can be produced by proton reduction (i.e. by the process $H^+ + e^- \rightarrow H$); these will all usually unite with each other to give molecular hydrogen, but can attack other species present. Thus in the reduction of an arsenic-containing compound to arsine (AsH_3) or of an alkyl halide (C_2H_5Cl) to an alkane (C_2H_6) by a metal couple (Al–Zn–Cu) in aqueous acid, hydrogen atoms may participate in the reaction.

5.6 Deuterium

Deuterium, an isotope of hydrogen ^2_1H, is made by prolonged electrolysis of water, during which hydrogen is evolved preferentially to deuterium at the cathode. Consequently the residual water is enriched in deuterium oxide, D_2O, ('heavy water'). The D_2O finally obtained has a b.p. 374.2 K and a density at 293 K of 1.106 g cm^{-3} (water, 0.998 g cm^{-3}); electrolysis of D_2O gives deuterium which again has physical properties slightly different from those of hydrogen (for example, b.p. 24 K). Ordinary hydrogen contains about 1 part in 6000 of deuterium.

The slightly different physical properties of deuterium allow its concentration in ordinary hydrogen (or the concentration of a deuterium-containing compound in a hydrogen compound) to be determined. *Exchange* of deuterium and hydrogen occurs and can be used to elucidate the mechanism of reactions (i.e. the deuterium is a non-radioactive tracer). Methanol exchanges with deuterium oxide thus:

$$CH_3OH + D_2O \rightleftharpoons CH_3OD + HDO$$

The hydroxyl hydrogen exchanges but the hydrogen atoms of the CH$_3$ (methyl) group do not (*see* also Chapter 10).

*This method produces an endothermic hydride by direct means.

5.7   Tests for hydrogen

In general, hydrogen itself (and compounds containing hydrogen) when oxidized by heating with oxygen or with a metal oxide form water, for which tests are available. There are otherwise no chemical tests for hydrogen. The metal palladium will take up many times its own volume of hydrogen, to form a non-stoichiometric metal hydride (p. 103) and this property can be used to separate hydrogen from other gases which remain unaffected by the palladium.

5.8   Hydrogen on the large scale

Industrial hydrogen is produced from water and hydrocarbons (e.g. natural gas, represented as methane in the equation below) (*see* p. 164 also):

$$CH_4 + H_2O \rightarrow CO + 3H_2$$
$$CO + H_2O \rightarrow CO_2 + H_2$$

The possibility of using hydrogen gas as a fuel has prompted investigations of its production from water by methods which do not themselves require high energy inputs. Reaction of water with coal (essentially $C + H_2O \rightarrow CO + H_2$) is one possibility; others include the splitting of water using thermal or photochemical solar energy (i.e. by heat or light from the sun).

Summary

The principal reactions of hydrogen are summarized in *Figure 5.2.*

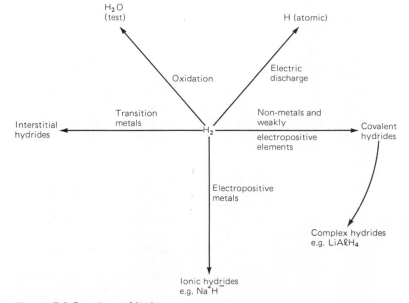

Figure 5.2 Reactions of hydrogen

Questions

1   Discuss the chemistry of the simple hydrides of the elements, indicating how
    they can be classified according to their structures.

                                                           Liverpool B.Sc., Part I

2   (a) Describe in detail the bonding which occurs in the compounds formed
         between hydrogen and
         (i)   sodium (in sodium hydride),
         (ii) carbon (in methane),
         (iii) nitrogen (in ammonia).
    (b) Describe the reactions, if any, which take place between water and the
         hydrides of the elements in (a).
    (b) Comment upon the significance of the relative values of the following
         boiling points of the halogen hydrides:

    HF   HCl   HBr   HI
    19.5 °C   − 85 °C   − 67 °C   − 36 °C

                                                                          JMB,A

3   Outline briefly one method for the preparation of each of the following:
    (a) NaH (from sodium),
    (b) CH_4 (from carbon),
    (c) PH_4I (from phosphorus).
    How do the following hydrides react with water: NaH, CH_4, SiH_4 and HI?
    Comment on these reactions in terms of the nature of the chemical bonds in
    these compounds. Suggest reasons for the increase in acidity in the series
    PH_3, H_2S, HCl. How would you seek to establish this order experimentally?

                                                                            C,A

4   Outline one method for the manufacture of hydrogen from either crude oil
    or natural gas. State two important uses of hydrogen. Give explanations and
    illustrate reactions for the following statements:
         (i)   The hydrides of the elements Na, P, S, Cl, show increasing acidity
               with increasing atomic number.
         (ii) The hydrides of the elements F, Cl, Br, I, show increasing reducing
               power with increasing atomic number.

                                                                            C,A

5   Discuss the following observations:
    (a) The boiling point of methane is considerably lower than that of the
         corresponding silicon hydride (SiH_4, monosilane), whereas the boiling
         points of ammonia and of water are higher than those of phosphine and
         of hydrogen sulphide respectively.
    (b) Phenylamine (aniline) is a weaker base than ammonia, but ethylamine is
         a stronger base than ammonia.
    (c) 1M aqueous solutions of hydrogen chloride, hydrogen bromide and
         hydrogen iodide have pH values of 0.09, 0.06 and 0.02 respectively,
         whereas the pH of a 1N aqueous solution of hydrogen fluoride is 1.7.

(d) Ionic compounds are normally readily soluble in water, but do not dissolve well in organic solvents.

6   Hydrogen resembles both the alkali-metals and the halogens in its chemical behaviour. Survey the evidence which leads to this conclusion.
Use the compounds which you have described to illustrate the changes in bond-type of the hydrides of elements in a period of the Periodic Table.

JMB,A

Chapter 6
Groups I and II

Lithium, sodium, potassium, rubidium, caesium; beryllium,
magnesium, calcium, strontium, barium

6.1 The elements

6.1.1 General characteristics

These elements form two groups, often called the alkali (Group I) and
alkaline earth (Group II) metals. Some of the physical properties usually
associated with metals — hardness, high m.p. and b.p. — are noticeably
lacking in these metals, but they all have a metallic appearance and are good
electrical conductors. *Table 6.1* gives some of the physical properties.

From *Table 6.1*, it is easy to see that Group II metals are more dense, are
harder and have higher m.p. and b.p. than the corresponding Group I metals.

In Chapter 2, a discussion of the theory of metallic bonding indicated that
the strength of such bonding generally depends on the ratio (number of
electrons available for bonding)/(atomic radius). The greater this ratio is, the
stronger are the bonds between the metal atoms. In the pre-transition metals,
this ratio is small and at a minimum in Group I with only one bonding
electron. Metallic bond strength is greater in Group II but there are still only
two bonding electrons available, hence the metals are still relatively soft and
have low melting and boiling points. Hardness, m.p. and b.p. all decrease
steadily down Group I, the metallic bond strength decreasing with increasing
atomic radius. These changes are not so well marked in Group II but note
that beryllium and, to a lesser extent, magnesium are hard metals, as a result
of their small atomic size; this property, when coupled with their low density,
makes them of some technological importance (p. 113).

A full discussion of the changes in ionization energy with group and period
position has been given in Chapter 2. These data are given again in *Table 6.2*.

6.1.2 Formation of ions

We note first that the elements are all electropositive, having relatively low
ionization energies, and are, in consequence, very reactive. The enthalpy
change required for the process M(metal $\rightarrow$ M^+(g) for Group I, or
M(metal) $\rightarrow$ M^{2+}(g) for Group II is at a maximum at the top of each group,
and it is, therefore, not surprising to find that lithium, beryllium and, to some
extent, magnesium do form some covalent compounds. Most solid
compounds of Group I and II elements, however, have ionic structures and
the properties associated with such structures — high m.p. and b.p.,

Table 6.1 Selected properties of the elements of Groups I and II

Element	Atomic number	Outer electrons	Density g cm⁻³	m.p./K	b.p./K	Hardness (Brinell)
Li	3	$2s^1$	0.535	452	1609	0.06
Na	11	$3s^1$	0.971	370.9	1155.9	0.07
K	19	$4s^1$	0.862	336.5	1035	0.04
Rb	37	$5s^1$	1.532	312	973	0.03
Cs	55	$6s^1$	1.90	301.5	943	0.02
Be	4	$2s^2$	1.86	1553	3243	—
Mg	12	$3s^2$	1.75	924	1380	30—40
Ca	20	$4s^2$	1.55	1124	1760	23
Sr	38	$5s^2$	2.6	1073	1639	20
Ba	56	$6s^2$	3.59	998	1910	—

Table 6.2 Further properties of the elements of Groups I and II

	Ionization energy* kJ mol⁻¹	Metallic radius nm	Ionic radius nm	Heat of vaporization at 298 K kJ mol⁻¹	Hydration energy of gaseous ion kJ mol⁻¹	$E^{\ominus}/V$
Li	520	0.152	0.060	152.5	519	−3.04
Na	496	0.186	0.095	108.6	406	−2.71
K	419	0.227	0.133	90.0	322	−2.92
Rb	403	0.248	0.148	85.8	293	−2.93
Cs	376	0.263	0.169	78.8	264	−2.92
Be	2657	0.112	0.031	326	2494	−1.85
Mg	2187	0.160	0.065	149	1921	−2.37
Ca	1735	0.197	0.099	177	1577	−2.87
Sr	1613	0.215	0.113	164	1443	−2.89
Ba	1467	0.221	0.135	178	1305	−2.91

*For Li—Cs, first ionization energy; Be—Ba, sum of first and second ionization energies.

solubility in water rather than in organic solvents and electrical conductance when molten.

6.1.3 Ions in solution

The hydration energies (strictly, hydration enthalpies) fall, as expected, as we descend either Group, and are larger for Group II than for Group I ions. The solubilities of the salts of Groups I and II are determined by a balance between lattice energy, hydration energy and the entropy change in going from solid to solution, and only a few generalizations are possible. Thus high charge and low ionic radii tend to produce insolubility (for example salts of lithium, beryllium and magnesium, especially those with doubly charged anions such as carbonate CO_3^{2-}). At the other end of the scale, low charge and large radii also produce low solubility, for example salts of potassium, rubidium and caesium containing large anions such as the tetraphenylborate anion (p. 124). In between, solubility is the rule for all Group I salts, and for most Group II salts containing singly-charged negative ions; for many Group II salts with doubly- or triply-charged anions (for example CO_3^{2-}, SO_4^{2-}, PO_4^{3-}) insolubility is often observed.

The decreasing tendency to form salts with water of crystallization (as a group is descended) is again in line with the falling hydration energy. For example, both sodium sulphate and carbonate form hydrates but neither of the corresponding potassium salts do; the sulphates of Group II elements show a similar trend $MgSO_4.7H_2O$, $CaSO_4.2H_2O$, $BaSO_4$. For the most part, however, the chemistry of the Group I and II elements is that of the metal and the ions M^+ for Group I and M^{2+} for Group II. As already noted the two head elements, lithium and beryllium, tend to form covalent compounds; the beryllium ion Be^{2+}, because of its very small radius and double charge, has also some peculiar properties in solution, which are examined later (p. 122).

6.1.4 Occurrence and extraction

The alkali metals of Group I are found chiefly as the chlorides (in the Earth's crust and in sea water), and also as sulphates and carbonates. Lithium occurs as the aluminosilicate minerals, *spodumene* and *lepidolite*. Of the Group II metals (beryllium to barium) beryllium, the rarest, occurs as the aluminosilicate, *beryl*; magnesium is found as the carbonate and (with calcium) as the double carbonate *dolomite*; calcium, strontium and barium all occur as carbonates, calcium carbonate being very plentiful as limestone.

The general characteristics of all these elements generally preclude their extraction by any method involving aqueous solution. For the lighter, less volatile metals (Li, Na, Be, Mg, Ca) electrolysis of a fused salt (usually the chloride), or of a mixture of salts, is used. The heavier, more volatile metals in each group can all be similarly obtained by electrolysis, but it is usually more convenient to take advantage of their volatility and obtain them from their oxides or chlorides by displacement, i.e. by general reactions such as

$$3M_2O + 2M^{III} \rightarrow M_2^{III}O_3 + 6M\uparrow$$
$$MCl + M^I \rightarrow M^ICl + M\uparrow$$

Thus potassium is obtained by heating potassium chloride with sodium, and barium by reduction of barium oxide with aluminium.

Sodium is important in many technical processes and is therefore prepared in considerable quantity. Almost all of it is now made by electrolysis of the fused sodium chloride, using the *Downs cell* (*see Figure 6.1*). The graphite anode is cylindrical and is surrounded by the steel gauze diaphragm and the concentric cylindrical cathode (also of steel). The electrolyte is usually a mixture of sodium chloride and calcium chloride; the latter is added to reduce the m.p. of the sodium chloride to approximately 800 K. (Some

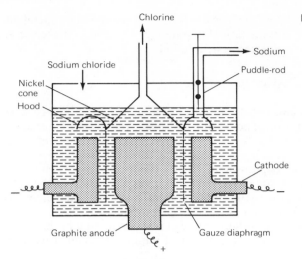

Chlorine

Figure 6.1 The Downs cell

Sodium

Sodium chloride

Puddle-rod

Nickel cone

Hood

Cathode

Graphite anode

Gauze diaphragm

calcium is therefore liberated with the sodium.) The gap between anode and cathode is kept as small as possible to reduce resistance: the heat developed by the current maintains the temperature of the cell. Chlorine is set free at the anode surface, rises into the nickel cone and can be collected. Sodium, liberated at the cathode, is prevented by the diaphragm from passing into the anode region; the molten sodium collects under the circular hood and rises up the pipe, being assisted if necessary by the puddle-rod. The calcium, being almost immiscible with sodium and much more dense, can readily be separated from the molten sodium. The graphite anode wears away and must be renewed from time to time.

6.1.5   Uses

Lithium finds use in high-strength glass, and its use as a cathode in high energy density batteries (which might be used in cars) has been extensively investigated. Much sodium is used, as an alloy with lead, in a reaction with chloroethane to produce tetraethyllead, the 'anti-knock' additive in petrol. Sodium is used to produce sodium peroxide and sodium hydride. Liquid sodium, with its high thermal conductivity, is used as a heat exchange liquid in fast-breeder nuclear reactors, and in sodium-filled electrical transmission lines. Potassium is used to make potassium superoxide KO_2 which reacts with water and carbon dioxide to give oxygen:

$$4KO_2 + 2H_2O + 4CO_2 \rightarrow 4KHCO_3 + 3O_2$$

and which is therefore used as an emergency source of oxygen in, for example, mines and submarines. Sodium–potassium alloys have the same thermal properties as liquid sodium, with the additional advantage that they are liquid at ordinary temperatures.

Beryllium is added to copper to produce an alloy with greatly increased wear resistance; it is used for current-carrying springs and non-sparking safety tools. It is also used as a neutron moderator and reflector in nuclear reactors. Much magnesium is used to prepare light metal alloys; other uses include the extraction of titanium (p. 325) and in the removal of oxygen and sulphur from steels; calcium finds a similar use.

6.1.6   Biological importance

Sodium and potassium ions are found in all animal cells and, usually, the concentration of potassium ions inside the cell is greater than that of sodium. In many cells, this concentration difference is maintained by a 'sodium pump', a process for which the energy is supplied by the hydrolysis of adenosine triphosphate (ATP). Diffusion of excess of potassium ions outwards through the cell wall gives the inside of the cell a net negative charge (owing to the anions present) and a potential difference is established across the cell wall. In a nerve cell, a momentary change in the permeability of the cell wall to sodium ions can reverse the sign of this potential difference, and this produces the electrical impulse associated with the action of the nerve.

The ability of living organisms to differentiate between the chemically similar sodium and potassium ions must depend upon some difference between these two ions in aqueous solution. Essentially, this difference is one of *size* of the hydrated ions, which in turn means a difference in the *force* of electrostatic (coulombic) attraction between the hydrated cation and a negatively-charged site in the cell membrane; thus a site may be able to accept the smaller ion $Na^+(aq)$ and reject the larger $K^+(aq)$. This same mechanism of selectivity operates in other 'ion-selection' processes, notably in ion-exchange resins.

All organisms seem to have an absolute need for magnesium. In plants, the magnesium complex chlorophyll is the prime agent in photosynthesis. In animals, magnesium functions as an enzyme activator; the enzyme which catalyses the ATP hydrolysis mentioned above is an important example.

Calcium plays an important part in structure-building in living organisms, perhaps mainly because of its ability to link together phosphate-containing materials. Calcium ions in the cell play a vital part in muscle contraction.

6.1.7   Reactions of the metals

In general, the metals of Groups I and II can combine, more or less readily, with many less electropositive elements. The reactivity towards most reagents, for example dry oxygen and dry bromine, increases as the size of the atom increases and the ionization energy falls. However, when reacting with very small non-metallic elements, for example carbon and nitrogen, the reverse is true, since the very small cation and the very small anion produced in the reaction form a very strong crystal lattice. The lattice energy evolved is sufficiently great to more than compensate for the large ionization energy of the small atom. Hence, although all Group II elements form nitrides, only lithium amongst the alkali metals is able to do so.

Most of the metals react with water and, therefore, with any aqueous solution giving effectively M^+ (Group I) and M^{2+} (Group II) ions:

Group I: $2M + 2H_2O \rightarrow 2M^+(aq) + 2OH^- + H_2\uparrow$
Group II: $M + 2H_2O \rightarrow M^{2+}(aq) + 2OH^- + H_2\uparrow$

The reactions with water are summarized in *Table 6.3*. Since the metals are powerful reducing agents (p. 89) they cannot be prepared in aqueous solution; electrolysis of the fused anhydrous halides is usually employed using a graphite anode.

Table 6.3 Reactions with water

Element	Li	Na	K	Rb	Cs
Reaction Conditions	All react with cold water to produce MOH Vigour of reaction increasing $\longrightarrow$				
Basic properties of products	All basic, base strength increasing $\longrightarrow$				

Element	Be	Mg	Ca	Sr	Ba
Reaction conditions	Does not react with water	Very slowly with water, readily with steam	React with cold water, vigour of reaction increasing $\longrightarrow$		
Basic properties of product	Be(OH)$_2$ amphoteric	MgO insoluble	slightly soluble	$\xrightarrow{\text{M(OH)}_2}$ soluble	
	Base strength increasing $\longrightarrow$				

The alkali metals have the interesting property of dissolving in some non-aqueous solvents, notably liquid ammonia, to give clear coloured solutions which are excellent reducing agents and are often used as such in organic chemistry. Sodium (for example) forms an intensely blue solution in liquid ammonia and here the outer ($3s$) electron of each sodium atom is believed to become associated with the solvent ammonia in some way, i.e. the solution contains $[Na(NH_3)_x]^+$ and $[e(NH_3)_y]^-$ species.

The solution is energetically unstable (Chapter 3); the sodium slowly reacts with the ammonia solvent thus:

$2Na + 2NH_3 \rightarrow 2NaNH_2 + H_2\uparrow$
$\qquad\qquad\qquad$ sodium amide
$\qquad\qquad\qquad$ (sodamide)

a reaction which can also be written

$2e^- + 2NH_3 \rightarrow 2NH_2^- + H_2\uparrow$
$\qquad\qquad\qquad$ amide ion

This reaction is catalysed by such ions as iron(III) and should be compared with the reaction with water

$$2Na + 2H_2O \rightarrow 2NaOH + H_2\uparrow$$

6.2 Compounds of Group I and II elements

6.2.1 General

For the most part is it true to say that the chemistry of the alkali and alkaline earth metal compounds is not that of the metal ion but rather that of the anion with which the ion is associated. Where appropriate, therefore, the chemistry of these compounds will be discussed in other sections, for example nitrates with Group V compounds, sulphates with Group VI compounds, and only a few compounds will be discussed here.

6.2.2 The hydrides

All Group I and II elements, except beryllium, form hydrides by direct combination with hydrogen. The hydrides of the metals except those of beryllium and magnesium, are white mainly ionic solids, all Group I hydrides having the sodium chloride lattice structure. All the hydrides are stable in dry air but react with water, the vigour of the reaction increasing with the molecular mass of the hydride for any particular group.

$$MH + H_2O \rightarrow MOH + H_2\uparrow$$
$$MH_2 + 2H_2O \rightarrow M(OH)_2 + H_2\uparrow$$

This reaction is due to the very strong basic property of the hydride ion H^- which behaves as a powerful proton acceptor and is therefore strongly basic, i.e.

$$H^- + H_2O \rightarrow H_2\uparrow + OH^-$$

When the molten ionic hydrides are electrolysed, all yield hydrogen at the anode, the metal at the cathode.

The hydrides of Group I, especially lithium hydride, react with the hydrides of trivalent metals of Group III to form interesting complex hydrides, probably the most important being lithium aluminium hydride (lithium tetrahydridoaluminate) $LiAlH_4$, well known as a reducing agent in organic chemistry.

The hydrides of beryllium and magnesium are both largely covalent, magnesium hydride having a 'rutile' (p. 31) structure, while beryllium hydride forms an electron-deficient chain structure. The bonding in these metal hydrides is not simple and requires an explanation which goes beyond the scope of this book.

6.2.3   The halides

Group I metals combine directly with all the halogens. The reactions are exothermic, the greatest heats of formation being found when the elements combine with fluorine. Except for the formation of the fluorides, the heat of formation of a given halide increases as the group is descended and the ionization energies of the metallic elements fall. The reverse is true for the fluorides, and the heat of formation falls as the group is descended. This is due to the high lattice energies produced from the 'combination' of the small fluoride anion and the metal cation (p. 66). (Similar variations are also noted with other small anions, for example nitride, carbide.)

All the Group I halides can be regarded as ionic*, this fact being reflected in their high m.p. and b.p. and the ability of the melt to conduct electricity. All except lithium fluoride are soluble in water, the insolubility of the lithium fluoride being a result of the high lattice energy, which is sufficiently large more than to compensate for the high hydration energies of the lithium and fluoride ions (p. 70). Group II metals also form halides by direct combination. The trends in heat of formation and m.p., however, whilst following the general pattern of the corresponding Group I compounds, are not so regular.

As a consequence of the high ionization energy of beryllium its halides are essentially covalent, with comparatively low m.p., the melts being non-conducting and (except beryllium fluoride) dissolving in many organic solvents.

The lower members in Group II form essentially ionic halides, with magnesium having intermediate properties, and both magnesium bromide and iodide dissolve in organic solvents.

The lattice energies of the Group II fluorides are generally greater than those for the corresponding Group I fluorides; consequently all but beryllium fluoride are insoluble. (The solubility of beryllium fluoride is explained by the high hydration energy of the beryllium ion, cf. LiF.) The high hydration energy of the Be^{2+} ion† results in hydrolysis in neutral or alkaline aqueous solution; in this reaction the beryllium halides closely resemble the aluminium halides (another example of a diagonal relationship — p. 16).

The magnesium ion having a high hydration energy (*Table 6.2*) also shows hydrolysis but to a lesser extent (than either Be^{2+} or Al^{3+}). The chloride forms several hydrates which decompose on heating to give a basic salt, a reaction most simply represented as (cf. p. 39):

$$MgCl_2.2H_2O \ \rightarrow \ Mg(OH)Cl \ + \ HCl\uparrow \ + \ H_2O$$

Other Group II halides are essentially ionic and therefore have relatively high m.p., the melts acting as conductors, and they are soluble in water but not in organic solvents.

The properties of the halides are summarized in *Table 6.4*.

---

*Lithium bromide and iodide probably have some degree of covalency but this does not affect the general conclusion.

†Note that the Be^{2+} ion has a coordination number of 4 whereas most cations have a coordination number of six. This is again the result of the very small size.

Table 6.4 Summary of the properties of halides of Groups I and II

Element	Li	Na	K	Rb	Cs
Fluorides	Insoluble	Soluble →			
		Heat of formation decreasing →			
		Melting point decreasing →			
Chlorides	Hydrated deliquescent	Anhydrous →			
		Heat of formation increasing →			
		Melting point decreasing →			
Bromides and iodides	Soluble in organic solvents	Insoluble in organic solvents →			
		Heat of formation increasing →			
		Melting point decreasing →			

Element	Be	Mg	Ca	Sr	Ba
Fluorides	Soluble in water	Sparingly soluble in water	Insoluble in water →		
Chlorides, bromides and iodides	Covalent when anhydrous. Soluble in organic solvents. Hydrolysed by water	Soluble in water →			

6.2.4   The oxides and hydroxides

The white solid oxides $M_2^I O$ and $M^{II}O$ are formed by direct union of the elements. The oxides $M_2^I O$ and the oxides $M^{II}O$ of calcium down to radium have ionic lattices and are all highly basic; they react exothermically with water to give the hydroxides, with acids to give salts, and with carbon dioxide to give carbonates. For example

$$Na_2O + H_2O \rightarrow 2NaOH$$
$$BaO + CO_2 \rightarrow BaCO_3$$

Magnesium oxide is almost inert towards water, but dissolves in acids to give salts; beryllium oxide is inert and almost insoluble in water or in acids.

Group I elements, except lithium, form *peroxides* $M_2^I O_2$ with excess of oxygen, and potassium, rubidium and caesium will form *superoxides* MO_2. These per- and super-oxides are best prepared by passing oxygen into a solution of the metal in liquid ammonia. It is believed that the large ions O_2^{2-} and O_2^- are only stable in lattices with larger cations — hence lithium (small cation) forms only the normal oxide Li_2O. The elements of Group II also form peroxides.

The hydroxides M^IOH are all soluble in water, in which they behave as strong bases, for example

$$KOH \rightarrow K^+ + OH^-$$

The hydroxides $M^{II}(OH)_2$ are generally less soluble and are of lower base strength. The Group I hydroxides are almost unique in possessing good solubility — most metal hydroxides are insoluble or sparingly soluble; hence sodium hydroxide and, to a lesser extent potassium hydroxide, are widely used as sources of the hydroxide ion OH^- both in the laboratory and on a large scale.

Sodium hydroxide is manufactured by electrolysis of concentrated aqueous sodium chloride; the other product of the electrolysis, chlorine, is equally important and hence separation of anode and cathode products is necessary. This is achieved either by a diaphragm (for example in the *Hooker* electrolytic cell) or by using a mercury cathode which takes up the sodium formed at the cathode as an amalgam (the *Kellner–Solvay* cell). The amalgam, after removal from the electrolyte cell, is treated with water to give sodium hydroxide and mercury. The mercury cell is more costly to operate but gives a purer product.

Potassium hydroxide is similar to sodium hydroxide but is a stronger base; it is also more soluble in ethanol and the solution is sometimes used as a reagent ('alcoholic potash'). The other hydroxides of Group I are similar, increasing in base strength down the group*; all are hygroscopic solids which attack the skin — hence the old names, 'caustic soda' (NaOH), 'caustic potash' (KOH) — and react with carbon dioxide in the air to give carbonates:

$$2OH^- + CO_2 \rightarrow CO_3^{2-} + H_2O$$

With excess of carbon dioxide, i.e. if the gas is passed through a solution of the hydroxide, a hydrogencarbonate is formed:

$$OH^- + CO_2 \rightarrow HCO_3^-$$

The reaction between $Ca(OH)_2$ and CO_2 to produce sparingly soluble $CaCO_3$ is the common test for carbon dioxide.

Beryllium hydroxide is obtained as a white gelatinous precipitate when OH^- ions are added to a solution of a beryllium salt. It is only sparingly soluble in water, and is weakly basic, dissolving in strong acids to give the hydrated beryllium ion $[Be(H_2O)_4]^{2+}$, but also dissolving in solutions containing the hydroxide ion to give the *tetrahydroxoberyllate*(II) ion $[Be(OH)_4]^{2-}$; addition of acid first reprecipitates the hydroxide $Be(OH)_2$ (as a white gelatinous hydrated precipitate) and then re-dissolves it to give the

*With the smaller cations (Li^+, Na^+) there is some association of the OH^- ion with the cation in solution, and this results in a lower base strength.

hydrated ion; hence we have the sequence*

$$[Be(H_2O)_4]^{2+} \underset{H^+}{\overset{OH^-}{\rightleftharpoons}} [Be(OH)_2(H_2O)_2] \downarrow \underset{H^+}{\overset{OH^-}{\rightleftharpoons}} [Be(OH)_4]^{2-}$$

This behaviour distinguishes beryllium hydroxide from the other hydroxides of Group II which are not amphoteric; this amphoterism is also shown by aluminium hydroxide in Group III, and it has been discussed more fully in Chapter 2, where we saw it as characteristic of small ions of high charge, i.e. Be^{2+} and Al^{3+}.

The other Group II hydroxides are sparingly soluble in water, the solubility increasing down the group; magnesium hydroxide is precipitated only by an appreciable concentration of hydroxide ion (not by ammonium hydroxide in presence of ammonium chloride) and the others are not precipitated.

The properties of the hydroxides are summarized in *Table 6.5*.

Table 6.5 Summary of the properties of hydroxides

Element	Li	Na	K	Rb	Cs
MOH	All soluble	Base strength increasing →			
Element	Be	Mg	Ca	Sr	Ba
M(OH)₂	Insoluble			Solubility increasing →	
	Amphoteric			Base strength increasing →	

6.3   The carbonates and hydrogencarbonates

As with the hydroxides, we find that whilst the carbonates of most metals are insoluble, those of alkali metals are soluble, so that they provide a good source of the carbonate ion CO_3^{2-} in solution; the alkali metal carbonates, except that of lithium, are stable to heat. Group II carbonates are generally insoluble in water and less stable to heat, losing carbon dioxide reversibly at high temperatures.

A further peculiarity of the Group I and II carbonates is the ability to form the *hydrogencarbonate* or bicarbonate ion HCO_3^-:

$$CO_3^{2-} + H_3O^+ \rightleftharpoons HCO_3^- + H_2O$$

This ion is produced by the prolonged passage of carbon dioxide through neutral or alkaline solutions containing Group I or II ions (except lithium or

*The species involved are more complicated than this sequence indicates, see note on p. 40; the simplified representation is, however, quite adequate.

Table 6.6 Decomposition temperatures*/K of some carbonates

Group I	T/K	Group II	T/K
Li_2CO_3	1 540	$BeCO_3$	370
Na_2CO_3	very high	$MgCO_3$	470
K_2CO_3	very high	$CaCO_3$	1 170
Rb_2CO_3	very high	$SrCO_3$	1 550
Cs_2CO_3	very high	$BaCO_3$	1 630

*The temperature at which the pressure of CO_2 reaches 1 atmosphere.

beryllium which do not form a hydrogencarbonate). The hydrogencarbonates of Group I elements can be isolated as solids but these solids readily decompose when heated to form the carbonate with the evolution of carbon dioxide and water, for example

$$2NaHCO_3 \rightarrow Na_2CO_3 + H_2O + CO_2$$

Group II hydrogencarbonates have insufficient thermal stability for them to be isolated as solids. However, in areas where natural deposits of calcium and magnesium carbonates are found a reaction between the carbonate, water and carbon dioxide occurs:

$$M^{II}CO_3 + CO_2 + H_2O \rightarrow M^{2+} + 2HCO_3^-$$
Insoluble   In solution   In solution

This produces sufficient concentrations of magnesium and calcium ions to render the water *hard*, that is to say, it fails to lather with soap. Hardness in water is considered in Chapter 10 (p. 241). The above reaction is readily reversed by boiling the water when the magnesium and calcium ions responsible for the hardness are removed as the insoluble carbonate.

Some carbonates are important industrial chemicals. Calcium carbonate occurs naturally in several forms, including limestone, and is used in the production of *quicklime*, calcium oxide CaO, *slaked (or hydrated) lime*, calcium hydroxide $Ca(OH)_2$ and cement.

Several million tons of sodium carbonate are used every year, almost one third of this being used in glass making and the rest being used for a variety of purposes including paper manufacture, chemicals, and as a water softener in soap powder. Sodium sesquicarbonate, $Na_2CO_3.NaHCO_3.2H_2O$, occurs naturally in the United States of America and approximately 1 000 000 tons of sodium carbonate are produced from this annually. Until recently almost all the sodium carbonate required commercially in the UK (5 000 000 tons annually) was manufactured by the soda–ammonia process but some is now produced by carbonation of sodium hydroxide, surplus to requirements, made during the electrolysis of brine:

$$2NaOH + CO_2 \rightarrow Na_2CO_3 + H_2O$$

The soda–ammonia process occurs in two main stages. First, brine is saturated with ammonia gas and this 'ammoniacal brine' is then treated with carbon dioxide. The equilibrium

$$CO_2 + 2H_2O \rightleftharpoons HCO_3^- + H_3O^+$$

is moved to the right by the competition of the ammonia for protons, i.e.

$$NH_3 + H_3O^+ \rightleftharpoons NH_4^+ + H_2O$$

The ions then present are NH_4^+, HCO_3^-, Cl^- and Na^+ and the least soluble salt, sodium hydrogencarbonate, is precipitated when ionic concentrations increase, and is removed by vacuum filtration.

When heated, sodium hydrogencarbonate readily decomposes evolving carbon dioxide, a reaction which leads to its use as baking powder when the carbon dioxide evolved 'aerates' the dough. In the soda–ammonia process the carbon dioxide evolved is used to supplement the main carbon dioxide supply obtained by heating calcium carbonate:

$$CaCO_3 \rightarrow CaO + CO_2$$

The calcium oxide so produced is slaked to give a suspension of calcium hydroxide and this is heated with the filtrate from the carbonator which contains ammonium chloride:

$$2NH_4Cl + Ca(OH)_2 \rightarrow CaCl_2 + 2NH_3\uparrow + 2H_2O$$

The ammonia gas is used again and the only by-product, calcium chloride, is used to melt snow, prevent freezing of coal in transit and as an antidust treatment since it is hygroscopic and forms a solution of low freezing point.

6.4 Abnormal properties of lithium and beryllium

As any group is descended the size of the atom and number of electrons shielding the outer electrons from the nucleus increases and the ionization energy falls (*see Table 6.2*).

Shielding of the outer electrons is least for the small lithium and beryllium atoms and their ionization energies are consequently higher than other members of their respective groups. In the case of beryllium the higher ionization energy results in the bonding in many beryllium compounds being covalent rather than ionic. (This tendency is shown to a much lesser extent by magnesium which forms some covalent compounds.)

The small lithium Li^+ and beryllium Be^{2+} ions have high charge–radius ratios and consequently exert particularly strong attractions on other ions and on polar molecules. These attractions result in both high lattice and hydration energies and it is these high energies which account for many of the abnormal properties of the ionic compounds of lithium and beryllium.

In view of the ionization energies the electrode potentials for lithium and beryllium might be expected to be higher than for sodium and magnesium. Relevant values are given in *Table 6.7*. Ionization energy refers to the process $Li(g) \rightarrow Li^+(g) + e^-$, whereas the electrode potential measured in aqueous solution also includes the enthalpy of atomization and the energy of hydration of the $Li^+(g)$ ion once formed, i.e.

$$Li^+(g) + xH_2O \rightarrow Li^+(aq)$$

Table 6.7 Comparative electrode potentials

Reaction	$E^{\ominus}/V$
$Li^+(aq) + e^- \rightarrow Li(s)$	-3.04
$Na^+(aq) + e^- \rightarrow Na(s)$	-2.71
$Be^{2+}(aq) + e^- \rightarrow Be(s)$	-1.85
$Mg^{2+}(aq) + e^- \rightarrow Mg(s)$	-2.37

This hydration energy is large and in the case of lithium compensates for the high ionization energy. The value of the second ionization energy of beryllium (the energy to remove the second electron) is so great that even the large hydration energy of the Be^{2+} cannot compensate for it, and $E^{\ominus}$ is less negative.

The hydroxide of lithium, although soluble in water, is a weak base owing to the great attraction between the Li^+ and OH^- ions (p. 66); the hydroxide of beryllium is really a neutral, insoluble beryllium complex $[Be(OH)_2(H_2O)_2]$ (p. 120).

When considering the fluorides, the high hydration energy of the small fluoride ion, F^-, must also be considered (p. 70). The lattice energy of beryllium fluoride is high but the combined hydration energies of the Be^{2+} and F^- ions are sufficient for the BeF_2 to dissolve, whilst the other fluorides of Group II elements having lower M^{2+} hydration energy are insoluble in spite of lower lattice energies. The insolubility of lithium fluoride results from the high lattice energy which in this case is not exceeded by the combined hydration energies. Other Group I fluorides dissolve since the lattice energies are smaller and are exceeded by the combined hydration energies.

In this discussion, entropy factors have been ignored and in certain cases where the difference between lattice energy and hydration energy is small it is the entropy changes which determine whether a substance will or will not dissolve. Each case must be considered individually and the relevant data obtained (*see* Chapter 3), when irregular behaviour will often be found to have a logical explanation.

The abnormal properties of lithium and beryllium are summarized in *Tables 6.8* and *6.9*.

6.5   Tests for the cations

6.5.1   Group I

All the cations of Group I produce a characteristic colour in a flame (lithium, red; sodium, yellow; potassium, violet; rubidium, dark red; caesium, blue). The test may be applied quantitatively by atomizing an aqueous solution containing Group I cations into a flame and determining the intensities of emission over the visible spectrum with a spectrophotometer (*flame photometry*).

The larger cations of Group I (K, Rb, Cs) can be precipitated from aqueous solution as white solids by addition of the reagent sodium tetraphenyl-borate, $NaB(C_6H_5)_4$. Sodium can be precipitated as the yellow sodium zinc uranium oxide ethanoate (sodium zinc uranyl acetate), $NaZn(UO_2)_3$-$(CH_3COO)_9.9H_2O$, by adding a clear solution of 'zinc uranyl acetate' in dilute ethanoic acid to a solution of a sodium salt.

Table 6.8 Summary of the chemistry of lithium

	Li	Na	K	Rb	Cs
Element	Hard metal	Soft metals →			
Hydroxide	Not a strong base	Strong bases →			
Fluoride	Only slightly soluble in water	Readily soluble in water →			
Chloride	Slightly hydrolysed in hot solution	Not hydrolysed →			
Bromide and iodide	Soluble in many organic solvents	Insoluble in most organic solvents →			
Carbonate	Evolves carbon dioxide on heating	Stable to heat →			

Table 6.9 Summary of the chemistry of beryllium

	Be	Mg	Ca	Sr	Ba
Hydroxide	Amphoteric	Basic →			
Fluoride	Soluble in water	Sparingly soluble to soluble in water →			
Chloride	Partly covalent	Ionic →			
Other compounds	Often covalent	Ionic →			

6.5.2 Group II

Calcium, strontium and barium produce characteristic flame colours like the Group I cations (calcium, orange; strontium, red; barium, green) and flame photometry can be used for their estimation. All give insoluble carbonates in neutral solution.

Magnesium is slowly precipitated as the white magnesium ammonium tetraoxophosphate(V), $MgNH_4PO_4.6H_2O$, when a solution of disodium hydrogentetraoxophosphate(V) is added to a solution of a magnesium salt in the presence of ammonia and ammonium chloride.

Summary

1   The **metals** have low hardness, increasing from Group I to Group II with melting and boiling points decreasing down the groups.

3   Most compounds are ionic solids, and **ions** are hydrated in solution. Lithium, beryllium and magnesium can also form covalent compounds.

3   The **hydrides** are mainly salt-like and ionic.

4   The **halides** and **hydroxides** are summarized in *Tables 6.4* and *6.5*. Most form **peroxides** $M^I_2O_2$ and $M^{II}O_2$.

5   All except lithium and beryllium form hydrogencarbonates M^IHCO_3 and $M^{II}(HCO_3)_2$. Those of Group II exist only in solution.

Questions

1   By consideration of the trends in the properties of the Group I elements and their compounds, deduce possible answers to the following questions concerning the element francium (Fr, atomic number 87).
   (a) Which noble gas would have the same electronic configuration as the francium ion?
   (b) Give the formula of the compound formed between francium and hydrogen.
   (c) Write down the equation for the reaction of francium with water.
   (d) What further reaction would take place if the solution obtained in (c) were exposed to the atmosphere?
   (e) Why would the compound formed between francium and chlorine be soluble in water but insoluble in benzene?

                                                                JMB,A

2   The elements in Group II of the Periodic Table (alkaline earth metals) are, in alphabetical order, barium (Ba), beryllium (Be), calcium (Ca), magnesium (Mg), radium (Ra) and strontium (Sr).
   (a) Arrange these elements in order of increasing atomic numbers.
   (b) Write down the electronic configurations of any two of the above elements other than beryllium (Be), stating in each case the name of the element, for example Be would be $1s^22s^2$.

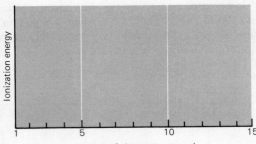

Number of electrons removed

(c) Indicate in the diagram how you would expect successive ionization energies of magnesium to vary with the number of electrons removed.

(d) (i) What type of chemical bonding is generally found in alkaline earth metal compounds?

(ii) What experiment would you carry out in order to demonstrate the presence of this type of bonding in alkaline earth metal compounds? Briefly indicate the results which you would expect to obtain.

(e) How does the solubility in water of the alkaline earth metal sulphates vary with the atomic weight of the metal?

L,A

3   'The properties of lithium resemble those of the alkaline earth metals rather than those of the alkali metals.' Discuss this statement.

Liverpool B.Sc., Part I

4   Explain why the Group I elements are:
(a) univalent,
(b) largely ionic in combination,
(c) strong reducing agents,
(d) poor complexing agents.

S,A

Chapter 7
Group III
Boron, aluminium, gallium, indium, thallium

Of the five Group III elements, only boron and aluminium are reasonably familiar elements. Aluminium is in fact the most abundant metal, and third most abundant element in the Earth's crust, but the other elements are rare and boron is the only one so far found in concentrated deposits.

The data in *Table 7.1* show that, as expected, density, ionic radius, and atomic radius increase with increasing atomic number. However, we should also note the marked differences in m.p. and liquid range of boron compared with the other Group III elements; here we have the first indication of the very large difference in properties between boron and the other elements in the group. Boron is in fact a non-metal, whilst the remaining elements are metals with closely related properties.

7.1 Oxidation state +3

Summation of the first three ionization energies of any Group III element indicates that the formation of an $E^{3+}(g)$ ion is difficult. In the case of boron the energy required is so large that under normal circumstances $B^{3+}(g), (s)$ or (aq) is never formed. The energy required is slightly less for aluminium but the simple ion $Al^{3+}(s)$ is found only in anhydrous aluminium fluoride and chlorate(VII), and even here there may be partial covalent bonding. Oxidation state +3 compounds of other Group III elements are largely covalent.

With the one exception of boron, all Group III elements form +3 ions in aqueous solution; these ions exist only as complexes, often with water, for example $[Al(H_2O)_6]^{3+}$, and are usually extensively hydrolysed (p. 40). The large hydration energy which helps to stabilize the ion is a major factor contributing to the low standard electrode potential of aluminium which, in view of the energy required to form $Al^{3+}(g)$, is rather unexpected. Since hydration energy decreases with increasing ionic size we can correctly predict that the standard electrode potential will decrease with increasing atomic number of the element. In the case of boron, however, the very small $B^{3+}(g)$ ion is unable to coordinate a sufficient number of water molecules to compensate for the high ionization energy; it can be stabilized by tetracoordination of certain ligands to form the boronium cation, for example, as shown at top of p. 129.

Table 7.1 Selected properties of the elements of Group III

Element	Atomic number	Outer electrons	Atomic radius nm	Radius of M$^+$ nm	Density g cm^{-3} (293 K)	m.p. K	b.p. K	Ionization energy kJ mol^{-1} 1st	2nd	3rd	$E^{\ominus}$/V
B	5	$2s^2 2p^1$	0.079	(0.020)	2.35	2600	2800	801	2428	3660	-0.87
Al	13	$3s^2 3p^1$	0.143	0.045	2.70	933	2600	578	1817	2745	-1.68
Ga	31	$3d^{10} 4s^2 4p^1$	0.153	0.062	5.91	303	2500	579	1979	2962	-0.52
In	49	$4d^{10} 5s^2 5p^1$	0.167	0.081	7.31	429	2340	558	1820	2705	-0.34
Tl	81	$5d^{10} 6s^2 6p^1$	0.171	0.095	11.85	574	1726	589	1970	2880	

$$\left[\begin{array}{c} H_3N \\ | \\ H_3N \overset{\displaystyle B \text{\tiny\hspace{0.2em}} H}{\diagdown} \\ H \end{array} \right]^+$$

7.2 Oxidation state +1

The outer electronic configuration of the Group III elements is ns^2np^1 and as we have seen on p. 26 the energy required to remove the first p electron from a given quantum level is less than that needed to remove one of a pair of s electrons occupying the same quantum level. This would indicate the possible existence of a $+1$ oxidation state when only the p electron was removed. However, as was seen in Chapter 4 several factors are involved in the stabilization of any oxidation state. It is found, in this case, that the stability of the $+1$ oxidation state increases regularly with increasing atomic number from aluminium to thallium, being (so far) unknown for boron but being generally the most stable oxidation state for thallium. Unipositive compounds of aluminium, gallium and indium (unlike those of thallium which are stabilized because of insolubility) disproportionate in water:

$$3M^+ \rightarrow M^{3+} + 2M$$

The tendency of elements of higher atomic number to retain the s electrons as an inert pair is also encountered in Group IV, and in this case it is found that for lead the most stable oxidation state is $+2$, achieved by loss of two p electrons.

7.3 Coordination number

By sharing its three outer electrons, boron forms planar, covalent BX_3 compounds (p. 141). By accepting an electron pair from a donor molecule or ion, boron can achieve a noble gas configuration whilst increasing its covalency to four, for example $H_3N \rightarrow BCl_3$, $K^+BF_4^-$. This is the maximum for boron and the second quantum level is now complete; these 4-coordinate species are tetrahedral (p. 32).

Aluminium also has a strong tendency to achieve a noble gas configuration by electron pair acceptance as shown in dimeric aluminium chloride,

in the adduct $H_3N \rightarrow AlCl_3$, and in $Li^+AlH_4^-$, in a similar manner to boron. In the case of aluminium, however, the third quantum level is not full since there are unfilled $3d$ orbitals available, and aluminium is able to coordinate up to a maximum of six ligands (molecules or ions) depending upon their size and shape, for example $[AlF_6]^{3-}$, $[Al(OH)_6]^{3-}$, $[Al(H_2O)_6]^{3+}$. The metal–ligand bonding in these complexes may be partly ionic and partly covalent in nature.

Gallium, indium and thallium resemble aluminium and form compounds with three, four and six ligands. The increase in coordination number, maximum between the first and second elements in a group, is characteristic of Groups III to VII: but the maximum coordination (6) of the second element, in purely inorganic compounds, is usually only seen with ligands that are small and electronegative, for example H_2O, F^-, OH^-. Thus, owing to its greater size, there are no corresponding stable compounds with the chloride ion, e.g. aluminium forms $[AlCl_4]^-$ but *not* $[AlCl_6]^{3-}$.

7.4   Properties of the elements

7.4.1   Occurrence and extraction

Boron

Boron does not occur free in nature; in minerals, it occurs as borates, for example, *kernite*, $Na_2B_4O_7.4H_2O$, and *borax*, $Na_2B_4O_7.10H_2O$; there are extensive deposits of these in the United States of America.

Boron can be obtained by heating boron trioxide with magnesium:

$$B_2O_3 + 3Mg \rightarrow 2B + 3MgO$$

The boron so obtained is an amorphous powder. It can be obtained in the crystalline state by reducing the vapour of boron tribromide with hydrogen, either in an electric arc or in contact with an electrically-heated tungsten filament:

$$2BBr_3 + 3H_2 \rightarrow 2B + 6HBr\uparrow$$

Pure boron in the form of a thin film can also be obtained by heating diborane to 1000 K:

$$B_2H_6 \rightarrow 2B + 3H_2\uparrow$$

Amorphous boron has not been obtained in the pure state. Crystalline boron is a black powder, extremely hard, with a metallic appearance but with very low electrical conductivity.

Aluminium

Aluminium is not found free but its compounds are so widespread that it is the most abundant metal in the Earth's crust. *Aluminosilicates* such as clay, kaolin (or china clay), mica and feldspar are well known and widely distributed. The oxide, Al_2O_3 occurs (anhydrous) as *corundum* and *emery*, and (hydrated) as *bauxite*. *Cryolite*, Na_3AlF_6, (sodium hexafluoroaluminate), is found extensively in Greenland.

Aluminium is obtained on a large scale by the electrolysis of the oxide, dissolved in fused cryolite. The oxide, occurring naturally as bauxite, $Al_2O_3.2H_2O$, usually contains silica and iron(III) oxide as impurities. These must be removed first, since aluminium, once prepared, cannot be freed from other metals (which will be deposited on electrolysis) by refining it. The crude oxide is dissolved under pressure in sodium hydroxide solution; the aluminium oxide and silica dissolve and the iron(III) oxide is left:

$$Al_2O_3 + 2OH^- + 7H_2O \rightleftharpoons 2[Al(OH)_4(H_2O)_2]^-$$

From the sodium aluminate solution, aluminium hydroxide is precipitated by passing in carbon dioxide:

$$2[Al(OH)_4(H_2O)_2]^- + H_2O + CO_2 \rightarrow 2[Al(OH)_3(H_2O)_3]\downarrow + CO_3^{2-}$$

Alternatively, the solution is 'seeded' with a little previously prepared aluminium hydroxide:

$$[Al(OH)_4(H_2O)_2]^- + H_2O \rightleftharpoons [Al(OH)_3(H_2O)_3]\downarrow + OH^-$$

The pure oxide is then obtained by heating the precipitated hydroxide:

$$2Al(OH)_3(H_2O)_3 \rightarrow Al_2O_3 + 6H_2O$$

The pure oxide is dissolved in molten cryolite in an iron bath lined with graphite which acts as the cathode (*see Figure 7.1*). The anode consists of

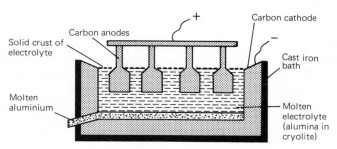

Figure 7.1 Extraction of aluminium

carbon rods suspended in the molten electrolyte. A low voltage must be used to avoid decomposition of the cryolite, and a very high current density is employed. (The proportion of the cost of this process for electric power is high; hence it is usually carried out where electric power is cheap and plentiful.) Molten aluminium collects on the floor of the graphite-lined bath and is run off at intervals, fresh alumina being added as required. The temperature of the bath (1100—1200 K) is maintained by the passage of the current. Oxygen is evolved at the anode, which is slowly attacked to form oxides of carbon and a little tetrafluoromethane, CF_4, may also be formed by slight electrolysis of the cryolite. A promising alternative to graphite for the bath lining is *silicon nitride*, Si_3N_4 which is very resistant to molten aluminium and cryolite. It is a non-conductor, and hence resistant cathodes made of titanium diboride (TiB_2) are used.

In a newer process, in which purification of the oxide is of much less importance, aluminium chloride vapour is passed through the fused oxide at about 1300 K, whereupon the following reaction occurs:

$$2Al_2O_3 + 2AlCl_3 \rightarrow 6AlCl + 3O_2$$

The aluminium monochloride vapour is unstable when cooled and disproportionates (p. 68) below 1100 K thus:

$$3AlCl \rightarrow AlCl_3 + 2Al$$

The aluminium trichloride is then recycled through the fused oxide.

Gallium, indium and thallium
Each of these elements can be extracted by reduction of the respective oxide at high temperature, using either carbon or hydrogen; or by electrolysis of an aqueous solution of a salt of the required element.

7.4.2 Reactions of the elements with acids

Boron, being chemically a non-metal, is resistant to attack by non-oxidizing acids but the other members of the group react as typical metals and evolve hydrogen. Aluminium, gallium and indium are oxidized to the $+3$ oxidation state, the simplified equation being

$$2M + 6H^+ \rightarrow 2M^{3+} + 3H_2$$

However, thallium is oxidized to the $+1$ oxidation state:

$$2Tl + 2H^+ \rightarrow 2Tl^+ + H_2$$

Strong oxidizing acids, for example hot concentrated sulphuric acid and nitric acid, attack finely divided boron to give 'boric acid' H_3BO_3. The metallic elements behave much as expected, the metal being oxidized whilst the acid is reduced. Bulk aluminium, however, is rendered 'passive' by both dilute and concentrated nitric acid and no action occurs; the passivity is due to the formation of an impervious oxide layer. Finely divided aluminium does dissolve slowly when heated in concentrated nitric acid.

7.4.3 Reactions of the elements with alkalis (sodium hydroxide)

Amorphous boron and the amphoteric elements, aluminium and gallium, are attacked by aqueous solutions of sodium hydroxide and hydrogen is liberated. Boron reacts slowly with boiling concentrated sodium hydroxide to give sodium polydioxoborate (metaborate) $Na_n^+(BO_2^-)_n$, but both aluminium and gallium will react at room temperature to produce hydroxoaluminate and hydroxogallate ions respectively:

$$2Al + 2NaOH + 10H_2O \rightarrow 2Na^+[Al(OH)_4(H_2O)_2]^- + 3H_2$$

The more metallic elements, indium and thallium, do not react in spite of the fact that $In(OH)_3$ is amphoteric.

7.4.4 Reactions of the elements with water

Neither boron nor aluminium reacts with water at room temperature but both react with steam at red heat liberating hydrogen:

$$2B + 6H_2O \rightarrow 2H_3BO_3 + 3H_2$$
$$2Al + 3H_2O \rightarrow Al_2O_3 + 3H_2$$

The electrode potential of aluminium would lead us to expect attack by water. The inertness to water is due to the formation of an unreactive layer of oxide on the metal surface. In the presence of mercury, aluminium readily forms an amalgam (destroying the original surface) which is, therefore, rapidly attacked by water. Since mercury can be readily displaced from its soluble salts by aluminium, contact with such salts must be avoided if rapid corrosion and weakening of aluminium structures is to be prevented.

In the absence of oxygen, gallium and indium are unaffected by water. Thallium, the most metallic element in Group III, reacts slowly with hot water and readily with steam to produce thallium(I) oxide, Tl_2O.

7.4.5 Reactions of the elements with air

Only thallium of the Group III elements is affected by air at room temperature and thallium(III) oxide is slowly formed. All the elements, however, burn in air when strongly heated and, with the exception of gallium, form the oxide M_2O_3: gallium forms a mixed oxide of composition GaO. In addition to oxide formation, boron and aluminium react at high temperature with the nitrogen in the air to form nitrides (BN and AlN).

7.4 Compounds of boron and aluminium

7.5.1 Hydrides

Boron forms a whole series of hydrides. The simplest of these is diborane, B_2H_6. It may be prepared by the reduction of boron trichloride in ether by lithium aluminium hydride. This is a general method for the preparation of non-metallic hydrides:

$$4BCl_3 + 3LiAlH_4 \rightarrow 2B_2H_6 + 3LiCl + 3AlCl_3$$

Diborane has a *geometric* structure similar to that of dimeric aluminium chloride, (p. 36) namely

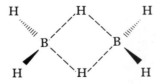

This is known as a 'hydrogen-bridge' structure. There are not enough electrons to make all the dotted-line bonds electron-pairs and hence it is an example of an *electron-deficient* compound. The structure of diborane may be alternatively shown as drawn in *Figure 7.2(a)* and (*b*).

All the available valency electrons, including those of the bridge hydrogens, are used as shown in (*a*), leaving the bridge hydrogens as protons,

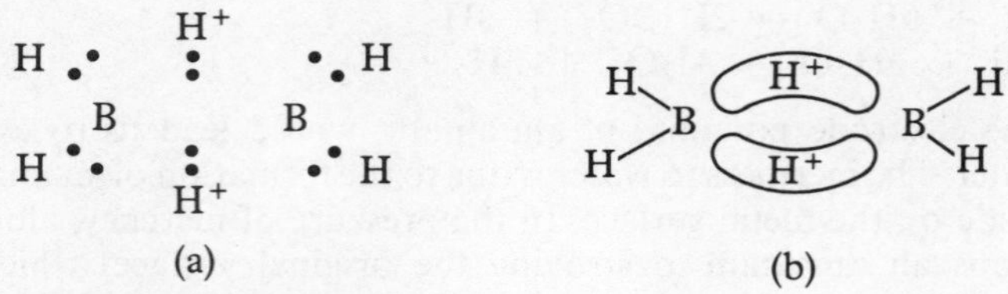

H ∙∙ ：∙ ∙∙H
H^+

B   B

H ∙∙∙ ： ∙∙H
H^+

H·,   ／H⁺﹨   ·,H
·B   B·
H／   ﹨H⁺／   ﹨H

(a)   (b)

Figure 7.2 The structure of diborane

H^+. The orbitals linking the boron atoms are not like those in ethene but form two banana-shaped 'clouds', as shown in (b); and the protons are embedded in these 'clouds'. (There is no tendency for diborane to act as an acid by losing these protons, as they are too firmly held.) Diborane is an inflammable gas which is immediately decomposed by water:

$$B_2H_6 + 6H_2O \rightarrow 2H_3BO_3 + 6H_2$$
boric acid

Borane, BH_3

Borane does not exist as such, but a donor molecule can break up diborane and form an adduct, thus:

$$B_2H_6 + 2N(CH_3)_3 \rightarrow 2(CH_3)_3N \rightarrow BH_3$$
trimethylamine

In this case the covalency of boron is brought up to four because the donor molecule supplies the necessary electrons. The adduct formed, trimethylamine–borane, is a stable white solid. Other compounds of a similar kind are known, all derived from the simple structure $H_3N \rightarrow BH_3$. This compound is *isoelectronic* with ethane, i.e. it contains the same number of electrons and has the same shape:

$\quad$ H $\quad$ H $\qquad\qquad$ H $\quad$ H

H ：N→B：H $\qquad\qquad$ H ：C：C：H

$\quad$ H $\quad$ H $\qquad\qquad$ H $\quad$ H

ammonia—borane $\qquad\qquad$ ethane

There are similar analogues to other aliphatic hydrocarbons, for example $H_2N \rightarrow BH_2$, which is isoelectronic with ethene, and a most interesting compound called borazine (cyclotriborazane), $B_3N_3H_6$, which possesses physical properties remarkably like those of the aromatic analogue benzene, C_6H_6. Borazine has, in fact, a ring structure like benzene:

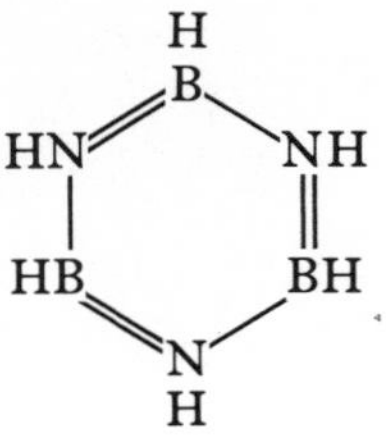

borazine

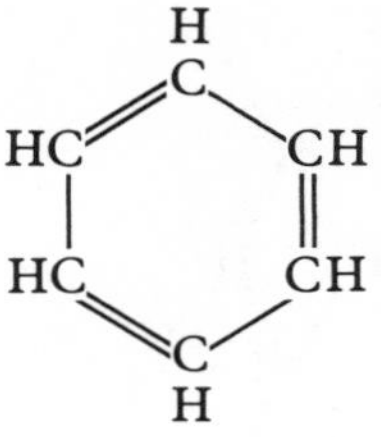

benzene

There is the possibility of building up an extensive systematic chemistry of compounds containing boron–nitrogen bonds, analogous to the chemistry of carbon–carbon bonds; but the reactivity of the B—N bond is much greater than that of the C—C bond, so that we get physical, but not chemical, resemblances between analogous compounds.

There is one other important way in which borane can be stabilized. Diborane reacts with a suspension of lithium hydride in dry ether thus

$$2LiH + B_2H_6 \rightarrow 2LiBH_4$$
lithium tetrahydridoborate
'lithium borohydride'

Here, the essential reaction is the formation of the *tetrahydridoborate* ion and again the covalency of boron is brough up to four, i.e.:

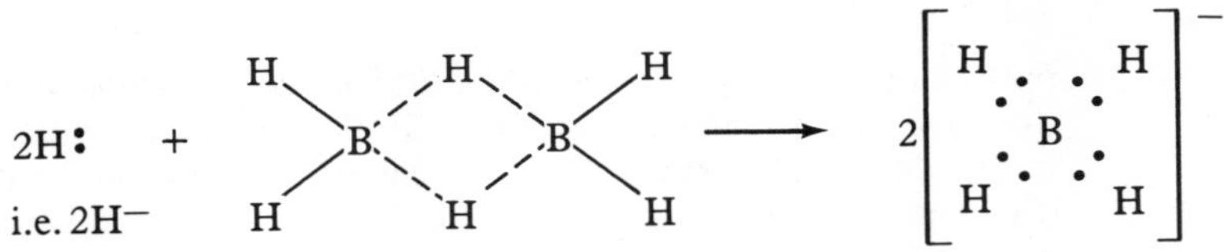

The alkali metal tetrahydridoborate are salts; those of sodium and potassium are stable in aqueous solution, but yield hydrogen in the presence of a catalyst. They are excellent reducing agents, reducing for example iron(III) to iron(II), and silver ions to the metal; their reducing power is used in organic chemistry, for example to reduce aldehydes to alcohols. They can undergo metathetic reactions to produce other borohydrides, for example

$$3LiBH_4 + AlCl_3 \xrightarrow{\text{ether}} Al(BH_4)_3 + 3LiCl$$
aluminium
tetrahydridoborate

Aluminium tetrahydridoborate is a volatile liquid. It is the most volatile aluminium compound known. It is covalent and does not contain ions but has a 'hydrogen-bridge' structure like that of diborane, i.e. each boron atom is attached to the aluminium by two hydrogen bridges:

$$
\begin{array}{c}
\text{H} \qquad \text{H} \\
\diagdown \quad \diagup \\
\text{B} \\
\diagup \quad \diagdown \\
\text{H} \qquad \text{H} \\
\text{H} - - \text{Al} - - \text{H} \\
\text{H} - \text{B} - - - \text{H} \quad \text{H} - - - - \text{B} - \text{H} \\
\diagup \qquad\qquad\qquad \diagdown \\
\text{H} \qquad\qquad\qquad \text{H}
\end{array}
$$

Other boron hydrides are known, most of them having the general formula B_nH_{n+4}, for example pentaborane, B_5H_9, decaborane $B_{10}H_{14}$. Each can be made by heating diborane in suitable conditions; for example at 420 K, decaborane is obtained. Boron hydrides have been tried as rocket fuels.

Aluminium hydride, $(AlH_3)_n$

When lithium hydride is allowed to react with aluminium chloride in ether solution, two reactions occur:

$$3LiH + AlCl_3 \rightarrow AlH_3 + 3LiCl\downarrow$$
$$4LiH + AlCl_3 \rightarrow LiAlH_4 + 3LiCl\downarrow$$

In the absence of excess of lithium hydride, aluminium hydride slowly precipitates as a white polymer $(AlH_3)_n$. With excess of lithium hydride, the reaction:

$$AlH_3 + H^- \rightarrow [AlH_4]^-$$

may be assumed to occur, forming *lithium tetrahydridoaluminate* (*aluminium hydride*), which remains in solution. In both cases, the aluminium increases its covalency. The extent of this increase is unknown in the polymer $(AlH_3)_n$ (the structure of this compound is not known with certainty but it is electron-deficient). In the tetrahedral ion $[AlH_4]^-$ the covalency has been increased to four.

Aluminium hydride loses hydrogen on heating. It reacts slowly with diborane to give aluminium tetrahydridoborate:

$$2(AlH_3)_n + 3nB_2H_6 \rightarrow 2nAl(BH_4)_3$$

7.5.2   Oxides and hydroxides

Boron trioxide, B_2O_3 is the anhydride of boric acid, H_3BO_3 and can be prepared by heating the acid:

$$2H_3BO_3 \rightarrow B_2O_3 + 3H_2O$$

Boron trioxide is not particularly soluble in water but it slowly dissolves to form both dioxoboric acid ('metaboric acid', HBO_2) and trioxoboric acid ('orthoboric acid', H_3BO_3). It is a dimorphous oxide and exists as either a glassy or a crystalline solid. Boron trioxide is an acidic oxide and combines with metal oxides and hydroxides to form borates, some of which have characteristic colours — a fact utilized in analysis as the 'borax bead test', cf. alumina p. 138. 'Boric acid' H_3BO_3. properly called trioxoboric acid, can be prepared by adding excess of hydrochloric or sulphuric acid to a hot saturated solution of borax, sodium heptaoxotetraborate, $Na_2B_4O_7$, when the only moderately soluble boric acid separates as white flaky crystals on cooling. Boric acid behaves as a very weak monobasic acid; it is a Lewis acid and its acidity is due to an initial acceptance of a lone pair of electrons from water rather than direct proton donation as in the case of Lowry–Brønsted acids, i.e.

$$
\text{HO}{\overset{\text{H}}{\underset{\text{O}}{\overset{\text{O}}{\text{B}}}}}\text{H}
\;+\;
:\!\text{O}\!\!\diagup^{\text{H}}_{\diagdown\text{H}}
\;+\; H_2O
\longrightarrow
H_3O^+ \;+\;
\left[\; \text{HO}\,{\overset{\text{H}}{\underset{\text{O}}{\overset{\text{O}}{\text{B}}}}}:\text{OH} \;\right]^-
$$

In the presence of glycerol or mannitol (polyhydroxo compounds)* boric acid behaves as a much stronger acid; the reaction can be represented as:

$$
\begin{array}{c} -\text{C}-\text{OH} \\ | \\ | \\ -\text{C}-\text{OH} \\ | \end{array}
\;+\; \text{HO}-\!\overset{\text{O}\!-\!\text{H}}{\underset{\text{O}\!-\!\text{H}}{\text{B}}}
\;+\;
\begin{array}{c} \text{HO}-\text{C}- \\ | \\ | \\ \text{HO}-\text{C}- \\ | \end{array}
\longrightarrow
\left[\begin{array}{c} -\text{C}-\text{O} \diagdown \diagup \text{O}-\text{C}- \\ | \qquad \text{B} \qquad | \\ -\text{C}-\text{O} \diagup \diagdown \text{O}-\text{C}- \\ | \end{array}\right]^-
\;+\; H_3O^+ \;+\; 2H_2O
$$

The acid can then be titrated with sodium hydroxide using phenolphthalein as the indicator. Boric acid was known as 'boracic acid' and was used extensively as a mild antiseptic. *Borates* are rarely simple salts although a few salts of formula MBO_3 (where M is a trivalent metal) are known. More commonly, the 'borate' anion is built up of BO_3 units into chains, rings or sheets, just as silicates are built up from units of the group SiO_4. Sodium heptaoxotetraborate (borax) $Na_2B_4O_7.10H_2O$ is alkaline in solution since it is hydrolysed. It can be titrated against hydrochloric acid using methyl red or methyl orange as the indicator:

$$B_4O_7^{2-} \;+\; 2H^+ \;+\; 5H_2O \;\to\; 4H_3BO_3$$

Borax is used in the production of pyrex glass, ceramics, as a flux in soldering and welding, and in laundering to impart a glaze to linen.

Sodium 'perborate' $NaBO_2.H_2O_2.3H_2O$, or more correctly sodium dioxoborate peroxohydrate, is an important additive to washing powders, behaving in water like a mixture of sodium borate and hydrogen peroxide (a

*Two of the hydroxo groups must be on the same side of the —C—C—chain, i.e. the structure must be *cis* (p. 157).

mild bleach). It is manufactured by treating a solution of borax with sodium peroxide followed by hydrogen peroxide or by the electrolysis of a solution containing borax and sodium borate with platinum electrodes.

Aluminium oxide, alumina Al_2O_3

Aluminium oxide occurs naturally as *emery* (an impure form) and as *corundum*. Corundum is a crystalline form which may be coloured by traces of impurity, for example as *ruby* (red) and *sapphire* (blue). Small synthetic rubies and sapphires have been made by heating alumina with the colouring oxide in an oxy-hydrogen flame.

Aluminium oxide can be prepared in the laboratory by heating the hydroxide (p. 139) or by heating powdered aluminium in air, when the oxide is formed together with some nitride. The reaction

$$4Al + 3O_2 \rightarrow 2Al_2O_3$$

is strongly exothermic and aluminium can be used to reduce some other metallic oxides to the metal, for example manganese, chromium and iron:

$$Fe_2O_3 + 2Al \rightarrow 2Fe + Al_2O_3$$

Reduction by aluminium has been used to produce molten iron *in situ* for welding steel and as a method of extracting metals.

Aluminium oxide is a white solid, insoluble in water, with a very high melting point. If heated above red heat, it becomes insoluble in acids and alkalis, and can only be brought into solution by first fusing it with sodium or potassium hydroxide, whereupon an aluminate is formed.

Alumina exists in several different crystalline forms. These have different capacities for *adsorbing* other substances on to the surface, from solution. If a mixture of coloured organic substances in solution is passed through a vertical glass tube packed with powdered alumina, the various substances separate out as coloured zones along the tube, and are thereby separated. Chlorophyll can be separated into its four constituents by this method. This was an early example of *chromatography*. Alumina refractories containing more than 45 per cent Al_2O_3 have high resistance to abrasion and attack by acids and are being used where ability to withstand high temperatures is essential. They have a working range up to 2000 K.

Aluminium hydroxide

A white gelatinous precipitate of aluminium hydroxide is obtained when a base is added to an aqueous solution of an aluminium salt. Addition of an excess of caustic alkali causes the precipitate to redissolve, the whole process being reversed by the addition of a strong acid; the actual substance present at any time depends on the position of the equilibrium. The equilibria involved have been discussed on p. 40; essentially they involve the species

$$[Al[H_2O]_6]^{3+} \quad \ldots[Al(OH)_3(H_2O)_3]\ldots \quad [Al(OH)_6]^{3-}$$

$$\xrightarrow{\text{alkali}}$$
$$\xleftarrow{\text{acid}}$$

Therefore, when an anhydrous aluminium salt is dissolved in water initially, the octahedral ion $[Al(H_2O)_6]^{3+}$ is formed by hydration of the Al^{3+} ion. However, since some hydrolysis occurs, the solution will contain H_3O^+ and be acidic. Addition of any molecule or ion which removes H_3O^+, for example alkali, or even sodium carbonate, will cause the equilibrium to be displaced to the right and hydrated aluminium hydroxide is precipitated:

$$H_3O^+ + CO_3^{2-} \rightarrow H_2O + CO_2$$

Addition of an excess of alkali displaces the equilibrium further and finally the hexahydroxoaluminate(III) ion $[Al(OH)_6]^{3-}$ is formed. Addition of H_3O^+ causes the displacement of equilibrium to the left.

On standing, gelatinous aluminium hydroxide, which may initially have even more water occluded than indicated above, is converted into a form insoluble in both acids and alkalis, which is probably a hydrated form of the oxide Al_2O_3. Both forms, however, have strong *ad*sorptive power and will *ad*sorb dyes, a property long used used by the textile trade to assist in the dyeing of fabrics, and more recently of rayon. The cloth is first impregnated with an aluminium salt (for example sulphate or acetate) whereupon addition of a little alkali, such as sodium carbonate, causes aluminium hydroxide to deposit in the pores of the material. The presence of this aluminium hydroxide *in* the cloth helps the dye to 'bite' by *ad*sorbing it — hence the name *mordant* (Latin *mordere* = to bite) dye process.

Sheet aluminium can be given a colour by a similar process. The aluminium is first made the anode in a bath of 'chromic acid' (p. 332) when, instead of oxygen being evolved, the aluminium becomes coated with a very adherent film of aluminium oxide which is very *ad*sorbent. If a dye is added to the bath the oxide film is coloured, this colour being incorporated in a film which also makes the remaining aluminium resistant to corrosion. This process is called 'anodizing' aluminium.

Salts containing the hydroxoaluminate ions $[Al(OH)_4(H_2O)_2]^-$ and $[Al(OH)_6]^{3-}$ are known in solution but on heating they behave rather like aluminium hydroxide and form hydrated aluminates. The structure of these solid compounds is not known with certainty but an approximate formula might be $NaAlO_2.xH_2O$. Many aluminates occur in minerals, for example the *spinels* of general formula $M^{II}(AlO_2)_2$ where M may be Mg, Zn or Fe: these have a mixed oxide structure, i.e. consist essentially of M^{2+}, Al^{3+} and O^{2-} ions.

7.5.3   The halides

Boron and aluminium halides show many similarities but also surprising differences. *Table 7.2* gives the melting and boiling points of the MX_3 halides. Boron halides are all covalently bonded with melting and boiling points increasing as expected with the increasing relative molecular mass. All boron trihalides exist as monomers in the vapour state and have regular trigonal planar configurations. They are electron-deficient compounds since in each halide the boron atom has only six electrons in its second quantum level and consequently they are electron pair acceptor molecules, i.e. Lewis acids. The ready hydrolysis of all the boron halides probably begins with the formation of a coordination compound with water, the oxygen atom donating a pair of

Table 7.2 Melting and boiling points of halides

Halide	m.p./K boron	m.p./K aluminium	b.p./K boron	b.p./K aluminium
Fluoride	144	1530 (sublimes)	174	1530 (sublimes)
Chloride	166	453 (2 atm.)	285	453 (sublimes)
Bromide	227	371	364	528
Iodide	323	453	483	654

electrons; this is rapidly followed by loss of hydrogen chloride, this process continuing to give finally $B(OH)_3$, i.e. boric acid.

The melting and boiling points of the aluminium halides, in contrast to the boron compounds, are irregular. It might reasonably be expected that aluminium, being a more metallic element than boron, would form an ionic fluoride and indeed the fact that it remains solid until 1564 K, when it sublimes, would tend to confirm this, although it should not be concluded that the fluoride is, therefore, wholly ionic. The crystal structure is such that each aluminium has a coordination number of six, being surrounded by six fluoride ions.

All the other aluminium halides are covalently bonded with aluminium showing a coordination number of four towards these larger halogen atoms. The four halogen atoms arrange themselves approximately tetrahedrally around the aluminium and dimeric molecules are produced with the configuration given below:

X = a halogen atom

These molecules exist in the solid halides, explaining the low melting points of these halides, and also in the vapour phase at temperatures not too far above the boiling point. At higher temperatures, however, dissociation into trigonal planar monomers, analogous to the boron halides, occurs.

The monomers are electron pair acceptors, and donor molecules are often able to split the dimeric halide molecules to form adducts; thus, whilst the dimeric halides persist in solvents such as benzene, donor solvents such as pyridine and ether appear to contain monomers since adduct formation occurs. Aluminium halides, with the one exception of the fluoride, resemble the corresponding boron halides in that they are readily hydrolysed by water.

Fluorides

Boron trifluoride is a colourless, reactive gas which can be prepared by heating boron trioxide and fluorspar with concentrated sulphuric acid:

$$B_2O_3 + 3CaF_2 + 3H_2SO_4 \rightarrow 2BF_3 + 3CaSO_4 + 3H_2O$$

or by the direct combination of the elements. The gas must be collected and kept under rigorously dry conditions; it fumes in moist air and reacts vigorously with water forming boric acid and tetrafluoroboric acid, $H^+BF_4^-$:

$$4BF_3 + 6H_2O \rightarrow 3H_3O^+ + 3BF_4^- + H_3BO_3$$

The BF_4^- ion has a regular tetrahedral configuration. The most important property of boron trifluoride is its great capacity to act as an electron pair acceptor (Lewis acid). Some examples of adducts are:

$$H_3N \rightarrow BF_3, \qquad \begin{matrix} C_2H_5 \\ \diagdown \\ O \rightarrow BF_3, \\ \diagup \\ C_2H_5 \end{matrix} \qquad H_2S \rightarrow BF_3$$

In each case the configuration around the boron changes from trigonal planar to tetrahedral on adduct formation. Because of this ability to form additional compounds, boron trifluoride is an important catalyst and is used in many organic reactions, notably polymerization, esterification, and Friedel–Crafts acylation and alkylations.

Aluminium fluoride is a white solid which sublimes without melting at 1530 K. Like boron trifluoride, it can be prepared by the direct combination of the elements but it can also be prepared by reacting aluminium hydroxide with gaseous hydrogen fluoride. Aluminium fluoride is chemically unreactive; it does not react with cold water in which it is only sparingly soluble, and it is attacked only slowly even by fused potassium hydroxide. Hydrofluoric acid dissolves it forming the octahedral hexafluoroaluminate ion, $[AlF_6]^{3-}$. The sodium salt of this ion, Na_3AlF_6, occurs naturally as cryolite (p. 130) but in insufficient quantities to meet the demand for it. It is produced industrially in large quantities by the action of hydrogen fluoride on sodium aluminate:

$$6HF + Na_3Al(OH)_6 \rightarrow Na_3AlF_6 + 6H_2O$$

Chlorides

Both boron and aluminium chlorides can be prepared by the direct combination of the elements. Boron trichloride can also be prepared by passing chlorine gas over a strongly heated mixture of boron trioxide and carbon. Like boron trifluoride, this is a covalent compound and a gas at ordinary temperature and pressure (boiling point 285 K). It reacts vigorously with water, the mechanism probably involving initial coordination of a water molecule (p. 140), and hydrochloric acid is obtained:

$$BCl_3 + 3H_2O \rightarrow H_3BO_3 + 3HCl$$

It forms an ion BCl_4^- only under special circumstances, and never in aqueous solutions (cf. BF_3). Like the trifluoride, it is an electron pair acceptor, but the adducts formed tend to decompose more readily. Unlike the corresponding aluminium chloride, boron trichloride exists only as the monomer.

Aluminium chloride can be prepared not only by the direct combination of the elements but also by the passage of dry hydrogen chloride over heated aluminium:

$$2Al + 3Cl_2 \rightarrow Al_2Cl_6$$
$$2Al + 6HCl \rightarrow Al_2Cl_6 + 3H_2$$

Pure anhydrous aluminium chloride is a white solid at room temperature. It is composed of double molecules in which a chlorine atom attached to one aluminium atom donates a pair of electrons to the neighbouring aluminium atom thus giving each aluminium the electronic configuration of a noble gas. By doing so each aluminium takes up an approximately tetrahedral arrangement (p. 36). It is not surprising that electron pair donors are able to split the dimer to form adducts, and ether, for example, forms the adduct

$$C_2H_5 \diagdown O \rightarrow AlCl_3 \diagup C_2H_5$$

in which aluminium again has a noble gas electronic configuration and tetrahedral symmetry.

When heated above 673 K the dimer, Al_2Cl_6, begins to dissociate into the monomer in which the aluminium has a regular trigonal planar configuration.

Aluminium chloride is used extensively in organic chemistry as a catalyst, for example in the Friedel–Crafts reaction:

$$C_6H_6 + C_2H_5Cl \xrightarrow{AlCl_3} C_6H_5C_2H_5 + HCl$$

It is believed that an intermediate complex ion $[AlCl_4]^-$ is formed thus:

$$C_2H_5Cl + AlCl_3 \rightleftharpoons C_2H_5^+ + AlCl_4^-$$

The $C_2H_5^+$ is a *carbonium ion* (cf. ammonium NH_4^+) (or *carbocation*) and reacts with the benzene:

$$C_6H_6 + C_2H_5^+ \rightarrow C_6H_5C_2H_5 + H^+$$

and then hydrogen chloride and aluminium chloride are formed:

$$H^+ + AlCl_4^- \rightarrow HCl + AlCl_3$$

Bromides and iodides

The tribromide and triiodide of both boron and aluminium can be made by the direct combination of the elements although better methods are known for each halide. The properties of each halide closely resemble those of the chloride.

Both aluminium tribromide and triiodide are dimeric in the solid state. As expected the solids dissolve in non-polar solvents without the break-up of these dimeric units.

Nitrides

When boron and aluminium burn in air small quantities of nitride are formed.

Boron nitride can be prepared by allowing ammonia to react with boron trichloride. The first product is boron amide which decomposes on heating to give the nitride:

$$BCl_3 + 6NH_3 \rightarrow B(NH_2)_3 + 3NH_4Cl$$
$$\text{boron amide}$$
$$B(NH_2)_3 \rightarrow BN + 2NH_3\uparrow$$

Boron nitride is chemically unreactive, and can be melted at 3000 K by heating under pressure. It is a covalent compound, but the lack of volatility is due to the formation of 'giant molecules' as in graphite or diamond (p. 150). The bond B—N is isoelectronic with C—C.

By subjecting boron nitride (a white powder) to high pressure and temperature small crystals of a substance harder than diamond, known as *borazon*, are obtained. This pressure–temperature treatment changes the structure from the original graphite-like 'layer' structure (p. 150) to a diamond-like structure; this hard form can withstand temperatures up to 2000 K.

Aluminium nitride can also be prepared by heating a mixture of aluminium oxide and carbon in nitrogen in an electric arc furnace:

$$Al_2O_3 + N_2 + 3C \rightarrow 2AlN + 3CO$$

It is stable up to 2000 K and melts under pressure at 2500 K. The crystal structure of aluminium nitride resembles that of boron nitride and diamond, but unlike both of these it is rapidly and exothermically hydrolysed by cold water:

$$AlN + 3H_2O \rightarrow Al(OH)_3 + NH_3$$

7.5.4   Other compounds

Alums

These are *double salts* which have the general formula

$$M^IM^{III}(SO_4)_2.12H_2O$$

where M^I may be an alkali metal or ammonium, and M^{III} may be aluminium, chromium, iron, manganese, cobalt and others in oxidation state $+3$. 'Alum' is $KAl(SO_4)_2.12H_2O$. They are double salts, not complex salts, i.e. they contain the ions (for example) K^+, $[Al(H_2O)_6]^{3+}$ and SO_4^{2-}.

7.5.5 Uses of Group III elements and compounds

Many of the uses of boron and aluminium compounds have already been discussed. The elements and a number of other compounds also have important applications.

Boron

Metal borides, for example those of molybdenum and titanium, are being increasingly used in aircraft, space craft, and high speed metal cutting tools. These borides are extremely hard and can withstand high temperatures. The element boron is a good neutron absorber and is used for shielding and in control rods for nuclear reactors. Its burning characteristics lead to its use in flares.

Aluminium

Industrial apparatus and many domestic articles (for example pans and kettles) are made from aluminium. Aluminium powder is used in anti-corrosion paints and in explosives (for example ammonal). Weight for weight, aluminium is a better electrical conductor than copper, so that wires may be made from it. It is used in overhead cables — aluminium wires being twisted round steel wires, the latter giving greater mechanical strength. Aluminium foil is used for wrapping foodstuffs (called tin foil because tin was previously used). Aluminium deposited from the vapour on to glass can form excellent mirrors which do not tarnish. Aluminium alloys are used extensively in the aircraft and motor industries, for example as *duralumin* and *magnalium*. A mixed oxide $Na_2O.11Al_2O_3$ is used as a solid electrolyte in batteries.

Gallium, indium, thallium

Intermetallic compounds with gallium are used as semiconductors. Indium is used to coat other metals to protect against corrosion, especially in engine bearings; it is also a constituent of low-melting alloys used in safety sprinklers. The toxicity of thallium compounds has limited the use of the metal but it does find use as a constituent of high-endurance alloys for bearings.

7.5.6 Tests for boron and aluminium

Boron

Volatile boron compounds burn with a green flame. If a solid borate is mixed with methanol and concentrated sulphuric acid, the volatile compound boron trimethoxide, $B(OCH_3)_3$, is formed and ignition of the alcohol therefore produces a green flame:

$$3CH_3OH + H_3BO_3 \rightarrow B(OCH_3)_3 + 3H_2O$$

The water formed is taken up by the concentrated sulphuric acid.

Aluminium

1 Addition of ammonium hydroxide to a solution of an aluminium salt gives a white gelatinous precipitate of aluminium hydroxide, $Al(OH)_3$, insoluble in

excess. Sodium hydroxide gives the same precipitate, but in this case, it does dissolve in excess.

2   Addition of ammonium hydroxide to an aluminium salt in solution, in presence of alizarin, gives a pink precipitate.

Summary

Usual oxidation state $+3$ (and $+1$ for thallium). No simple B^{3+} ions, others form tripositive ions. Covalent compounds are trigonal planar, act as electron acceptors and form tetracoordinate tetrahedral species (B, Al) or hexacoordinate octahedral species (Al). Form electron-deficient compounds, e.g. B_2H_6 and complex hydrides, e.g. $LiAlH_4$. Oxides are amphoteric.

Questions

1   The properties of the head element of a main group in the periodic table resemble those of the second element in the next group. Discuss this 'diagonal relationship' with particular reference to
     (a) lithium and magnesium,
     (b) beryllium and aluminium.

                                                          Liverpool B.Sc., Part I

2   Outline the extraction of pure aluminium from bauxite. (Details of the purification of the bauxite are not required.)
     (a) Magnesium chloride is a high melting-point solid, aluminium chloride is a solid which sublimes readily at about 480 K, and tetrachlorosilane is a volatile liquid. Explain the nature of the chemical bonding in these chlorides and show how this accounts for the above differences in volatility.
     (b) Explain why the freezing point of an aqueous solution of sodium hydroxide is unchanged when aluminium oxide is dissolved in the solution.

                                                                              C,A

3   Describe the laboratory preparation, from aluminium, of
     (a) anhydrous aluminium chloride,
     (b) potassium aluminium sulphate dodecahydrate.
        Why is potassium aluminium sulphate not soluble in benzene? A compound M has the composition $C = 50.0\%$; $H = 12.5\%$; $Al = 37.5\%$. 0.360 g of M reacts with an excess of water to evolve 0.336 l of gas N and leave a white gelatinous precipitate R. R dissolves in aqueous sodium hydroxide and in hydrochloric acid. 20 cm^3 of N require 40 cm^3 of oxygen for complete combustion, carbon dioxide and water being the only products. Identify compounds N and R, suggest a structural formula for M, and write an

equation for the reaction of **M** with water. (All gas volumes were measured at s.t.p.)

[H = 1.0; C = 12.0; O = 16.0; Al = 27.0; molar volume of a gas = 22.4 l at s.t.p.]

C,A

4   (a) Write an equation to show how aluminium can be converted into anhydrous aluminium chloride in the laboratory.
     (b) State two necessary conditions for this preparation.
     (c) Write equations (one in each case) to show what happens when (i) boron trichloride and (ii) aluminium chloride are added to an excess of water.
     (d) Describe what you would see if aqueous sodium hydroxide were added dropwise to excess to a dilute aqueous solution of aluminium chloride.
     (e) Give the formula of the aluminium species formed after an excess of sodium hydroxide has been added.

JMB,A

Chapter 8
Group IV
Carbon, silicon, germanium, tin, lead

8.1 Summary of general characteristics

In this group the outer quantum level has a full s level and two electrons in the corresponding p level. As the size of the atom increases the ionization energy changes (*see Table 8.1*) and these changes are reflected in the gradual change from a typical non-metallic element, carbon, to the weakly metallic element, lead. Hence the oxides of carbon and silicon are acidic whilst those of tin and lead are amphoteric.

8.1.1 Oxidation states

Gain of electrons
Only the carbon atom can gain four electrons; this only happens when it is combined with very small multipositive ions (Be^{2+}, Al^{3+}) to give methanides (p. 179), and this state may be regarded as exceptional.

Loss of electrons
The oxidation state $+4$ involves both the s and p electrons. The oxidation state $+2$, involving only the p electrons, becomes increasingly important with increasing atomic size, and the two s electrons are retained as an inert pair. There are no stable compounds of carbon and silicon in this $+2$ oxidation state; it is uncommon (and strongly reducing) in germanium, less strongly reducing and commonly found in tin and it is the most stable oxidation state for lead. Only tin and lead are capable of forming $+2$ ions which occur both in the solid state and in solution, where the ions are stabilized by solvation.

The oxidation state $+4$ is predominantly covalent and the stability of compounds with this oxidation state generally decreases with increasing atomic size (*Figure 8.1*). It is the most stable oxidation state for silicon, germanium and tin, but for lead the oxidation state $+4$ is found to be less stable than oxidation state $+2$ and hence lead(IV) compounds have oxidizing properties (for example, *see* p. 174).

The concept of oxidation states is best applied only to germanium, tin and lead, for the chemistry of carbon and silicon is almost wholly defined in terms of covalency with the carbon and silicon atoms sharing all their four outer quantum level electrons. These are often tetrahedrally arranged around the central atom. There are compounds of carbon in which the valency appears

Table 8.1 Selected properties of the elements of Group IV

Element	Atomic no.	Outer electrons	Atomic radius nm	Density at 298 K g cm^{-3}	m.p. K	b.p. K	Ionization energy kJ mol^{-1} 1st	2nd	3rd	4th	Electro-negativity (Pauling)	Enthalpy of atomization kJ mol^{-1}
C	6	$2s^22p^2$	0.077	3.53* 2.25†	3823* 4000†	5100*	1086	2353	4618	6512	2.5	714
Si	14	$3s^23p^2$	0.118	2.33	1683	2950	786	1577	3228	4355	1.8	440
Ge	32	$3d^{10}4s^24p^2$	0.122	5.5	1210	3100	760	1537	3301	4410	1.8	377
Sn	50	$4d^{10}5s^25p^2$	0.162	7.31‡	505	2960	708	1411	2942	3928	1.8	301
Pb	82	$5d^{10}6s^26p^2$	0.175	11.35	601	2024	715	1450	3080	4082	1.8	196

* diamond.
† graphite.
‡ white tin.

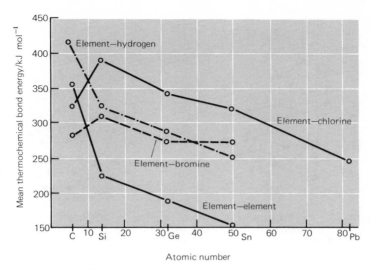

Figure 8.1 Mean thermochemical bond energies for representative bonds in compounds of Group IV elements

to be less than four but, with the exception of carbon monoxide, double or triple bonds are formed in such a way as to make the covalency of carbon always four. The exceptional structure of carbon monoxide makes the molecule an electron donor (pp. 162, 163). Silicon does not form equivalent double- or triple-bonded molecules.

Silicon, germanium, tin and lead can make use of unfilled d orbitals to expand their covalency beyond four and each of these elements is able (but only with a few ligands) to increase its covalency to six. Hence silicon in oxidation state $+4$ forms the octahedral hexafluorosilicate complex ion $[SiF_6]^{2-}$ (but not $[SiCl_6]^{2-}$). Tin and lead in oxidation state $+4$ form the hexahydroxo complex ions, hexahydroxostannate(IV), $[Sn(OH)_6]^{2-}$ and hexahydroxoplumbate(IV) respectively when excess of alkali is added to an aqueous solution containing hydrated tin(IV) and lead(IV) ions.

Carbon, however, is unable to form similar complexes since the energy required to promote electrons to the next higher energy level, the $3s$, is too great and there are no available d orbitals in its second quantum level.

8.2 Occurrence and extraction of the elements

8.2.1 Carbon

Pure carbon occurs naturally in two modifications, *diamond* and *graphite*. In both these forms the carbon atoms are linked by covalent bonds to give giant molecules (*Figure 8.2*).

Diamond
Diamonds are found in South Africa, India, South America and Russia. The largest ever found was the Cullinan diamond which weighed about 600 g.

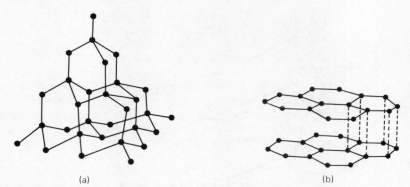

Figure 8.2 The structures of (a) diamond and (b) graphite. In diamond
the carbon symmetry is tetrahedral (sp^3) with C–C bond length 15.4 nm. In
graphite the carbon symmetry is trigonal planar (sp^2) with C–C bond
length 14.2 nm and interplanar distance 33.5 nm

The structure is as shown in *Figure 8.2*. (There are four possible crystalline
arrangements all of which are found to occur naturally.) The interatomic
bonds are very strong (mean thermochemical bond energy 356 kJ mol^{-1}).
This high bond strength is reflected in the great hardness and high melting
point of diamond. Diamond also has a high refractive index and is the
densest form of carbon (density 3.5 g cm^{-3}). The many uses of diamond are
largely dependent on its great hardness, for example for cutting and grinding.

Very small synthetic diamonds have been made industrially by subjecting
graphite to pressures in the range 5.5—6.9 GN m^{-2} at temperatures between
1500 and 2700 K. The diamonds produced are very small but competitive
with natural diamonds for use in industrial cutting and grinding wheels.

Graphite
Graphite is found in Sri Lanka, Germany and the USA. It was formerly
mined in Cumberland. Its name (Greek, *grapho* = I write) indicates its use in
'lead' pencils. The structure of graphite is indicated in *Figure 8.2*. Each
carbon atom is joined to three others by six bonds, the arrangement being
trigonal planar. The remaining electron on each carbon atom is in a *p* orbital.
Sideways overlap of these orbitals gives a delocalized π bond over all the
carbon atoms in the layer (p. 159). It is this second bond which reduces the
C—C bond distance in graphite compared with that found in diamond. The
delocalized π bond readily explains the conductivity and colour of graphite,
properties absent from diamond which has no such delocalized bonding. The
planes of carbon atoms are held together by van der Waals forces which are
much weaker than either σ or π bonding and allow the planes to slide over
each other. Graphite is consequently anisotropic and much research has
been carried out in attempts to produce large single crystals. Graphite
manufactured on a large scale by the Acheson process, in which coke
containing a little silica is heated in an electric furnace in the absence of air for
many hours, does not produce large crystals. Single crystals of graphite,
almost free from defects, have been produced by striking an electric arc

between carbon rods. These 'whiskers' have very high tensile strength along the planes of carbon atoms but are very brittle.

So-called 'carbon fibres' have been produced by the controlled thermal degradation of certain acrylic textile fibres. The basic molecular orientation of the carbon atoms in the original fibre is retained. Plastics reinforced with carbon fibres are light in weight but have great strength, properties making them valuable to many industries and to the aero industry in particular.

A process in which hydrocarbons are heated above 2300 K gives a material called pyrographite. This has properties indicating considerable ordering of the graphite crystals present. The thermal conductivity along the planes of carbon atoms is almost 100 times that at right angles to the planes, a property which makes the material valuable in rocket nose cones where rapid conduction from the hot zone is required and low conduction through to the interior. Electric conductance along the planes is 1000 times that found at right angles to the planes.

Amorphous carbon

In addition to diamond and graphite, carbon appears to exist in a number of other forms, collectively called amorphous carbon. Four common examples are coke, animal charcoal, lampblack and sugar carbon which can be prepared by heating coal, bones, oil and sugar respectively in the virtual absence of air. X-Ray diffraction studies indicate that these and nearly all other forms of amorphous carbon are in fact microcrystalline graphite. Truly amorphous carbon, which gives random X-ray scattering, can be prepared by the low temperature decomposition of hexaiodobenzene, C_6I_6.

Charcoal and lampblack have enormous surface areas for a small volume of sample, and are able to adsorb large amounts of gas or liquid. The effectiveness of the carbon can be greatly increased by heating the sample in a stream of steam to 1100—1300 K when impurities adsorbed during the initial preparation are driven off. This 'activated' charcoal has particularly good adsorption properties and is used as a catalyst. Lampblack is used in making printing ink, pigments and as a filler for rubber to be used in tyres.

8.2.2 Silicon

After oxygen, silicon is the most abundant element in the Earth's crust. It occurs extensively as the oxide, silica, in various forms, for example, flint, quartz, sand, and as silicates in rocks and clays, but not as the free element, silicon. Silicon is prepared by reduction of silica, SiO_2. Powdered 'amorphous' silicon can be obtained by heating dry powdered silica with either powdered magnesium or a mixture of powdered aluminium and sulphur (this supplies additional heat). After the reaction has ceased, magnesium (or aluminium) oxide and any unchanged silica is removed by washing with hydrofluoric acid in a polythene vessel:

$$SiO_2 + 2Mg \rightarrow 2MgO + Si$$

(If an excess of magnesium is used, magnesium silicide, Mg_2Si, is also produced.) The silicon obtained is a light brown hygroscopic powder. Crystalline or 'metallic' silicon is obtained industrially by the reduction of silica with carbon in an electric arc furnace:

$$SiO_2 + 2C \rightarrow 2CO + Si$$

The formation of silicon carbide, SiC (carborundum), is prevented by the addition of a little iron; as much of the silicon is added to steel to increase its resistance to attack by acids, the presence of a trace of iron does not matter. (Addition of silicon to bronze is found to increase both the strength and the hardness of the bronze.) Silicon is also manufactured by the reaction between silicon tetrachloride (tetrachlorosilane) and zinc at 1300 K and by the reduction of trichlorosilane with hydrogen.

Crystalline silicon has the tetrahedral diamond arrangement, but since the mean thermochemical bond strength between the silicon atoms is less than that found between carbon atoms (Si—Si, 226 kJ mol^{-1}, C—C, 356 kJ mol^{-1}), silicon does not possess the great hardness found in diamond. Amorphous silicon (silicon powder) is microcrystalline silicon.

8.2.3   Germanium

Germanium is a greyish-white, brittle solid, obtained by reducing the dioxide, GeO$_2$, with hydrogen or carbon at red heat. Germanium is a rare element found in trace quantities in coke obtained from bituminous coal. When this coke is burnt, germanium dioxide, together with many other metal oxides, is deposited in the flue. The extraction of germanium dioxide from this mixture is a complex process. Impure germanium and silicon are both purified by zone refining and both can be obtained in a very high purity, for example silicon pure to one part in 10^{10} can be obtained*. Germanium, like silicon, crystallizes with a diamond structure, the mean thermochemical bond strength being Ge—Ge, 188 kJ mol^{-1}.

8.2.4   Tin

The common ore of tin is *tinstone* or *cassiterite*, SnO$_2$, found in Cornwall and in Germany and other countries. Major producers of tin include Malaysia and Bolivia. The price of tin has risen so sharply in recent years that previously disregarded deposits in Cornwall are now being re-examined. Tin is obtained from the tin dioxide, SnO$_2$, by reducing it with coal in a reverberatory furnace:

$$SnO_2 + 2C \rightarrow 2CO\uparrow + Sn$$

Before this treatment, the cassiterite content of the ore is increased by removing impurities such as clay, by washing and by roasting which drives off oxides of arsenic and sulphur. The crude tin obtained is often

*Silicon and germanium are now used extensively in semiconductors; for this purpose, extreme initial purity is needed, since the desired semiconducting properties are conferred by the introduction of only a few parts per million of either a Group III element (for example indium), giving rise to a 'deficiency' of electrons in the silicon or germanium crystal, or a Group V element (for example arsenic) giving a 'surplus' of electrons.

contaminated with iron and other metals. It is, therefore, remelted on an inclined hearth; the easily fusible tin melts away, leaving behind the less fusible impurities. The molten tin is finally stirred to bring it into intimate contact with air. Any remaining metal impurities are thereby oxidized to form a scum ('tin dross') on the surface and this can be skimmed off. Very pure tin can be obtained by zone refining.

Tin exists in three different forms (allotropes). 'Grey tin' has a diamond structure, a density of 5.75 g cm^{-3} and is stable below 286 K. 'White tin' exists as tetragonal crystals, has a density of 7.31 g cm^{-3} and is stable between 286 and 434 K. Between 434 K and the melting point of tin, 505 K, tin has a rhombic structure, hence the name 'rhombic tin', and a density of 6.56 g cm^{-3}.

8.2.5   Lead

The principal ore of lead is *galena*, PbS. Although there are some galena deposits in Great Britain, most of the United Kingdom's requirements must be imported. In the extraction of lead, the sulphide ore is first roasted together with quartz in a current of air:

$$2PbS + 3O_2 \rightarrow 2PbO + 2SO_2$$

Any lead(II) sulphate formed in this process is converted into lead(II) silicate by reaction with the quartz. The oxide produced is then mixed with limestone and coke and heated in a blast furnace. The following reactions occur:

$$PbO + C \rightarrow Pb + CO\uparrow$$
$$PbO + CO \rightarrow Pb + CO_2\uparrow$$
$$PbSiO_3 + CaO + CO \rightarrow Pb + CaSiO_3 + CO_2\uparrow$$

The last equation explains the function of the limestone. An older process, in which the ore was partially roasted, the air shut off and the temperature raised so that excess of sulphide reacted with the oxide produced to give lead, is now obsolete.

Crude lead contains traces of a number of metals. The desilvering of lead is considered later under silver (Chapter 14). Other metallic impurities are removed by remelting under controlled conditions whereupon arsenic and antimony form a scum of lead(II) arsenate and antimonate on the surface while copper forms an infusible alloy which also takes up any sulphur, and also appears on the surface. The removal of bismuth, a valuable by-product, from lead is accomplished by making the crude lead the anode in an electrolytic bath consisting of a solution of lead in fluorosilicic acid. Gelatin is added so that a smooth coherent deposit of lead is obtained on the pure lead cathode when the current is passed. The impurities here (i.e. all other metals) form a sludge in the electrolytic bath and are not deposited on the cathode.

Lead has only one form, a cubic metallic lattice. Thus we can see the change from non-metal to metal in the physical structure of the elements, occurring with increasing atomic mass of the elements carbon, silicon, germanium, tin and lead.

8.3 Typical reactions of the elements

8.3.1 Reactions with acids

Carbon

Dilute acids have no effect on any form of carbon, and diamond is resistant to attack by concentrated acids at room temperature but is oxidized by both concentrated sulphuric and concentrated nitric acid at about 500 K, when an additional oxidizing agent is present. Carbon dioxide is produced and the acids are reduced to gaseous oxides:

$$C + 4HNO_3 \rightarrow CO_2 + 2H_2O + 4NO_2$$
$$C + 2H_2SO_4 \rightarrow CO_2 + 2H_2O + 2SO_2$$

Graphite reacts rather differently with mixtures of oxidizing agents and concentrated oxoacids. A 'graphite oxide' is formed; the graphite swells because oxygen atoms become attached to some of the carbon atoms in the rings and distend the layer structure. 'Graphite oxide' is rather indefinite in composition. With concentrated sulphuric acid and an oxidizing agent a blue solution called 'graphite hydrogensulphate' is formed*; this has an approximate formula

$$(C_x)^+ HSO_4^-.2H_2SO_4$$

Amorphous carbon, having a far greater effective surface area than either diamond or graphite, is the most reactive form of carbon. It reacts with both hot concentrated sulphuric and hot concentrated nitric acids in the absence of additional oxidizing agents but is not attacked by hydrochloric acid.

Silicon

Silicon, like carbon, is unaffected by dilute acids. Powdered silicon dissolves incompletely in concentrated nitric acid to give insoluble silicon dioxide, SiO_2:

$$3Si + 4HNO_3 \rightarrow 3SiO_2 + 4NO + 2H_2O$$

Germanium

The gradual increase in electropositive character down the group is clearly shown in that, unlike both carbon and silicon, germanium very readily dissolves in both concentrated nitric and sulphuric acids; the hydrated germanium(IV) oxide is produced:

$$3Ge + 4HNO_3 \rightarrow 3GeO_2 + 4NO + 2H_2O$$

Germanium, however, does not react with either dilute sulphuric or dilute hydrochloric acid, unlike tin, the next element in the group.

*Graphite reacts with alkali metals, for example potassium, to form compounds which are non-stoichiometric but which all have limiting compositions (for example K_nC); in these, the alkali metal atoms are *intercalated* betweed the layers of carbon atoms. In the preparation of fluorine by electrolysis of a molten fluoride with graphite electrodes the solid compound $(CF)_n$, polycarbon fluoride is formed, with fluorine on each carbon atom, causing puckering of the rings.

Tin
Tin slowly dissolves in dilute hydrochloric, nitric and sulphuric acids, and is in fact the only Group IV element to do so. The reactions with more concentrated acid are rapid. With hydrochloric acid, tin gives a solution of tin(II) chloride, there being no further oxidation to the $+4$ oxidation state:

$$Sn + 2HCl \rightarrow SnCl_2 + H_2\uparrow$$

Concentrated nitric acid, however, is an oxidizing agent and tin reacts to give hydrated tin(IV) oxide in a partly precipitated, partly colloidal form, together with a small amount of tin(II) nitrate, $Sn(NO_3)_2$:

$$Sn + 4HNO_3 \rightarrow SnO_2\downarrow + 4NO_2 + 2H_2O$$

A similar oxidation reaction occurs with concentrated sulphuric acid but in this case hydrated tin(IV) ions remain in solution:

$$Sn + 4H_2SO_4 \rightarrow Sn(SO_4)_2 + 4H_2O + 2SO_2\uparrow$$

Lead
Lead reacts only briefly with dilute hydrochloric and sulphuric acids for both lead(II) chloride and lead(II) sulphate are insoluble and form a film on the lead which effectively prevents further attack. Lead, however, does slowly dissolve in both concentrated sulphuric and hydrochloric acids. The sulphuric acid is reduced to sulphur dioxide:

$$Pb + 2H_2SO_4 \rightarrow PbSO_4 + 2H_2O + SO_2\uparrow$$

Lead reacts slowly with hot concentrated hydrochloric acid since the lead(II) chloride dissolves in an excess of the hot hydrochloric acid to form the acid $H_2[Pb^{II}Cl_4]$:

$$Pb + 4HCl \rightarrow H_2[PbCl_4] + H_2\uparrow$$

Again, nitric acid readily dissolves lead but is unable to oxidize lead beyond the oxidation state $+2$. The reduction products of the nitric acid vary with the concentration of acid used, and a number of nitrogen oxides are usually obtained. Warm dilute nitric acid gives mainly nitrogen monoxide, NO,

$$3Pb + 8HNO_3 \rightarrow 3Pb(NO_3)_2 + 4H_2O + 2NO\uparrow$$

whilst cold concentrated acid gives mainly nitrogen dioxide, NO_2:

$$Pb + 4HNO_3 \rightarrow Pb(NO_3)_2 + 2H_2O + 2NO_2\uparrow$$

8.3.2   Reactions with alkalis

Carbon
Carbon does not react, even with molten alkali.

Silicon and germanium
Silicon and germanium readily react with even very dilute solutions of caustic alkali. Silicon is so sensitive to attack that it will dissolve when boiled

with water which has been in contact with glass*:

$$Si + 2OH^- + H_2O \rightarrow SiO_3^{2-} + 2H_2\uparrow$$
$$Ge + 2OH^- + H_2O \rightarrow GeO_3^{2-} + 2H_2\uparrow$$

Tin

Tin dissolves slowly in hot concentrated alkali forming a hexahydroxostannate(IV):

$$Sn + 4H_2O + 2OH^- \rightarrow [Sn(OH)_6]^{2-} + 2H_2\uparrow$$

Lead

Lead dissolves only very slowly in hot concentrated sodium hydroxide and forms hexahydroxoplumbate(II):

$$Pb + 4OH^- + 2H_2O \rightarrow [Pb(OH)_6]^{4-} + H_2\uparrow$$

Notice, again, that the lower oxidation state of lead is formed.

8.3.3   Reactions with oxygen

Carbon

All forms of carbon, if heated to a sufficiently high temperature, give carbon dioxide in a plentiful supply of air, and carbon monoxide if the supply is limited (p. 161):

$$C + O_2 \rightarrow CO_2 \qquad \Delta H = -394 \text{ kJ mol}^{-1}$$
$$C + \tfrac{1}{2}O_2 \rightarrow CO \qquad \Delta H = -111 \text{ kJ mol}^{-1}$$

Silicon

Silicon burns when heated in air to red heat giving silicon dioxide, SiO_2. Several crystalline forms of SiO_2 are known.

$$Si + O_2 \rightarrow SiO_2 \qquad \Delta H = -910 \text{ kJ mol}^{-1} \text{ (approximate)}$$

Note the much larger enthalpy of formation of silicon dioxide as compared with carbon dioxide; this arises in part because of greater strength in the Si—O bonds and also because the Si—Si bond in silicon is much weaker than the C—C bond (p. 152).

Tin

Ordinary white tin is not attacked by air at ordinary temperatures but on heating in air it forms tin(IV) oxide, SnO_2

$$Sn + O_2 \rightarrow SnO_2$$

Lead

Finely divided lead, when heated in air, forms first the lead(II) oxide, 'litharge', PbO, and then on further heating in an ample supply of air, dilead(II) lead(IV) oxide, 'red lead', Pb_3O_4. Lead, in a very finely divided

*The equations are simplified: the oxosilicates and germanates actually formed are complex.

state, when allowed to fall through air, ignites and a shower of sparks is produced. Such finely divided powder is said to be 'pyrophoric'. It can be prepared by carefully heating lead tartrate.

8.4 Compounds of Group IV elements

8.4.1 Hydrides

Carbon hydrides are commonly called hydrocarbons. They are very numerous and the study of these compounds is outside the scope of this book. Reference will therefore be made only to the main groups.

Alkanes
Methane, CH_4, is the first member of this series, all of which have the general formula C_nH_{2n+2}. Every carbon atom in any alkane molecule has a tetrahedral configuration and is joined to four other atoms. Alkanes are resistant to attack, at room temperature, by common acids, alkalis, oxidizing and reducing agents. However, all hydrocarbons burn in oxygen, the ultimate products being carbon dioxide and water; this reaction can be used to determine the empirical formula of hydrocarbons. For example,

$$C_4H_{10} + 6\tfrac{1}{2}O_2 \rightarrow 4CO_2 + 5H_2O$$

Alkanes also react with halogens to form substitution products.

Alkenes
Every member of this series must contain at least one double bond. The two carbon atoms making up the double bond are joined to only three other atoms and they are therefore said to be unsaturated. The carbon atoms of the double bond have a trigonal planar configuration and free rotation about the C—C bond is prevented by the π bond as indicated in *Figure 8.3*. The inability to rotate means that geometrical isomers can be produced, with substituents a and b, thus:

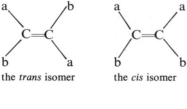

the *trans* isomer   the *cis* isomer

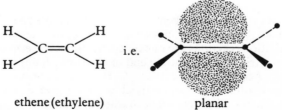

ethene (ethylene)   planar

Figure 8.3 Bonding in ethene, a planar molecule

The region of high electron density between the doubly bonded carbon atoms gives alkenes an additional reactivity and in addition to burning and reacting with halogens, alkenes will add on other molecules; for example:

$$H_2C\!\!=\!\!CH_2 + HBr \rightarrow CH_3CH_2Br$$

and will polymerize in the presence of a suitable catalyst:

$$nH_2C\!\!=\!\!CH_2 \xrightarrow{\text{catalyst}}$$

Ethene can add on to certain metal salts; it is believed that the extra electrons on the double bond can be donated to some extent; an example is the compound $PtCl_2.C_2H_4$ formed with platinum(II) chloride which has the structure

Alkynes

The essential feature of this series of hydrocarbons is the presence of a triple bond between two carbon atoms, one σ and two π, as shown in *Figure 8.4*.

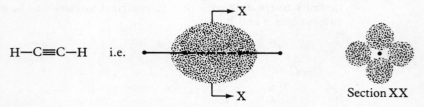

$$H\!-\!C\!\equiv\!C\!-\!H \quad \text{i.e.}$$

X

X

Section XX

Figure 8.4 Bonding in ethyne, a linear molecule

This gives a linear arrangement of bonds, and alkynes, like alkenes, are unsaturated. As might be expected, alkynes are very reactive although certain addition reactions are unexpectedly difficult. Terminal alkynes (ones in which the triple bond is at the end of a carbon chain) have slightly acidic properties. Acetylene or ethyne, C_2H_2, for example, reacts with an ammoniacal solution of copper(I) chloride to give a red solid, copper(I) dicarbide, Cu_2C_2, which is explosive when dry, Similarly, ammoniacal silver nitrate gives a white solid, silver dicarbide, Ag_2C_2. These two compounds contain the dicarbide ion $[C \equiv C]^{2-}$ as does calcium 'carbide' CaC_2, which should really be called calcium dicarbide. All dicarbides give ethyne when treated with a dilute acid.

Cyclic hydrocarbons

Carbon also forms numerous cyclic hydrides of which benzene, C_6H_6, is a well-known example. This has a planar, regular hexagonal structure often represented as a resonance hybrid between the structures in *Figure 8.5(a)*. Overlaps of the *p* orbitals (b) gives the structure shown in (c). All the C—C bond lengths are equal, as are all the C—H bond lengths, and the double bonds are 'delocalized'.

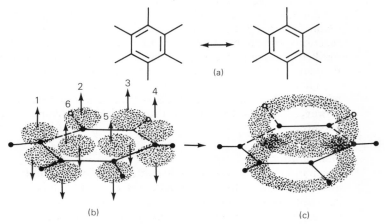

(a)

(b)   (c)

Figure 8.5 Bonding in benzene, a cylic molecule

Silicon

Silicon, unlike carbon, does not form a very large number of hydrides. A series of covalently bonded volatile hydrides called *silanes* analogous to the alkane hydrocarbons is known, with the general formula Si_nH_{2n+2}, but less than ten members of the series have so far been prepared. Mono- and di-silanes are more readily prepared by the reaction of the corresponding silicon chloride with lithium tetrahydridoaluminate in ether:

$$SiCl_4 + LiAlH_4 \rightarrow SiH_4\uparrow + LiCl\downarrow + AlCl_3$$

and

$$2Si_2Cl_6 + 3LiAlH_4 \rightarrow 2Si_2H_6\uparrow + 3LiCl\downarrow + 3AlCl_3$$

The Si—Si bond is weaker than the C—C bond (mean thermochemical bond energies are C—C in diamond, $356\,kJ\,mol^{-1}$, Si—Si in silicon, $226\,kJ\,mol^{-1}$) and catenation (the phenomenon of self-linkage between atoms of the same element) is consequently less marked with silicon than with carbon; the higher silanes decompose slowly even at room temperature. Silanes are far more sensitive to oxygen than alkanes and all the silanes are spontaneously inflammable in air, for example

$$SiH_4 + 2O_2 \rightarrow SiO_2 + 2H_2O$$

This greater reactivity of the silanes may be due to several factors, for example, the easier approach of an oxygen molecule (which may attach initially to the silane by use of the vacant silicon $3d$ orbitals) and the formation of strong Si—O bonds (stronger than C—O).

Halogen derivatives of silanes can be obtained but direct halogenation often occurs with explosive violence; the halogen derivatives are usually prepared by reacting the silane at low temperature with a carbon compound such as tetrachloromethane, in the presence of the corresponding aluminium halide which acts as a catalyst.

Silanes are very sensitive to attack by alkalis and will even react with water made alkaline by contact with glass; this reaction is in marked contrast to the reactions shown by alkanes. Unlike alkanes, silanes are found to have marked reducing properties and will reduce, for example, potassium manganate(VII) to manganese(IV) oxide, and iron(III) to iron(II).

In addition to the volatile silanes, silicon also forms non-volatile hydrides with formulae $(SiH_2)_x$ but little is known about their structure. Silicon, however, does *not* form unsaturated hydrides corresponding to the simple alkenes.

Germanium

Germanium forms a series of hydrides of general formula Ge_nH_{2n+2} which are quite similar to the corresponding silanes. Only a small number of germanes have so far been prepared. Germanes are not as inflammable as the corresponding silanes (the Ge—O bond is not as strong as the Si—O bond) and they are also less reactive towards alkalis, monogermane being resistant to quite concentrated alkali.

Tin

The greater metallic nature of tin is clearly indicated here for tin forms only one hydride, stannane, SnH_4. It is best prepared by the reaction of lithium tetrahydridoaluminate and tin(IV) chlorde in ether:

$$LiAlH_4 + SnCl_4 \rightarrow SnH_4\uparrow + LiCl\downarrow + AlCl_3$$

It is a colourless gas which decomposes on heating above 420 K to give metallic tin, often deposited as a mirror, and hydrogen. It is a reducing agent and will reduce silver ions to silver and mercury(II) ions to mercury. Sn—Sn bonding is unknown in hydrides but does exist in alkyl and aryl compounds, for example $(CH_3)_3Sn$—$Sn(CH_3)_3$.

Lead

Lead, like tin, forms only one hydride, plumbane. This hydride is very unstable, dissociating into lead and hydrogen with great rapidity. It has not been possible to analyse it rigorously or determine any of its physical properties, but it is probably PbH_4. Although this hydride is unstable, some of its derivatives are stable; thus, for example, tetraethyllead, $Pb(C_2H_5)_4$, is one of the most stable compounds with lead in a formal oxidation state of +4. It is used as an 'antiknock' in petrol.

8.5   Oxides of Group IV elements

All Group IV elements form both a monoxide, MO, and a dioxide, MO_2. The stability of the monoxide increases with atomic mass of the Group IV elements from silicon to lead, and lead(II) oxide, PbO, is the most stable oxide of lead. The monoxide becomes more basic as the atomic mass of the Group IV elements increases, but no oxide in this Group is truly basic and even lead(II) oxide is amphoteric. Carbon monoxide has unusual properties and emphasizes the different properties of the group head element and its compounds.

The dioxides are all predominantly acidic but again acidity decreases with increasing atomic mass of the Group IV element and lead(IV) oxide, PbO_2, is amphoteric. The stability of the dioxides decreases with increasing atomic mass of the Group IV elements and although tin(IV) oxide, SnO_2, is the most stable oxide of tin, lead (IV) oxide is less stable than lead (II) oxide.

8.5.1   Oxides of carbon

Carbon monoxide, CO

Carbon monoxide is a colourless, odourless gas. It is extremely poisonous, since the haemoglobin of the blood (p. 348) reacts with carbon monoxide in preference to oxygen so preventing the haemoglobin from acting in its normal capacity as an oxygen carrier.

Carbon monoxide is formed by the incomplete combustion of carbon. It is prepared in the laboratory by dropping methanoic (formic) acid into warm concentrated sulphuric acid; the latter dehydrates the methanoic acid:

$$HCOOH \xrightarrow{\ H_2SO_4\ } CO\uparrow + H_2O$$

The gas is passed through sodium hydroxide solution to remove any sulphur dioxide or carbon dioxide produced in side reactions. Carbon monoxide is also obtained when an ethanedioate (oxalate) is heated with concentrated sulphuric acid:

$$C_2O_4^{2-} + H_2SO_4 \rightarrow CO\uparrow + CO_2\uparrow + H_2O + SO_4^{2-}$$

The carbon dioxide is removed by passage of the gas through a mixture of sodium and calcium hydroxides. Very pure carbon monoxide is produced by heating nickel tetracarbonyl (*see* p. 162):

$$Ni(CO)_4 \rightarrow Ni + 4CO\uparrow$$

The commercial production of carbon monoxide in the form of water gas is now largely obsolete. The production by the reaction between steam and hydrocarbons is considered later (p. 164).

The structure of carbon monoxide can be represented as a resonance hybrid between two structures

(The actual structure is more accurately represented as a resonance hybrid of $Ni(\leftarrow C\!\!=\!\!O)_4$ and $Ni(\!\!=\!\!C\!\!=\!\!O)_4$ with the valency shell of nickel further expanded.) Other examples are iron pentacarbonyl, $Fe(CO)_5$, and chromium hexacarbonyl, $Cr(CO)_6$, which have trigonal bipyramidal and octahedral configurations respectively.

Carbon monoxide burns with a characteristic blue flame in air or oxygen. The reaction

$$2CO + O_2 \rightarrow 2CO_2 \qquad \Delta H = -283 \text{ kJ mol}^{-1}$$

is very exothermic and as expected, therefore, carbon monoxide reacts with heated oxides of a number of metals, for example copper, lead, iron, reducing them to the metal. For example:

$$PbO + CO \rightarrow Pb + CO_2\uparrow$$

Carbon monoxide forms addition compounds. With chlorine in sunlight or in the presence of charcoal in the dark, carbonyl chloride (phosgene), $COCl_2$, is formed:

$$CO + Cl_2 \rightarrow COCl_2$$

With ammoniacal or hydrochloric acid solution of copper(I) chloride, carbon monoxide forms the addition compound

$$CuCl.CO.2H_2O$$

This reaction can be used to quantitatively remove carbon monoxide from gaseous mixtures.

Although carbon monoxide appears to be the anhydride of methanoic acid it does not react with water to give the acid; however, it will react with sodium hydroxide solution above 450 K, under pressure, to give sodium methanoate:

$$CO + NaOH \rightarrow HCOO^-Na^+$$

Carbon dioxide, CO_2

Carbon dioxide is present in air and escapes from fissures in the earth in volcanic regions and where 'mineral springs' occur. It may be prepared by:

(1)   the action of dilute acid on any metal carbonate or hydrogencarbonate, for example

$$CaCO_3 + 2HCl \rightarrow CaCl_2 + CO_2\uparrow + H_2O$$

(2)   the action of heat on a hydrogencarbonate,

$$2HCO_3^- \rightarrow H_2O + CO_2\uparrow + CO_3^{2-}$$

(3)   the action of heat on a metal carbonate, other than those of the alkali metals or barium (*see* later, p. 167). Industrially, carbon dioxide is obtained in large quantities by heating limestone:

$$CaCO_3 \rightarrow CaO + CO_2\uparrow$$

It is obtained as a by-product in the fermentation of sugars to give alcohols:

$$C_6H_{12}O_6 \xrightarrow[\text{catalyst}]{\text{enzyme}} 2C_2H_5OH + 2CO_2$$

Appreciable quantities are also obtained as a by-product in the manufacture of hydrogen from naphtha-gaseous hydrocarbons. In this process the gaseous hydrocarbon and superheated steam under a pressure of about 10 atmospheres and at a temperature of 1000 K are passed over a nickel–chromium catalyst. Carbon monoxide and hydrogen are produced:

$$C_nH_m + nH_2O \rightarrow nCO + \frac{(2n+m)}{2}H_2$$

The hydrocarbons used depend on availability. Natural gas is now being used by some large industrial organizations but others use petroleum from a refinery. The second stage in the process is the so-called 'water-gas shift' reaction; this reaction was originally used with 'water-gas' — a mixture of CO and H_2 obtained by passing superheated steam through white hot coke. The gaseous mixture containing an excess of steam, still at 10 atmospheres pressure, is passed at 700 K over an iron catalyst when the carbon monoxide reacts with the steam to form carbon dioxide and hydrogen:

$$CO + H_2O \rightarrow CO_2 + H_2$$

In one process the carbon dioxide is removed using potassium carbonate solution, potassium hydrogencarbonate being produced:

$$K_2CO_3 + H_2O + CO_2 \rightarrow 2KHCO_3$$

This reaction can be reversed by heat and the potassium carbonate and carbon dioxide recovered. (Other compounds which absorb carbon dioxide and evolve it again at a lower temperature are also in common use*.)

Structure of carbon dioxide
Carbon dioxide has a linear structure. The simple double-bonded formula, however, does not fully explain the structure since the measured carbon–oxygen bond lengths are equal but intermediate between those expected for a double and a triple bond. A more accurate representation is, therefore, obtained by considering carbon dioxide as a resonance hybrid of the three structures given below:

$$\overset{+}{O}\equiv C - \overset{-}{O} \quad \longleftrightarrow \quad O = C = O \quad \longleftrightarrow \quad \overset{-}{O} - C \equiv \overset{+}{O}$$

$$\text{(a)} \hspace{4cm} \text{(b)} \hspace{4cm} \text{(c)}$$

*Some of the carbon monoxide and hydrogen produced in the steam–naphtha reforming process react to form methane:

$$CO + 3H_2 \rightleftarrows CH_4 + H_2O$$

This reaction is an undesirable side reaction in the manufacture of hydrogen but utilized as a means of removing traces of carbon monoxide left at the end of the second stage reaction. The gases are passed over a nickel catalyst at 450 K when traces of carbon monoxide form methane. (Methane does not poison the catalyst in the Haber process — carbon monoxide does.)

Properties of carbon dioxide

Carbon dioxide is a colourless gas which is virtually odourless and tasteless. Its density, relative to air, is 1.53; hence it accumulates at the bottom of towers or wells in which it is being prepared, and may reach dangerous concentrations there. (Carbon dioxide does not support respiration, but it is not toxic.) Its critical point is 304 K, i.e. it may be compressed to a liquid below this temperature. However, if carbon dioxide is cooled rapidly (for example by allowing compressed gas to escape through a valve) solid carbon dioxide is formed. This sublimes at 195 K and atmospheric pressure; it is a white solid now much used as a refrigerant (known as 'dry ice' or 'Drikold'), since it leaves no residue after sublimation.

Chemically, carbon dioxide is not very reactive, and it is often used as an inactive gas to replace air when the latter might interact with a substance, for example in the preparation of chromium(II) salts (p. 336). Very reactive metals, for example the alkali metals and magnesium can, however, continue to burn in carbon dioxide if heated sufficiently, for example

$$4K + 3CO_2 \rightarrow 2K_2CO_3 + C$$

Carbon dioxide reacts with a solution of a metal hydroxide giving the carbonate, which may be precipitated, for example

$$Ca^{2+} + 2OH^- + CO_2 \rightarrow CaCO_3\downarrow + H_2O$$

This reaction is used as a test for carbon dioxide. Passage of an excess of carbon dioxide produces the soluble hydrogencarbonate:

$$CaCO_3 + CO_2 + H_2O \rightarrow Ca^{2+} + 2HCO_3^-$$

The hydrogencarbonate ion, produced in nature by this reaction, is one of the main causes of temporary hardness in water. Carbon dioxide is fairly soluble in water, 1 cm^3 dissolving 1.7 cm^3 of the gas at s.t.p. The variation of solubility with pressure does not obey Henry's law, since the reaction

$$CO_2 + H_2O \rightleftharpoons H_2CO_3$$

takes place to a small extent, forming carbonic acid (see below).

Uses of carbon dioxide

Carbon dioxide is used in the manufacture of sodium carbonate by the ammonia–soda process, urea, 2-hydroxybenzoic (salicyclic) acid (for aspirin), fire extinguishers and aerated water. Lesser amounts are used to transfer heat generated by an atomic reactor to water and so produce steam and electric power, whilst solid carbon dioxide is used as a refrigerant, a mixture of solid carbon dioxide and alcohol providing a good low-temperature bath (195 K) in which reactions can be carried out in the laboratory.

8.5.2   Carbonic acid and carbonates

The following equilibria apply to a solution of carbon dioxide in water:

$$CO_2 + G_2O \rightleftharpoons \underset{\substack{\text{carbonic} \\ \text{acid}}}{H_2CO_3} \rightleftharpoons H^+ + HCO_3^- \rightleftharpoons 2H^+ + CO_3^{2-}$$

The amount of carbonic acid present, undissociated or dissociated, is only about 1 per cent of the total concentration of dissolved carbon dioxide. Carbonic acid, in respect of its dissociation into hydrogen and hydrogencarbonate ions, is actually a stronger acid than ethanoic acid; the dissociation constant is:

$$K_a = \frac{[H^+][HCO_3^-]}{[H_2CO_3]} = 5 \times 10^{-4} \text{ mol } l^{-1}$$

(cf. $K_a = 1.8 \times 10^{-5}$ mol l^{-1} for ethanoic acid)

But a solution of carbon dioxide in water behaves as a very weak acid since the *effective* dissociation constant K' is given by:

$$K' = \frac{[H^+][HCO_3^-]}{[CO_2 + H_2CO_3]} = 4 \times 10^{-7} \text{ mol } l^{-1}$$

Since carbonic acid is a weak acid, its salts are hydrolysed in aqueous solution:

$$CO_3^{2-} + H_2O \rightleftharpoons OH^- + HCO_3^-$$
$$HCO_3^- + H_2O \rightleftharpoons OH^- + H_2CO_3$$

Although both these reactions lie largely to the left, soluble carbonates (i.e. those of the alkali metals) are alkaline in aqueous solution, and the hydrogencarbonates are very feebly alkaline. The equilibria are displaced to the right on addition of an acid and soluble carbonates can therefore be titrated with acids and indeed sodium carbonate is used as a standard base. The titration curve is given below for 0.1 M hydrochloric acid being added to 100 cm³ of 0.1 M alkali metal carbonate (*Figure 8.7*). At A all the CO_3^{2-} has been converted into HCO_3^- and at B all the HCO_3^- has been converted into CO_3^{2-}. Phenolphthalein changes colour between pH 8.3 and pH 10.0 and can be used to indicate point A whilst methyl orange, changing colour between pH 3.1 and pH 4.4, indicates point B.

Most metal carbonates are insoluble and they are precipitated either as the

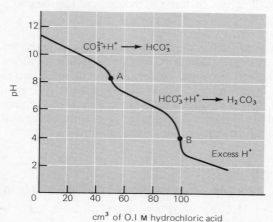

Figure 8.7 Titration of a soluble carbonate with hydrochloric acid

simple carbonate or as the basic carbonate when carbonate ions, as sodium carbonate solution, are added to a solution containing the metal ions.

Hydrogencarbonates of sodium, potassium and ammonium are known in the solid state and show hydrogen bonding in the crystal:

The broken lines indicate hydrogen bonds. The full lines are to show the structure, they do not simply represent single covalent bonds.

Magnesium and calcium hydrogencarbonates are known in solution and are responsible for temporary hardness in water.

Structure of the carbonate ion
The carbonate ion is planar and can be regarded as a resonance structure between the three forms given below (see also p. 38):

All the carbon–oxygen bonds are found to be of equal length and intermediate between carbon–oxygen single and double bond length.

Stability of carbonates and hydrogencarbonates to heat
The stability to heat of metal carbonates is related to the size and charge of the cation present. Carbonates formed by metal ions with large radius: charge ratios, for example, Na^+, K^+, Ba^{2+}, are stable to heat at high temperatures whilst those ions with low radius:charge ratios, for example, Li^+, Zn^{2+}, Cu^{2+} form carbonates which are relatively easily decomposed by heat, the effect being so marked with Fe^{3+} and Al^{3+} that neither of these ions is able to form a carbonate stable at room temperature. These changes in stability have been attributed to the amount of distortion of the carbonate ion that the metal ion causes; the greater this distortion the lower the stability of the carbonate. The hydrogencarbonate ion is unstable and decomposes on heating in either solid or solution thus:

$$2HCO_3^- \rightarrow H_2O + CO_2\uparrow + CO_3^{2-}$$

(If the hydrogencarbonate is in solution and the cation is Ca^{2+} or Mg^{2+}, the insoluble carbonate is precipitated; this reaction may be used, therefore, to remove hardness in water by precipitation of Ca^{2+} or Mg^{2+} ions.) The ease of decomposition of hydrogencarbonates affords a test to distinguish between a hydrogencarbonate and a carbonate; carbon dioxide is evolved by a hydrogencarbonate, but not by a carbonate, if it is heated, either as the solid or in solution, on a boiling water bath.

8.5.3   Other oxides of carbon

Carbon forms a number of oxides in addition to carbon monoxide and dioxide but they are beyond the scope of this book.

8.5.4   Oxides of silicon

Silicon monoxide, SiO

When silica (silicon dioxide) and silicon are heated *in vacuo* to 1700 K, there is evidence for SiO in the gaseous state. On cooling, a brown powder is obtained which rapidly disproportionates:

$$2SiO \rightarrow Si + SiO_2$$

Silicon dioxide, SiO$_2$

Silica is found naturally in several crystalline forms (e.g. *quartz*, *tridymite*, *cristobalite*) and as *kieselguhr*, a hydrated amorphous solid possessing great absorptive powers. It is not appropriate to refer to this oxide of silicon as a dioxide, since, in its crystalline forms, it forms 'giant molecules' in which each silicon atom is linked tetrahedrally to four oxygen atoms: the structure can be represented diagrammatically thus, the linkages extending three-dimensionally:

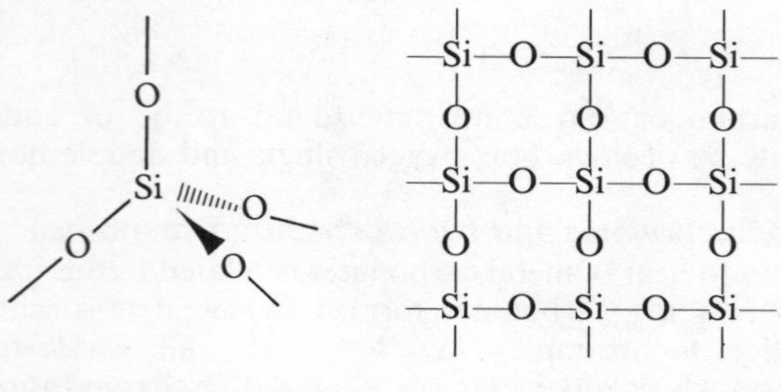

Pure silica may be obtained by hydrolysing silicon tetrafluoride or the tetrachloride (*see* the reactions above). When so prepared, silica is hydrated; it appears in fact as a *gel*, i.e. a colloidal system in which a liquid is dispersed in a solid. This gel when filtered off and dried, loses much of its water, and on heating can be made anhydrous; but formation of a solid gel takes place again when the anhydrous solid is exposed to a moist atmosphere, i.e. the solid absorbs water. Hence *silica gel* is a most useful drying agent, for it has a high capacity for absorbing water and it is also chemically inactive. Silica is attacked only by hydrofluoric acid, and by alkali to give silicates:

$$SiO_2 + 2OH^- \rightleftharpoons SiO_3^{2-} + H_2O$$

When silica is fused, *silica glass* is formed. This has advantages over ordinary glass in that it is much less easily fused (it softens at about 1800 K), and has a very low coefficient of expansion. It is, therefore, used for crucibles and other articles required to be infusible and to resist chemical attack. It is also used for certain optical plates and lenses, since it transmits ultraviolet light better than ordinary glass.

'Silicic acid' and the silicates

When acid is added to any soluble silicate, the following reaction occurs:

$$SiO_3^{2-}(aq) + 2H^+ \rightleftharpoons H_2SiO_3(aq) \rightarrow SiO_2.xH_2O$$

and the 'silicic acid' is converted into insoluble, hydrated silica similar to that already described.

A soluble silicate — a trioxosilicate — is obtained when silica is fused with sodium carbonate:

$$SiO_2 + Na_2CO_3 \rightarrow Na_2SiO_3 + CO_2\uparrow$$

This is in acid–base reaction, in which the base is the oxide ion O^{2-} (p. 80); the acidic oxide SiO_2 displaces the weaker acidic oxide CO_2 in the fused mixture. But in aqueous solution, where the O^{2-} ion cannot function as a strong base (p. 80), carbon dioxide displaces silica, which, therefore precipitates when the gas is passed through the aqueous silicate solution. In a fused mixture of silica and a nitrate or phosphate, the silica again displaces the weaker acidic oxides N_2O_5 and P_4O_{10}:

$$4KNO_3 + 2SiO_2 \rightarrow 2K_2SiO_3 + 2N_2O_5$$
$$2N_2O_5 \rightarrow 4NO_2 + O_2$$
$$2Ca_3(PO_4)_2 + 6SiO_2 \rightarrow 6CaSiO_3 + P_4O_{10}$$

This latter reaction is used in the extraction of phosphorus (p. 188).

The product of the fusion of silica with sodium carbonate, sodium silicate (strictly called sodium polytrioxosilicate but usually metasilicate), dissolves in water to give a clear, viscous solution known as 'waterglass'. It hydrolyses slowly and silica is precipitated. Besides the metasilicate, other silicates of sodium are known, e.g. the polytetraoxosilicate (orthosilicate), Na_4SiO_4. Only the silicates of the alkali metals are soluble in water. Other silicates, many of which occur naturally, are insoluble, and in these substances the polysilicate anions can have highly complicated structures, all of which are constructed from a unit of one silicon and four oxygen atoms arranged tetrahedrally (cf. the structure of silica). Some of these contain aluminium (the aluminosilicates) and some have important properties and uses.

The *zeolites* are aluminosilicates, having large, open-structured anions and balancing cations. Because of the open structure, *zeolites* can take up water molecules reversibly into the interstices of their structures. More importantly, they may be able to act as *molecular sieves*, by taking up from a gas mixture only molecules in a certain size range; the zeolite can then be taken out of the gas and the absorbed species pumped off. Thus the zeolite *mordenite* will occlude small molecules, e.g. nitrogen, argon*, but not, for example, methane or ethane. Synthetic zeolites possess the property of *ion-*

*Traces of oxygen can be removed from argon (required for an inert atmosphere in certain metallurgical processes). Oxygen molecules can pass through the spaces or windows 'end-ways' while the larger argon atoms are kept out.

exchange. The cations in a zeolite may move freely through the open structure, and hence replacement of one cation by another can occur without affecting the rest of the lattice. Many artificial ion-exchange zeolites have been made, and used to remove cations from water, e.g. the 'permutits', and more recently, ion-exchange materials with a framework of an organic polymer have been made and used extensively (e.g. in the purification of water, p. 242).

Clay and kaolin describe groups of substances with compositions which are similar chemically (they contain aluminium, silicon, oxygen and water) but with many different kinds of structure, the nature of which has been established by X-ray diffraction studies. The clays all possess a layer-like structure. When water is added to clay it enters between the layers and the clay swells and acquires plasticity thus enabling it to be moulded into bricks, pottery, and so on. On ignition or 'firing', these lose plasticity permanently acquiring thereby a fixed shape, hardness and strength. Kaolin is rather less 'plastic' than clay but can be moulded and then fired to give porcelain or 'china'.

Glass is the name given to any amorphous solid produced when a liquid solidifies. Glasses are non-crystalline and isotropic, i.e. their physical properties are independent of the direction in which they are measured. When a glass is heated, it does not melt at a fixed temperature but gradually softens until a liquid is obtained.

The word 'glass' commonly means the transparent substance obtained when white sand is fused with metal oxides or carbonates to give a mixture of silicates. Ordinary or 'soda-glass' has the approximate composition $Na_2O.CaO.6SiO_2$. (This is the composition obtained by analysis: it does not represent the compounds present.) If sodium is replaced by potassium the melting point is raised (Jena glass) and the use of lithium gives added strength; replacement of calcium by lead gives a higher refracting power (flint glass), and the SiO_2 may be partly replaced by 'P_2O_5' (crown glass). Addition of aluminium and boron oxides gives a glass with a low expansivity suitable for vessels which are to be heated, e.g. 'Pyrex'. Coloured glass is made by adding an oxide of a metal which gives a coloured silicate, e.g. cobalt (blue), iron(II) (green), copper(I) (red).

The brittle character of glass is an obvious disadvantage, and it is not easy to mould glass into curved shapes without loss of transparency. Hence glass has, in recent years, been replaced by transparent *plastics*; or the latter have been used to give glass resistance to breakage by bonding together layers of glass and plastic (safety glass). A plastic is usually composed of molecules of very high relative molecular mass ('high polymers') and the name plastic is given because many polymeric solids soften on heating (these are said to be *thermoplastic*) like glass. Most polymers are composed of long chains of carbon atoms (but see below) to which other groups may be attached along the chain; according to the nature of these groups, the chains may be rigid rods, kinked rods, or flexible, and able to form coils. Moreover, during the formation of a polymer, *branching* may occur, and *cross-linking* between the chains gives a three-dimensional structure. Usually, extensive cross-linking leads to hardness and complete insolubility. Polymers with little or no cross-linking will dissolve in some organic solvents; the polymer solid first swells in the solvent and on addition of more solvent forms a viscous solution. The higher the relative molecular mass of the polymer the greater is the viscosity. To give an otherwise hard and brittle polymer the properties of flexibility and resistance to shrinking, a very small amount of non-volatile solvent known as a *plasticizer* may be left with the solid polymer. Alternatively, two different kinds of chain molecules may be *co-polymerized* (giving something analogous to an alloy of two different metals) to give properties which are desirable.

Most high polymeric substances are composed of carbon chains, but a few contain other elements and one very important class will now be considered.

The silicones

In tetrachlorosilane, $SiCl_4$, chlorine atoms can be replaced by methyl or other alkyl groups to give, for example, CH_3SiCl_3 and $(CH_3)_2SiCl_2$. These two compounds are obtained when chloromethane is passed over a copper–silicon mixture at about 600 K, but they can be prepared by other methods. Hydrolysis then gives, for example:

$$(CH_3)_2SiCl_2 + 2H_2O \rightarrow (CH_3)_2Si(OH)_2 + 2HCl$$

The resultant compound then polymerizes by losing water thus:

$$
\begin{array}{ccccc}
CH_3 & CH_3 & CH_3 & CH_3 & CH_3 & CH_3 \\
| & | & | & | & | & | \\
HO{-}Si{-}\boxed{OH+H}\,O{-}Si{-}OH & \rightarrow & HO{-}Si{-}O{-}Si{-}O{-}Si\cdots O{-}Si{-}OH \\
| & | & | & | & | & | \\
CH_3 & CH_3 & CH_3 & CH_3 & CH_3 & CH_3
\end{array}
$$

Note that in the compound $(CH_3)_2Si(OH)_2$ the silicon atom can hold two OH groups, unlike carbon. It is this property that makes the existence of silicones possible. By variation of the compounds and conditions of hydrolysis, straight chains, rings and cross-linked polymers are obtained, for example:

$$
\begin{array}{ccc}
 & \vdots & \\
R & O & R \\
| & | & | \\
\cdots{-}Si{-}O{-}Si{-}O{-}Si{-}\cdots \\
| & | & | \\
R & | & R \\
 & O & \\
R & | & R \\
| & | & | \\
\cdots{-}Si{-}O{-}Si{-}O{-}Si{-}\cdots \\
| & | & | \\
R & O & R \\
 & \vdots &
\end{array}
$$

These are the silicones. According to the degree of cross-linking and length of the chain, they can be obtained in the form of oils or rubber-like solids. The silicone oils are not volatile on heating and can be heated to high temperatures without decomposition (and so are useful for high vacuum pumps and high-temperature oil baths) and can be cooled without becoming too viscous (hydrocarbon oils become viscous on cooling); hence silicone oils are used for low-temperature lubrication. Moreover, silicones are water-repellent, and have high relative permittivity so that they are useful for electrical capacitors.

Solid, rubbery silicones likewise retain their plasticity at low temperatures and are resistant to many forms of chemical attack; they are now incorporated in paints for resisting damp and for waterproofing. Silicones are also used in moulds to avoid sticking of the casting to the mould.

8.5.5   Oxides of germanium

Germanium(II) oxide, GeO

The existence of germanium(II) oxide is well established. It is a solid which can be made, for example, by the action of water on germanium dichloride, $GeCl_2$:

$$GeCl_2 + H_2O \rightarrow GeO + 2HCl$$

The product is a solid yellow hydrated oxide. If prepared by a method in the absence of water, a black anhydrous product is obtained. Germanium(II) oxide is stable in air at room temperature but is readily oxidized when heated in air or when treated at room temperature with, for example, nitric acid, hydrogen peroxide, or potassium manganate(VII). When heated in the absence of air it disproportionates at 800 K:

$$2GeO \rightarrow Ge + GeO_2$$

The yellow hydrated oxide is slightly acidic and forms germanates(II) (germanites). The increased stability of germanium(II) oxide compared with silicon(II) oxide clearly indicates the more metallic nature of germanium.

Germanium(IV) oxide

Germanium(IV) oxide occurs in two forms; one has a rutile lattice and melts at 1359 K whilst the other has a quartz lattice and a melting point of 1389 K. It can be prepared by oxidation of germanium using, for example, concentrated nitric acid, or by the hydrolysis of germanium tetrachloride:

$$Ge + 4HNO_3 \rightarrow GeO_2\downarrow + 4NO_2\uparrow + 2H_2O$$
$$GeCl_4 + 2H_2O \rightarrow GeO_2\downarrow + 4HCl$$

The anhydrous oxide is obtained by ignition of the hydrated oxide produced.

Germanium(IV) oxide is less acidic than silicon(IV) oxide but reacts readily with alkali forming germanates(IV), the greater reactivity of the germanium(IV) oxide being attributable to the slight solubility of the quartz form of GeO_2 in water. Germanium forms a few salts containing the anion $[Ge(OH)_6]^{2-}$ e.g. $Fe[Ge(OH)_6]$.

8.5.6   Oxides of tin

Tin (II) oxide

If a solution of a tin(II) salt is treated with a *small* amount of an alkali, tin(II) hydroxide is precipitated, the reaction being represented by the equation:

$$Sn^{2+} + 2OH^- \rightarrow Sn(OH)_2\downarrow$$

The precipitate obtained is in fact colloidal and has no definite composition. Careful drying of the precipitate gives the anhydrous oxide, SnO, which may also be prepared by heating tin(II) ethanedioate (oxalate):

$$SnC_2O_4 \rightarrow SnO + CO\uparrow + CO_2\uparrow$$

Tin(II) oxide is a dark-coloured powder which oxidizes spontaneously in air with the evolution of heat to give tin(IV) oxide, SnO_2:

$$2SnO + O_2 \rightarrow 2SnO_2$$

It is amphoteric; it gives tin(II) salts with dilute acids and hydroxostannates(II) with alkalis, for example:

$$SnO + 2HCl \rightarrow SnCl_2 + H_2O$$
$$SnO + H_2O + OH^- \rightleftharpoons [Sn(OH)_3]^-$$

Stannate(II) ions are powerful reducing agents. Since, for tin, the stability of oxidation state $+4$ is greater than that of oxidation state $+2$, tin(II) always has reducing properties, but these are greater in alkaline conditions than in acid (an example of the effect of pH on the redox potential, p. 92).

Tin(IV) *oxide,* SnO_2

Tin(IV) oxide occurs naturally, clearly indicating its high stability. It can be prepared either by heating tin in oxygen or by heating the hydrated oxide obtained when metallic tin reacts with concentrated nitric acid:

$$Sn + 4HNO_3 \rightarrow SnO_2\downarrow + 4NO_2\uparrow + 2H_2O$$

Tin(IV) oxide is insoluble in water, but if fused with sodium hydroxide and the mass extracted with water, sodium hexahydroxostannate(IV) is formed in solution:

$$SnO_2 + 2NaOH + 2H_2O \rightarrow Na_2[Sn(OH)_6]$$

If a dilute acid is added to this solution, a white gelatinous precipitate of the hydrated tin(IV) oxide is obtained. It was once thought that this was an acid and several formulae were suggested. However, it now seems likely that all these are different forms of the hydrated oxide, the differences arising from differences in particle size and degree of hydration. When some varieties of the hydrated tin(IV) oxide 'dissolve' in hydrochloric acid, this is really a breaking up of the particles to form a colloidal solution — a phenomenon known as *peptization.*

8.5.7 Oxides of lead

Lead(II) *oxide,* PbO

Lead(II) oxide is the most stable oxide of lead; it exists in two crystalline forms. One form is reddish yellow in colour, with a tetragonal lattice, and is called *litharge*. The other form, yellow in colour, has a rather greater density and a rhombic lattice; it is called *massicot*. Litharge is obtained when molten lead is oxidized by a blast of air. **By** more careful heating, or by heating lead carbonate or lead nitrate, massicot is obtained. Litharge is the stable form at room temperature, but massicot changes only very slowly to litharge under ordinary conditions.

Lead(II) oxide is the most basic oxide formed by a Group IV element. It dissolves easily in acids to give lead(II) salts but it also dissolves slowly in alkalis to give hydroxoplumbates(II) and must, therefore, be classed as an amphoteric oxide, for example:

$$PbO + 2H^+ \rightarrow Pb^{2+} + H_2O$$
$$PbO + 4OH^- + H_2O \rightarrow [Pb(OH)_6]^{4-}$$

Lead(II) oxide is easily reduced to the metal when heated with a reducing agent such as hydrogen, carbon or carbon monoxide, for example:

$$PbO + H_2 \rightarrow Pb + H_2O$$

Lead(IV) *oxide,* PbO_2

Lead(IV) oxide can be prepared by the action of an alkaline chlorate(I) solution on a lead(II) salt. The reaction can be considered in two stages:

1        $$Pb^{2+} + 2OH^- \rightarrow Pb(OH)_2\downarrow$$
                                white

The white precipitate of lead hydroxide [or hydrated lead(II) oxide] is then oxidized by the chlorate(I) to the brown dioxide:

2        $$Pb(OH)_2 + ClO^- \rightarrow PbO_2\downarrow + Cl^- + H_2O$$
                                brown

Lead(IV) oxide is also obtained when 'red lead', Pb_3O_4 (*see* below), is treated with dilute nitric acid:

$$Pb_3O_4 + 4HNO_3 \rightarrow 2Pb(NO_3)_2 + 2H_2O + PbO_2\downarrow$$

When heated above 600 K lead(IV) oxide decomposes into the more stable lead(II) oxide and oxygen:

$$2PbO_2 \rightarrow 2PbO + O_2\uparrow$$

Lead(IV) oxide is found to have a considerable oxidizing power, again indicating that the oxidation state $+2$ is generally more stable for lead than oxidation state $+4$. Concentrated hydrochloric acid, for example, reacts with PbO_2 at room temperature to form lead(II) chloride and chlorine:

$$PbO_2 + 4HCl \rightarrow PbCl_2 + Cl_2\uparrow + 2H_2O$$

If this reaction is carried out at 273 K some unstable lead(IV) chloride is initially formed (p. 179). Other oxidizing reactions of lead(IV) oxide include the evolution of oxygen when heated with concentrated sulphuric acid:

$$2PbO_2 + 2H_2SO_4 \rightarrow 2PbSO_4 + 2H_2O + O_2\uparrow$$

and the oxidation of sulphur to sulphur dioxide which then reacts with more lead(IV) oxide to form lead(II) sulphate:

$$PbO_2 + S \rightarrow Pb + SO_2$$
$$PbO_2 + SO_2 \rightarrow PbSO_4$$

Lead dioxide is slightly soluble in concentrated nitric acid and concentrated sulphuric acid, and it dissolves in fused alkalis. It therefore has amphoteric properties, although these are not well characterized since it is relatively inert.

Dilead(II) lead(IV) oxide, 'red lead', Pb_3O_4

Red lead is a brilliant red powder obtained by heating lead monoxide in air to about 800 K. This reaction is reversible, for if heated, red lead evolves oxygen at temperatures above 850 K.

$$6PbO + O_2 \rightleftharpoons 2Pb_3O_4$$

Red lead is insoluble in water. Like lead(II) oxide it can readily be reduced to lead. The structure of the solid, as the systematic name suggests, consists of two interpenetrating oxide structures, in which each Pb^{IV} atom is surrounded octahedrally by six oxygen atoms, and each Pb^{II} by three (pyramidal) oxygen atoms, the oxygen atoms being shared between these two units of structure. With dilute nitric acid the lead(II) part dissolves, and the lead(IV) part precipitates as lead(IV) oxide:

$$Pb_2[PbO_4] + 4HNO_3 \rightarrow 2Pb(NO_3)_2 + PbO_2 \downarrow + 2H_2O$$

Red lead is a useful ingredient of anti-rusting paints, in which it is mixed with linseed oil. If glycerol is added to this mixture, a cement suitable for luting (i.e. making airtight or watertight) joints in iron pipes or vessels is obtained.

8.6 Chlorides and other important halides of Group IV elements

All Group IV elements form tetrachlorides, MX_4, which are predominantly tetrahedral and covalent. Germanium, tin and lead also form dichlorides, these becoming increasingly ionic in character as the relative atomic mass of the Group IV element increases and the element becomes more metallic. Carbon and silicon form catenated halides which have properties similar to their tetrahalides.

8.6.1 Carbon

When carbon forms four covalent bonds with halogen atoms the second quantum level on the carbon is completely filled with electrons. Most of the reactions of the Group IV tetrahalides require initial donation by a Lewis base (p. 81) (e.g. water, ammonia) which attaches initially to the tetrahalide by donation of its electron pair. Hence, although the calculated free energy of a reaction may indicate that the reaction is energetically favourable, the reaction may still not proceed. Thus we find that the tetrahalides of carbon are chemically (kinetically) inert and, unlike all other Group IV element tetrahalides, they are not hydrolysed by water. *Carbon tetrafluoride* (tetrafluoromethane) is a gas, b.p. 145 K, and is made by direct combination of carbon and fluorine; it is also the main product of burning fluorine in benzene vapour. *Carbon tetrachloride* (tetrachloromethane) is a liquid, b.p.

350 K, and is prepared by the action of chlorine on carbon disulphide (p. 180) in the presence of a catalyst, usually manganese(II) chloride or iron(III) chloride:

$$CS_2 \ + \ 3Cl_2 \xrightarrow{\ 300\ K\ } CCl_4 \ + \ S_2Cl_2$$

Further reaction then occurs between the disulphur dichloride and the carbon disulphide:

$$2S_2Cl_2 \ + \ CS_2 \xrightarrow{\ 330\ K\ } CCl_4 \ + \ 6S$$

Tetrachloromethane is an excellent solvent for organic substances. It has been used in dry-cleaning and in fire-extinguishers, but it has now largely been replaced because it is highly toxic, causing damage to liver and kidneys. 1,1,1-Trichloroethane is the most commonly used dry-cleaning solvent and fluorocarbons are used in many fire-extinguishers.

8.6.2   Silicon

Silicon tetrafluoride (*tetrafluorosilane*) is formed when hydrogen fluoride reacts with silica or a silicate:

$$4HF \ + \ SiO_2 \ \rightarrow \ SiF_4{\uparrow} \ + \ 2H_2O$$

The hydrogen fluoride is conveniently produced *in situ* by the action of concentrated sulphuric acid on calcium fluoride:

$$CaF_2 \ + \ H_2SO_4 \ \rightarrow \ CaSO_4 \ + \ 2HF$$

Tetrafluorosilane is a colourless gas, b.p. 187 K, the molecule having, like the tetrahalides of carbon, a tetrahedral covalent structure. It reacts with water to form hydrated silica (silica gel, see p. 168) and hexafluorosilicic acid, the latter product being obtained by a reaction between the hydrogen fluoride produced and excess of tetrafluorosilane:

$$SiF_4 \ + \ 2H_2O \ \rightarrow \ SiO_2{\downarrow} \ + \ 4HF$$
$$SiF_4 \ + \ 2HF \ \rightarrow \ H_2SiF_6$$

Silicon tetrachloride (*tetrachlorosilane*) is a colourless liquid, b.p. 216.2 K, and again the molecule has a covalent structure. It can be prepared by direct combination or by the following reaction

$$SiO_2 \ + \ 2Cl_2 \ + \ 2C \ \rightarrow \ SiCl_4{\uparrow} \ + \ 2CO{\uparrow}$$

Tetrachlorosilane is hydrolysed by water:

$$SiCl_4 \ + \ 2H_2O \ \rightarrow \ 4HCl \ + \ SiO_2{\downarrow}$$

Silica gel is again obtained but silicon does not form the corresponding hexachlorosilicic acid since the small silicon atom is unable to coordinate six chlorine ligands.

Silicon difluoride is obtained as a very reactive gas when silicon tetrafluoride and silicon are heated together. It polymerizes rapidly to give $(SiF_2)_n$, a solid.

8.6.3   Germanium

Germanium forms bivalent compounds with all the halogens. *Germanium*(II) *chloride* can be prepared by passing the vapour of germanium(IV) chloride (*see* below) over heated germanium. The reaction is reversible and disproportionation of germanium(II) chloride is complete at about 720 K at atmospheric pressure:

$$GeCl_4 + Ge \rightleftharpoons 2GeCl_2$$

[Germanium(I) fluoride can be prepared by a similar process using a slightly lower temperature.]

Germanium(II) chloride is hyrolysed by water; the reaction can be represented as

$$GeCl_2 + 2H_2O \rightarrow Ge(OH)_2 + 2HCl$$

but the product $Ge(OH)_2$ may be a hydrated oxide. With hydrogen chloride gas, the reaction is an addition:

$$GeCl_2 + HCl \rightarrow GeCl_3H \text{ [analogous to trichloromethane, (chloroform)}$$
$$CCl_3H]$$

In concentrated hydrochloric acid solution, the reaction is

$$GeCl_2 + Cl^- \rightarrow [GeCl_3]^-$$

and salts of this anion are known.

Germanium(IV) *chloride* can be prepared by passing chlorine over germanium at a temperature of 370—450 K:

$$Ge + 2Cl_2 \rightarrow GeCl_4$$

It has a covalently bonded structure and is a colourless liquid at room temperature; it is hydrolysed reversibly by water, all the germanium being recoverable by distilling the product with concentrated hydrochloric acid:

$$GeCl_4 + 2H_2O \rightleftharpoons GeO_2 + 4HCl$$

8.6.4   Tin

Tin(II) *chloride*

This chloride is prepared by dissolving tin in concentrated hydrochloric acid; on cooling, the solution deposits crystals of *hydrated* tin(II) chloride, $SnCl_2.2H_2O$ ('tin salt'). The *anhydrous* chloride is prepared by heating tin in a current of hydrogen chloride:

$$Sn + 2HCl \rightarrow \overset{\displaystyle \ddot{S}n}{\underset{\displaystyle Cl \qquad Cl}{\diagup \quad \diagdown}} + H_2$$

The hydrated salt is decomposed by heat:

$$SnCl_2.2H_2O \rightleftharpoons Sn(OH)Cl + HCl + H_2O$$

This reaction proceeds slowly in aqueous solution, so that the basic salt,

Sn(OH)Cl, is slowly precipitated. Addition of excess of hydrochloric acid gives the acids of formulae $HSnCl_3$ and H_2SnCl_4 Salts of these acids containing the ions $SnCl_3^-$ and $SnCl_4^{2-}$ [chlorostannates(II)] are known.

A solution of tin(II) chloride is a reducing agent:

$$Sn^{4+}(aq) + 2e^- \rightarrow Sn^{2+}(aq) \qquad E^\ominus = 0.15 \text{ V}$$

Hence it reduces *mercury*(II) *chloride*, first to the white insoluble mercury(I) chloride and then, if in excess to mercury:

$$2HgCl_2 + SnCl_2 \rightarrow SnCl_4 + Hg_2Cl_2\downarrow$$
$$\text{white}$$
$$Hg_2Cl_2 + SnCl_2 \rightarrow 2Hg\downarrow + SnCl_4$$

It reduces *iron*(III) to *iron*(II) salts:

$$2Fe^{3+} + Sn^{2+} \rightarrow Sn^{4+} + 2Fe^{2+}$$

This provides a method of estimating an iron(III) salt. After reduction the iron(II) salt is titrated with manganate(VII) solution.

It reduces *nitrobenzene* (in the presence of hydrochloric acid) to phenylammonium chloride:

$$C_6H_5NO_2 + 7HCl + 3SnCl_2 \rightarrow C_6H_5NH_2.HCl + 2H_2O + 3SnCl_4$$

It reduces *benzenediazonium chloride* to phenylhydrazine hydrochloride:

$$[C_6H_5.N_2]Cl + 4HCl + 2SnCl_2 \rightarrow C_6H_5NH.NH_2.HCl + 2SnCl_4$$

Tin(II) chloride is slowly oxidized in air, but keeping a piece of tin metal in the solution prevents this.

Tin(IV) *chloride,* $SnCl_4$

Stannic chloride is prepared by treating metallic tin with chlorine:

$$Sn + 2Cl_2 \rightarrow SnCl_4$$

(This reaction has been used to recover tin from scarp tinplate.) Tin(IV) chloride is a colourless liquid, which fumes in air owing to hydrolysis:

$$SnCl_4 + 2H_2O \rightleftharpoons SnO_2 + 4HCl$$
$$\text{hydrated}$$

It is soluble in organic solvents (a characteristic of a covalent compound), but dissolves in water and can form hydrates (a characteristic of an ionic compound). Hence the hydrated Sn^{4+} must be formed in water and undergo hydrolysis thus (cf. aluminium):

$$[Sn(H_2O)_x]^{4+} \rightleftharpoons [Sn(OH)(H_2O)_{x-1}]^{3+} + H^+ \rightleftharpoons [Sn(OH)_2(H_2O)_{x-2}]^{2+} + 2H^+$$

This process goes on until (if alkali is added) the final product is $[Sn(OH)_6]^{2-}$. (If alkali is not added, hydrolysis ultimately gives the hydrated oxide in accordance with the equation above.) The hydrolysis can be suppressed by addition of hydrochloric acid, and with excess of this, hexachlorostannic(IV) acid is formed:

$$SnCl_4 + 2HCl \rightarrow H_2Sn^{IV}Cl_6$$

Salts of this acid are known and ammonium hexachlorostannate(IV) $(NH_4)_2SnCl_6$, is used as a mordant (p. 139).

8.6.5   Lead

Lead(II) chloride

The solid is essentially ionic, made up of Pb^{2+} and Cl^- ions. The vapour contains bent molecules of $PbCl_2$ (cf. $SnCl_2$). Lead chloride is precipitated when hydrochloric acid (or a solution of a chloride) is added to a cold solution of a lead(II) salt. It dissolves in hot water but, on cooling, is slowly precipitated in crystalline form. It dissolves in excess of concentrated hydrochloric acid to give the acid $H_2[Pb^{II}Cl_4]$.

Lead(II) iodide

The solid has a layer structure (p. 378). Lead(II) iodide, like lead(II) chloride, is soluble in hot water but on cooling appears in the form of glistening golden 'spangles'. This reaction is used as a test for lead(II) ions in solution.

Lead(IV) chloride

Unlike solid lead(II) chloride which is ionic and dissolves in water to form hydrated Pb^{2+} and Cl^- ions, lead(IV) chloride is an essentially covalent volatile compound which is violently hydrolysed by water.

Lead(IV) chloride is formed from cold concentrated hydrochloric acid and lead(IV) oxide as described earlier. It readily evolves chlorine by the reversible reaction:

$$PbCl_4 \rightleftharpoons PbCl_2 + Cl_2\uparrow$$

Hence, if chlorine is passed into a cold suspension (in hydrochloric acid) of lead(II) chloride, lead(IV) chloride is formed. Addition of ammonium chloride gives the complex salt *ammonium hexachloroplumbate*(IV) as a yellow precipitate:

$$2NH_4Cl + PbCl_4 \rightarrow (NH_4)_2Pb^{IV}Cl_6\downarrow$$

This is filtered off and cold concentrated sulphuric acid added, whereupon lead(IV) chloride separates as an oily yellow liquid:

$$(NH_4)_2PbCl_6 + H_2SO_4 \rightarrow (NH_4)_2SO_4 + PbCl_4 + 2HCl$$

8.7   Other important compounds

8.7.1   Carbon

Carbides

These can be divided into three groups:

The salt-like carbides: Among these are aluminium tricarbide (*methanide*) Al_4C_3 (containing essentially C^{4-} ions in the crystal lattice) and the rather more common *dicarbides* containing the C_2^{2-} (acetylide or ethynide) ion, for example calcium dicarbide CaC_2; these carbides are hydrolysed by water yielding methane and ethyne respectively:

$$Al_4C_3 + 12H_2O \rightarrow 4Al(OH)_3 + 3CH_4\uparrow$$
$$CaC_2 + 2H_2O \rightarrow Ca(OH)_2 + C_2H_2\uparrow$$

The covalent carbides: These include boron carbide B_4C and silicon carbide SiC; the latter is made by heating a mixture of silica and coke in an electric furnace to about 2000 K:

$$SiO_2 + 3C \rightarrow SiC + 2CO\uparrow$$

The process is carried out alongside the similar one for producing graphite. Silicon carbide when pure is colourless, but technical silicon carbide (carborundum) is usually grey. These carbides have a diamond-like structure, i.e. covalent bonds extend throughout their crystals, and they are therefore of high melting point and chemically inert. Both are used as abrasives, and boron carbide is used in radiation shielding.

The interstitial carbides: These are formed by the transition metals (e.g. titanium, iron) and have the general formula M_xC. They are often non-stoichiometric — the carbon atoms can occupy some or all of the small spaces between the larger metal atoms, the arrangement of which remains essentially the same as in the pure metal (cf. the interstitial hydrides).

Carbon disulphide, CS_2

This was formerly manufactured by passing sulphur vapour over white hot coal or charcoal. An equilibrium was established and the carbon disulphide vapour was condensed, allowing the reaction to proceed:

$$C + 2S \rightleftharpoons CS_2$$

Large quantities are now manufactured by the reaction between sulphur vapour and methane at a temperature of 900—1000 K in the presence of a clay catalyst:

$$CH_4 + 4S \rightarrow CS_2 + 2H_2S$$

The CS_2 is then removed, after cooling, by a solvent. The molecule has a covalent linear structure $S{=}C{=}S$.

Carbon disulphide is a volatile, evil-smelling liquid, although if carefully purified, the unpleasant smell is removed, as it is due to impurity. The vapour is inflammable and can form explosive mixtures in air:

$$2CS_2 + 5O_2 \rightarrow 2CO + 4SO_2$$

It is also decomposed by water above 420 K:

$$CS_2 + 2H_2O \rightarrow CO_2 + 2H_2S$$

Carbon disulphide is an excellent solvent for fats, oils, rubber, sulphur, bromine and iodine, and is used industrially as a solvent for extraction. It is also used in the production of *viscose rayon*; when added to wood cellulose impregnated with sodium hydroxide solution, a viscous solution of 'cellulose xanthate' is formed, and this can be extruded through a fine nozzle into acid, which decomposes the xanthate to give a glossy thread of cellulose.

8.7.2   Lead

Lead(II) carbonate

Lead(II) carbonate occurs naturally as *cerussite*. It is prepared in the laboratory by passing carbon dioxide through, or adding sodium hydrogencarbonate to, a cold dilute solution of lead(II) nitrate or lead(II) ethanoate:

$$Pb^{2+} + 2HCO_3^- \rightarrow PbCO_3\downarrow + CO_2\uparrow + H_2O$$

If the normal carbonate is used, the *basic carbonate* or *white lead*, $Pb(OH)_2.2PbCO_3$, is precipitated. The basic carbonate was used extensively as a base in paints but is now less common having been largely replaced by either titanium dioxide or zinc oxide. Paints made with white lead are not only poisonous but blacken in urban atmospheres owing to the formation of lead sulphide and it is hardly surprising that their use is declining.

Lead(II) chromate(VI), PbCrO₄

Lead(II) chromate(VI) is precipitated when a soluble chromate(VI) or dichromate(VI) is added to a solution of a lead salt in neutral or slightly acid solution:

$$Pb^{2+} + CrO_4^{2-} \rightarrow PbCrO_4\downarrow$$
$$2Pb^{2+} + Cr_2O_7^{2-} + H_2O \rightarrow 2PbCrO_4\downarrow + 2H^+$$

The precipitation of lead(II) chromate is used to estimate lead gravimetrically; the yellow precipitate of lead(II) chromate is filtered off, dried and weighed. Lead(II) chromate is used as a pigment under the name 'chrome yellow'.

The lead accumulator

The most widely-used storage battery is the lead accumulator. Each cell consists essentially of two lead plates immersed in an electrolyte of sulphuric acid. The lead plates are usually perforated and one is packed with lead(IV) oxide, the other with spongy lead. An inert porous insulator acts as a separator between the plates. When the cell is producing current, the following reactions occur:

Lead(IV) oxide plate (positive):

$$PbO_2 + 4H^+ + 2e^- \rightarrow Pb^{2+} + 2H_2O$$

followed by:

$$Pb^{2+} + SO_4^{2-} \rightarrow PbSO_4$$

Spongy lead plate (negative):

$$Pb \rightarrow Pb^{2+} + 2e^-$$

followed by:

$$Pb^{2+} + SO_4^{2-} \rightarrow PbSO_4$$

Hence the overall chemical reaction in the cell during discharge is:

$$PbO_2 + Pb + 2H_2SO_4 \rightarrow 2PbSO_4 + 2H_2O$$

Hence sulphuric acid is used up and insoluble lead(II) sulphate deposited on both plates. This process maintains a potential difference between the two plates of about 2 V. If now a larger potential difference than this is applied externally to the cell (making the positive plate the anode) then the above overall reaction is reversed, so that lead dioxide is deposited on the anode, lead is deposited on the cathode, and sulphuric acid is re-formed. Hence in the electrolyte we have:

$$\text{sulphuric acid} \xrightleftharpoons[\text{charge}]{\text{discharge}} \text{water}$$

The density of the electrolyte, measured by a hydrometer, forms a useful indicator of the state of charge or discharge of the battery.

If the charging process continues after all the lead sulphate has been used up, then the charging voltage rises. Hydrogen is liberated from the lead electrode, and oxygen is liberated from the lead dioxide electrode. The accumulator is then said to be 'gassing'.

8.8 Tests for Group IV elements

Carbon
All carbon compounds, if oxidized by either oxygen or an oxide [such as copper(II) oxide] yield carbon dioxide, which gives a precipitate of calcium carbonate when passed into aqueous calcium hydroxide.

Silicon
All silicon compounds on oxidation yield silica or silicates; these are difficult to detect but silica (given by silicates after acid treatment) is insoluble in all acids except hydrofluoric acid.

Tin
In presence of hydrochloric acid, tin(II) in aqueous solution (1) is precipitated by hydrogen sulphide as *brown* SnS, and (2) will reduce mercury(II) chloride first to mercury(I) chloride (white precipitate) and then to metallic mercury.

Tin(IV) in aqueous acid gives a *yellow* precipitate with hydrogen sulphide, and no reaction with mercury(II) chloride.

Lead
Lead(II) in aqueous solution gives on addition of the appropriate anion (1) a white precipitate of lead(II) chloride, (2) a yellow precipitate of lead(II) chromate and (3) a yellow precipitate of lead(II) iodide which dissolves on heating and reappears on cooling in the form of glistening 'spangles'.

Summary

For a summary, *see Table 8.2.*

Questions

1   Compare and contrast the chemistry of silicon, germanium, tin and lead by
     referring to the properties and bond types of their oxides and chlorides.
     Give brief experimental details to indicate how you could prepare in the
     laboratory a sample of either tin(IV) chloride or tin(IV) iodide. How far does
     the chemistry of the oxides and chlorides of carbon support the statement
     that 'the head element of a group in the Periodic Table is not typical of that
     group'?

                                                                              JMB,A

2   What physical and chemical tests could you apply to the oxides and chlorides
     of Group IV elements to show the changes in their properties as the atomic
     number of the element increases? At the bottom of Group IV tin and lead
     exhibit two oxidation states. Why are these elements not classified as
     'transition' metals?

                                                                      N, Phys. Sci., A

3   (a) State two physical and two chemical properties which clearly illustrate
          the differences between a typical metal and a typical non-metal.
     (b) 'For any given group in the Periodic Table, the metallic character of the
          element increases with the increase in relative atomic mass of the
          element'.
          Discuss this statement as it applies to the Group IV elements, C, Si, Ge,
          Sn, Pb, indicating any properties of carbon which appear anomalous.
          Illustrate your answer by considering:
          (i)   the physical properties of the elements,
          (ii) the reaction of the oxides with sodium hydroxide,
          (iii) the reaction of the chlorides with water,
          (iv) the stability of the hydrides to heat,
          (v)   the changes in the stability of oxidation state (IV) with increase in
                atomic mass of the element.

                                                                              JMB,A

4   The chemical properties of the elements in a given group of the Periodic
     Table change with increasing atomic number.
     (a) Explain the main factors responsible for this, illustrating your answer by
          reference to the Group IVB elements, carbon to lead.
     (b) Apply the factors outlined under (a) to predict the main chemical
          properties and bonding relationships of the last three members of Group
          V of the Periodic Table containing the elements nitrogen, phosphorus,
          arsenic, antimony and bismuth.

                                                                                 L,S

Table 8.2 Summary of properties of Group IV

	C	Si	Ge	Sn	Pb
Element	Diamond (giant covalent) Graphite (layer structure)	Diamond-like, less hard	Diamond-like, less hard	Metallic, soft	Metallic, soft
Oxidation states	-4 (carbides) $+4$ (usually covalent)	$+4$ usually covalent $+2$ reactive, unstable	$+4$ usually covalent $+2$ reactive, unstable	$+4$ covalent $+2$ ionic, reducing	$+4$ covalent, oxidizing $+2$ ionic
Reactions: with acid with alkali		Silicates	Hydrated GeO_2 Germanates	Salts or oxide	Pb^{II} salts Hydroxo-anions $M^{II}(OH)_6^{4-}$
with oxygen	Excess gives CO_2 Limited gives CO	SiO_2	Little action	SnO_2	PbO then Pb_3O_4
Compounds: hydrides	Numerous, covalent	Form mainly MH_4, decreasing stability $\longrightarrow$			
oxides	CO (gaseous) CO_2 (gaseous, acidic)	SiO_2 (solid, acidic)	GeO_2 (solid, amphoteric)	SnO_2 (solid, amphoteric) SnO (solid, basic)	PbO_2, solid. PbO, Pb_3O_4 solid, amphoteric
Oxo-anions	Simple HCO_3^-, CO_3^{2-}	Polymeric oxo-anions	Polymeric oxo-anions		
Hydroxo-anions				Hydroxo-anions $[M^{IV}(OH)_6]^{2-}$, $[M^{II}(OH)_6]^{4-}$ $\longrightarrow$	
Halides	CX_4, covalent, resist hydrolysis	MX_4, covalent, easily hydrolysed $\longrightarrow$		SnX_2 ions in solution	PbX_2 ions in solution

5   Give an account of the chemical properties of the element tin and describe
        four of its principal compounds. The element germanium (Mendeléef's
        ekasilicon) lies in Group IV of the Periodic Table below carbon and silicon
        and above tin and lead. What properties would you predict for this element,
        for its oxide GeO_2 and for its chloride $GeCl_4$?

                                                                        O and C.S.

6   By reference to the elements carbon, silicon, tin and lead, show how the
        properties of an element and those of its compounds can be related to:
        (a) the group in the Periodic Table in which the element occurs,
        (b) its position in that group.

7   (a) Which of the oxides of the elements of Group IV (C, Si, Ge, Sn and Pb) is
                 (i)   the strongest oxidizing agent,
                 (ii) the strongest reducing agent?
        (b) What is the oxidation state of the Group IV element given in (a)(i)?
        (c) Name one substance which can be oxidized by the oxide given in (a)(i).
        (d) Which halide of tin is
                 (i)   thermally most stable,
                 (ii) thermally least stable?
        (e) Explain your answers to (d)(i) and (d)(ii).
        (f) A Group IV element A dissolves in warm dilute nitric acid to give a
             solution which, when treated with dilute hydrochloric acid in the cold,
             gives a white precipitate B which dissolves on heating. Addition of
             aqueous potassium iodide to the solution gives a yellow precipitate
             which dissolves on boiling to give a colourless solution. On cooling, a
             golden yellow crystalline substance C precipitates. The precipitate
             dissolves in excess of potassium iodide giving a clear solution D.
                 (i)   Identify the element A.
                 (ii) What is the formula of the white precipitate B?
                 (iii) What is the formula of the golden yellow crystalline substance C?
                 (iv) What is the formula of the metallic species present in solution D?
                                                                        JMB,A

Chapter 9
Group V
Nitrogen, phosphorus, arsenic, antimony, bismuth

9.1 Summary of general characteristics

Table 9.1 gives some of the physical properties of Group V elements. The data in *Table 9.1* clearly indicate the increase in electropositive character of the elements from nitrogen to bismuth. Nitrogen is a gas consisting entirely of diatomic molecules but the other elements are normally solids. From phosphorus to bismuth the elements show an increasingly metallic appearance, and arsenic, antimony and bismuth are electrical conductors. Their chemical behaviour is in agreement with this, the hydrides MH_3, for example, decreasing in stability. Arsenic, antimony and bismuth are all capable of forming tripositive cationic species in solution. The oxides become increasingly basic and bismuth(III) hydroxide $Bi(OH)_3$ is insoluble in alkali, but readily soluble in acids to form salts.

The outer quantum level of the Group V elements contains five electrons, but there is no tendency for the elements at the top of the group to lose these and form positive ions. Nitrogen and phosphorus are, in fact, typical non-metals, having acidic oxides which react with alkalis to give salts. Nitrogen, the head element, shows many notable differences from the other Group V elements, the distinction arising from the inability of nitrogen to expand the number of electrons in its outer quantum level beyond eight. (The other Group V elements are able to use d orbitals in their outer quantum level for further expansion.) The nitrogen atom can (a) share three electrons to give a covalency of three, leaving a lone pair of electrons on the nitrogen atom, (b) share three electrons and donate the unshared pair to an acceptor atom or molecule, as in

$$NH_4^+ \qquad H_3N \rightarrow AlCl_3 \qquad H-O-N{\overset{\displaystyle O}{\underset{\displaystyle O}{<}}}$$

when nitrogen achieves its maximum covalency of four, (c) acquire three electrons when combining with very electropositive elements to form the nitride ion, N^{3-}.

The other Group V elements can behave in a similar manner but their atoms have an increasing reluctance to accept electrons, and to donate the lone pair. These atoms can, however, increase their covalency to five, for example in the vapour of phosphorus pentachloride, or even to six, for example in the ions $[PF_6]^-$, $[PCl_6]^-$. Hence phosphorus, arsenic, antimony and bismuth are able to form both trivalent and quinquevalent compounds

Table 9.1 Selected properties of the elements

Element	Atomic number	Outer electrons	Atomic radius nm	m.p./K	b.p./K	First ionization energy kJ mol^{-1}	Electro-negativity (Pauling)
N	7	$2s^2 2p^3$	0.070*	63	77	1403	3.0
P	15	$3s^2 3p^3$	0.110*	317†	554†	1012	2.1
As	33	$3d^{10} 4s^2 4p^3$	0.125	1090‡	sublimes	947	2.0
Sb	51	$4d^{10} 5s^2 5p^3$	0.145	903	1910	834	1.9
Bi	83	$5d^{10} 6s^2 6p^3$	0.170	545	1832	703	1.9

*covalent radius.
†white P.
‡under pressure.

but as we go from phosphorus to bismuth it becomes increasingly more difficult to achieve a quinquevalent state — thus phosphorus(V) oxide, P_4O_{10}, is readily obtained by burning phosphorus in excess of air, but the corresponding oxides of antimony and bismuth require the action of strong oxidizing agents for their preparation and bismuth(V) oxide is particularly unstable.

9.2 Occurrence and extraction of the elements

9.2.1 Nitrogen

Nitrogen is an essential constituent of all living matter, being one of the elements present in proteins. Proteins are synthesized by plants from nitrogen compounds in the soil, usually with the help of bacteria although some plants can absorb and utilize free gaseous nitrogen. The replacement of nitrogen compounds in the soil is essential for continued growth of crops; hence the manufacture of fertilizers such as ammonium or nitrate salts is a major industry since, because they are water soluble, inorganic nitrogen compounds are only rarely found in nature. Deposits of sodium nitrate are found in Chile and a few other regions which have a dry climate. By far the greatest and most important source of nitrogen is the atmosphere, which consists of about 78 per cent nitrogen by volume and, therefore, acts as a reservoir (p. 189).

Industrially, elemental nitrogen is extracted from the air by the fractional distillation of liquid air from which carbon dioxide and water have been removed. The major fractions are nitrogen, b.p. 77 K and oxygen, b.p. 90 K, together with smaller quantities of the noble gases.

In the laboratory nitrogen can be made by the oxidation of the ammonium ion (p. 198).

9.2.2   Phosphorus

Phosphorus, like nitrogen, is an essential constituent of living matter where it may be partly in combination (as phosphate groups) with organic groups, for example in lecithin and egg yolk, or mainly in inorganic form, as calcium phosphate(V), in bones and teeth.

A number of phosphorus-containing minerals occur in nature; these are almost always salts of phosphoric(V) acid, notably the calcium salts, for example *phosphorite* or *hydroxyapatite* $3Ca_3(PO_4)_2.Ca(OH)_2$, *apatite* $3Ca_3(PO_4)_2.CaF_2$. Other minerals are *vivianite* $Fe_3(PO_4)_2.8H_2O$ and aluminium phosphate. Elemental phosphorus is manufactured on a large scale, the world production exceeding 1 million tons annually. A phosphorus-containing rock, usually apatite, is mixed with sand, SiO_2, and coke and the mixture is heated in an electric furnace at about 1700 K. At this temperature the non-volatile silica displaces the more volatile phosphorus(V) oxide from the phosphate:

$$2Ca_3(PO_4)_2 + 6SiO_2 \rightarrow 6CaSiO_3 + P_4O_{10}$$

The phosphorus(V) oxide is then reduced by coke, and phosphorus vapour and carbon monoxide are produced:

$$P_4O_{10} + 10C \rightarrow 10CO\uparrow + P_4\uparrow$$

These gases leave the furnace at about 600 K, pass through electrostatic precipitators to remove dust, and the phosphorus is then condensed out.

9.2.3   Arsenic, antimony and bismuth

Each of these elements occurs naturally as a sulphide ore: arsenic as *realgar* As_4S_4, *orpiment* As_4S_6 and *arsenical pyrites* with approximate formula FeAsS; antimony as *stibnite* Sb_2S_3; and bismuth as Bi_2S_3.

The method of extraction is similar for each element in involving first the roasting of the sulphide ore when the oxide is produced, for example

$$Sb_2S_3 + 5O_2 \rightarrow Sb_2O_4 + 3SO_2$$

followed by reduction of the oxide with carbon, for example

$$As_4O_6 + 6C \rightarrow As_4 + 6CO\uparrow$$

9.3   Properties of the elements

The main physical properties of these elements have been given in *Table 9.1*.

9.3.1   Allotropes

Solid phosphorus, arsenic and antimony exist in well known allotropic modifications. Phosphorus has three main allotropic forms, white, red and black. White phosphorus is a wax-like solid made up of tetrahedral P_4 molecules with a strained P—P—P angle of 60 degrees; these also occur in liquid phosphorus. The reactivity of white phosphorus is attributed largely to this strained structure. The rather less reactive red allotrope can be made by heating white phosphorus at 670 K for several hours; at slightly higher temperatures, ~ 690 K, red phosphorus sublimes, the vapour condensing to re-form white phosphorus. If, however, red phosphorus is heated in a vacuum and the vapour rapidly condensed, apparently another modification, violet phosphorus, is obtained. It is probable that violet phosphorus is a polymer of high relative molecular mass which on heating breaks down into P_2 molecules. These on cooling normally dimerize to form P_4 molecules, i.e. white phosphorus, but *in vacuo* link up again to give the polymerized violet allotrope. Red phosphorus may have a structure intermediate between that of violet phosphorus and white phosphorus, or it may be essentially similar to the violet species.

Black phosphorus is formed when white phosphorus is heated under very high pressure (12 000 atmospheres). Black phosphorus has a well-established corrugated sheet structure with each phosphorus atom bonded to three neighbours. The bonding forces between layers are weak and give rise to flaky crystals which conduct electricity, properties similar to those of graphite. It is less reactive than either white or red phosphorus.

Arsenic and antimony resemble phosphorus in having several allotropic modifications. Both have an unstable yellow allotrope. These allotropes can be obtained by rapid condensation of the vapours which presumably, like phosphorus vapour, contain As_4 and Sb_4 molecules respectively. No such yellow allotrope is known for bismuth. The ordinary form of arsenic, stable at room temperature, is a grey metallic-looking brittle solid which has some power to conduct electricity*. Under ordinary conditions antimony and bismuth are silvery white and reddish white metallic elements respectively.

9.4   Chemical reactivity of the elements

9.4.1   Reaction with air

Nitrogen

The dissociation energy of the $N\equiv N$ bond is very large, 946 kJ mol^{-1}, and dissociation of nitrogen molecules into atoms is not readily effected until very high temperatures, being only slight even at 3000 K. It is the high bond energy coupled with the absence of bond polarity that explains the low reactivity of nitrogen, in sharp contrast to other triple bond structures† such as

$$-C\equiv N \qquad\qquad -C\equiv O \qquad\qquad -C\equiv C-$$

---

*The incorporation of minute amounts of arsenic in semi-conductors has been mentioned (p. 152).

†Certain living systems can 'fix' atmospheric nitrogen, using a metalloenzyme called *nitrogenase*. Attempts are being made to imitate this mode of fixation by synthesizing transition metal complexes in which molecular nitrogen, N_2, is present as a ligand. The problem of easy conversion of this into (for example) NH_3 or NO_3^- remains to be solved.

Nitrogen does, however, combine with oxygen to a small extent when a mixture of the gases is subjected to high temperature or an electric discharge, the initial product being nitrogen monoxide, NO.

Phosphorus

White phosphorus is very reactive. It has an appreciable vapour pressure at room temperature and inflames in dry air at about 320 K or at even lower temperatures if finely divided, In air at room temperature it emits a faint green light called *phosphorescence*; the reaction occurring is a complex oxidation process, but this happens only at certain partial pressures of oxygen. It is necessary, therefore, to store white phosphorus under water, unlike the less reactive red and black allotropes which do not react with air at room temperature. Both red and black phosphorus burn to form oxides when heated in air, the red form igniting at temperatures exceeding 600 K, the actual temperature depending on purity. Black phosphorus does not ignite until even higher temperatures.

Arsenic, antimony and bismuth

None of the common allotropic forms of these metals is affected by air unless they are heated, when all burn to arsenic(III) oxide, antimony(III) oxide or bismuth(III) oxide.

9.4.2   Reaction with acids

Hydrochloric and dilute sulphuric acids have no appreciable action at room temperature on the pure Group V elements.

Concentrated sulphuric acid and nitric acid — powerful oxidizing agents — attack all the elements except nitrogen, particularly when the acids are warm. The products obtained reflect changes in stability of the oxidation states $+5$ and $+3$ of the Group V elements.

Both white and red phosphorus dissolve in, for example, concentrated nitric acid to form phosphoric(V) acid, the reaction between hot acid and white phosphorus being particularly violent.

Arsenic dissolves in concentrated nitric acid forming arsenic(V) acid, H_3AsO_4, but in dilute nitric acid and concentrated sulphuric acid the main product is the arsenic(III) acid, H_3AsO_3. The more metallic element, antimony, dissolves to form antimony(III) oxide Sb_4O_6 with moderately concentrated nitric acid, but antimony(V) oxide Sb_2O_5 (structure unknown) with the more concentrated acid. Bismuth, however, forms the salt bismuth(III) nitrate $Bi(NO_3)_3.5H_2O$.

9.4.3   Reaction with alkalis

The change from non-metallic to metallic properties of the Group V elements as the relative atomic mass of the element increases is shown in their reactions with alkalis.

The head element *nitrogen* does not react. White *phosphorus*, however, reacts when warmed with a concentrated solution of a strong alkali to form phosphine, a reaction which can be regarded as a disproportionation reaction of phosphorus:

$$P_4 + 3KOH + 3H_2O \rightarrow 3KH_2PO_2 + PH_3\uparrow$$

potassium
phosphinate
(hypophosphite)

phosphine

The phosphine produced is impure and contains small quantities of diphosphane, P_2H_4 (p. 202).

Arsenic, unlike phosphorus, is only slightly attacked by boiling sodium hydroxide; more rapid attack takes place with the fused alkali; an arsenate(III) is obtained in both cases,

$$As_4 + 12OH^- \rightarrow 4AsO_3^{3-} + 6H_2\uparrow$$

cf. aluminium (p. 132). Arsine is not formed in this reaction.

Antimony and bismuth do not react with sodium hydroxide.

9.4.4   Reaction with halogens

Nitrogen does form a number of binary compounds with the halogens but none of these can be prepared by the direct combination of the elements and they are dealt with below (p. 220). The other Group V elements all form halides by direct combination.

Phosphorus
White and red phosphorus combine directly with chlorine, bromine and iodine, the red allotrope reacting in each case at a slightly higher temperature. The reactions are very vigorous and white phosphorus is spontaneously inflammable in chlorine at room temperature. Both chlorine and bromine first form a trihalide:

$$P_4 + 6X_2 \rightarrow 4PX_3 \qquad (X = Cl \text{ or } Br)$$

but this is converted into a pentahalide by excess of the halogen. No pentaiodide is known (p. 227).

Arsenic, antimony and bismuth
A complete set of trihalides of arsenic, antimony and bismuth can be prepared by the direct combination of the elements although other methods of preparation can sometimes by used. The vigour of the direct combination reaction for a given metal decreases from fluorine to iodine (except in the case of bismuth which does not react readily with fluorine) and for a given halogen, from arsenic to bismuth.

In addition to the trihalides, arsenic and antimony form pentafluorides and pentachlorides.

9.5   Hydrides of Group V elements

All Group V elements form covalent hydrides MH_3. Some physical data for these hydrides are given below in *Table 9.2*. The abnormal values of the

Table 9.2 Properties of hydrides of Group V elements

Hydride	m.p./K	b.p./K	Mean thermochemical bond energy/kJ mol^{-1}
NH_3	195	240	391
PH_3	140	183	322
AsH_3	157	218	247
SbH_3	185	256	—
BiH_3	—	295	—

melting and boiling points of ammonia are explained by hydrogen bonding (p. 45). The thermal stabilities of the hydrides decrease rapidly from ammonia to bismuthine as indicated by the mean thermochemical bond energies of the M—H bond, and both stibine, SbH_3, and bismuthine, BiH_3, are very unstable. All the Group V hydrides are reducing agents, the reducing power increasing from NH_3 to BiH_3, as thermal stability decreases.

These stability changes are in accordance with the change from a non-metal to a weak metal for the Group V elements nitrogen to bismuth.

Nitrogen, phosphorus and arsenic form more than one hydride. Nitrogen forms several but of these only ammonia, NH_3, hydrazine, N_2H_4 and hydrogen azide N_3H (and the ammonia derivative hydroxylamine) will be considered. Phosphorus and arsenic form the hydrides diphosphane P_2H_4 and diarsane As_2H_4 respectively, but both of these hydrides are very unstable.

9.5.1   Hydrides of nitrogen

Ammonia NH_3

Ammonia is manufactured by the direct combination of the elements

$$N_2 + 3H_2 \rightleftharpoons 2NH_3 \qquad \Delta H = -92.0 \text{ kJ mol}^{-1}$$

The production by this method was developed originally by Haber after whom the the process is now named. Since the reaction is reversible and the production of ammonia is an exothermic process it can easily be deduced that high yields of ammonia will be obtained at a high total pressure and low temperature. However, the time required to reach equilibrium is so great at low temperatures that it is more economical to work at a higher temperature and get nearer to a poorer equilibrium position more quickly. In practice, a temperature of about 770 K is used and a pressure between 200 and 1000 atmospheres. Even under these conditions equilibrium is only slowly established and a catalyst is necessary. Iron mixed with alumina is commonly used as a catalyst, the effect of the alumina being to reduce loss of iron surface by melting or sintering of the iron at the high temperature used. The development of a catalyst capable of quickly establishing an equilibrium at a lower temperature is most desirable as this would give a great yield of ammonia and indeed much work has been done in this field.

The hydrogen required for ammonia production is largely obtained by the steam re-forming of naphtha (p. 164). Nitrogen is produced by the

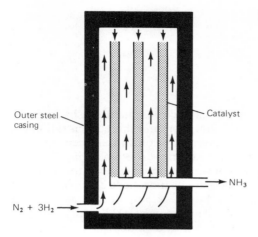

Figure 9.1 The Haber process

fractional distillation of liquid air. The purified gases are mixed in a 1:3 nitrogen to hydrogen ratio and passed into the catalyst vessel (*Figure 9.1*). The catalyst vessel consists of a steel tower containing relatively thin-walled tubes packed with the catalyst; the incoming gases pass up between these tubes and down through them, and the heat generated as the gases pass down the catalyst tubes warms the incoming gases. The gas emerging from the catalyst vessel contains about 10 per cent of ammonia; on cooling, this liquefies (since the pressure is high) and the unconverted hydrogen and nitrogen are returned to the inlet and passed again over the catalyst.

In the laboratory ammonia is obtained when any ammonium salt is heated with an alkali, either solid or in solution:

$$NH_4^+ + OH^- \rightarrow NH_3\uparrow + H_2O$$

It is best prepared by heating an intimate mixture of solid ammonium chloride and quicklime:

$$2NH_4Cl + CaO \rightarrow CaCl_2 + 2NH_3 + H_2O$$

After being dried over quicklime, calcium oxide CaO, the ammonia is collected by upward delivery. (N.B.) Both of the common drying agents, calcium chloride and concentrated sulphuric acid, combine with the gas.)

Ammonia is also produced when an ionic nitride is hydrolysed, for example magnesium nitride, produced when magnesium burns in nitrogen:

$$Mg_3N_2 + 6H_2O \rightarrow 3Mg(OH)_2 + 2NH_3\uparrow$$

Properties of ammonia. Ammonia is a colourless gas at room temperature and atmospheric pressure with a characteristic pungent smell. It is easily liquefied either by cooling (b.p. 240 K) or under a pressure of 8—9 atmospheres at ordinary temperature. Some of its physical and many of its chemical properties are best understood in terms of its structure. Like the other group head elements, nitrogen has no 2d orbitals available for bond formation and it is limited to a maximum of four single bonds. Ammonia has a basic tetrahedral arrangement with a lone pair occupying one position:

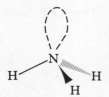

Because of the lone pair of electrons, ammonia has a dipole moment (high electron density at the lone pair) and this concentration of negative charge can attract (positive) hydrogen atoms in adjacent molecules giving fairly strong intermolecular forces, i.e. hydrogen bonding. Consequently ammonia has a high latent heat of vaporization and a relatively high boiling point (*see* Table 9.2 and p. 45), facts at one time made use of in refrigeration employing ammonia. The great solublity of ammonia in water (1 volume of water dissolves 1300 volumes of ammonia at 273 K) can be attributed to hydrogen bonding between ammonia and water molecules. (N.B. Concentrated ammonia solution has a density of 0.880 g cm^{-3} and contains 35 per cent of ammonia.) The reaction:

$$NH_3 + H_2O \rightleftharpoons NH_3.H_2O$$

is exothermic and can easily be reversed by heat, all the ammonia being evolved on boiling.

A second reaction also occurs:

$$NH_3.H_2O \rightleftharpoons NH_4^+ + OH^-$$

For this second reaction $K_{298} = 1.81 \times 10^{-5}$ and hence pK_b for ammonia solution is 4.75. The entity $NH_3.H_2O$ is often referred to as ammonium hydroxide, NH_4OH, a formula which would imply that either nitrogen has a covalency of five, an impossible arrangement, or that NH_4OH existed as the ions NH_4^+ and OH^-. It is possible to crystallize two hydrates from concentrated ammonia solution but neither of these hydrates is ionic. Hence use of the term 'ammonium hydroxide' is to be discouraged in favour of 'ammonia solution'.

Chemical properties of ammonia

These may, for convenience, be divided into a number of topics but all are closely related depending very largely on the presence of the lone pair of electrons on the nitrogen atom.

Ammonia as a donor molecule. Because of the presence of the lone pair of electrons on the nitrogen atom, ammonia can behave as an electron pair donor. For example, ammonia abstracts a proton from a water molecule producing the tetrahedral ammonium, NH_4^+, ion and forms the compounds $H_3N \rightarrow AlCl_3$ and $H_3N \rightarrow BCl_3$.

The commonly observed behaviour of ammonia as a ligand is due to the lone pair of electrons on the nitrogen atom, and ammonia forms numerous complex *ammines* with both transition elements and typical metals; the bonding varies from weak ion–dipole attraction to strong covalent bonding. (For examples of ammonia as a ligand, *see* pp. 39, 320.) The formation of the ammine $CaCl_2.8NH_3$ explains why calcium chloride cannot be used to dry ammonia gas.

Ammonia as a base. The ammonia molecule has a powerful affinity for protons and hence ammonia gas will react with gaseous hydrogen-containing compounds which are acidic, for example hydrogen chloride:

$$NH_3 + HCl \underset{\text{heat}}{\overset{\text{cool}}{\rightleftharpoons}} NH_4Cl \text{ (i.e. } NH_4^+ Cl^-)$$

(N.B. A trace of water is required to make the forward reaction proceed at a realistic rate.)

Ammonia will react with aqueous acids, for example

$$2NH_3 + H_2SO_4(aq) \rightarrow (NH_4)_2SO_4$$

which is more correctly written

$$2NH_3 + 2H_3O^+ + SO_4^{2-} \rightarrow 2NH_4^+ + 2H_2O + SO_4^{2-}$$

Aqueous ammonia can also behave as a weak base giving hydroxide ions in solution. However, addition of aqueous ammonia to a solution of a cation which normally forms an insoluble hydroxide may not always precipitate the latter, because (a) the ammonia may form a complex ammine with the cation and (b) because the concentration of hydroxide ions available in aqueous ammonia may be insufficient to exceed the solubility product of the cation hydroxide. Effects (a) and (b) may operate simultaneously. The hydroxyl ion concentration of aqueous ammonia can be further reduced by the addition of ammonium chloride; hence this mixture can be used to precipitate the hydroxides of, for example, aluminium and chromium(III) but not nickel(II) or cobalt(II).

Because of ammine formation, when ammonia solution is added slowly to a metal ion in solution, the hydroxide may first be precipitated and then redissolve when excess of ammonia solution is added; this is due to the formation of a complex ammine ion, for example with copper(II) and nickel(II) salts in aqueous solution.

Ammonia as a reducing agent. Ammonia gas will not burn in air but it does burn in oxygen with a yellowish flame after ignition. A convenient apparatus is shown in *Figure 9.2.* By reversing the gas supplies it can easily be shown that oxygen will also burn in ammonia.

In the presence of catalyst, usually platinum, ammonia is oxidized by oxygen (and air) to nitrogen monoxide NO. This reaction, used to obtain nitric acid from ammonia (p. 211), can be demonstrated in the laboratory using the apparatus shown in *Figure 9.3*; the oxygen rate should be slow, or ignition can occur.

Using the apparatus shown in *Figure 9.2* it can be shown that ammonia gas will burn in chlorine gas, the ignition being spontaneous in this case:

$$2NH_3 + 3Cl_2 \rightarrow N_2 + 6HCl$$
$$6HCl + 6NH_3 \rightarrow 6NH_4Cl$$

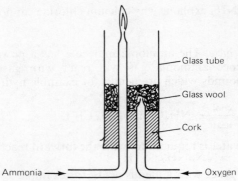

Figure 9.2 Apparatus for combustion of ammonia in oxygen

$$4NH_3 + 3O_2 \rightarrow 2N_2 + 6H_2O$$

Glass tube

Glass wool

Cork

Ammonia →   ← Oxygen

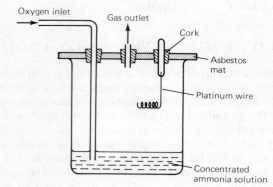

Oxygen inlet

Gas outlet

Cork

Figure 9.3 Catalytic oxidation of ammonia

$$4NH_3 + 5O_2 \rightarrow 4NO + 6H_2O$$

Asbestos mat

Platinum wire

Concentrated ammonia solution

If ammonia is used in large excess and the chlorine diluted with nitrogen, *chloramine*, NH_2Cl, is formed:

$$NH_3 + Cl_2 \rightarrow NH_2Cl + HCl$$

When chlorine gas is in excess a highly explosive substance, nitrogen trichloride, NCl_3, is formed:

$$2NH_3 + 6Cl_2 \rightarrow 2NCl_3 + 6HCl$$

When chlorine is passed into aqueous ammonia, ammonium chloride and nitrogen are formed. If, however, sodium chlorate(I) (hypochlorite) is used instead of chlorine, chloramine is first formed:

$$NH_3 + OCl^- \rightarrow NH_2Cl + OH^-$$

Normally the chloramine immediately undergoes further reaction, giving off nitrogen:

$$2NH_2Cl + OCl^- + 2OH^- \rightarrow N_2\uparrow + 3Cl^- + 3H_2O$$

but in the presence of glue or gelatin the chloramine reacts with more ammonia to give *hydrazine*:

$$NH_2Cl + NH_3 + OH^- \rightarrow N_2H_4 + Cl^- + H_2O$$

It is thought that the function of the glue or gelatin is to combine with very slight traces of heavy metal cations, for example Cu^{2+}, which are known to catalyse the nitrogen-forming reaction.

Ammonia will reduce metallic oxides which are reduced by hydrogen [for example copper(II) oxide, CuO, lead(II) oxide, PbO], being itself oxidized to nitrogen:

$$2NH_3 + 3PbO \rightarrow 3Pb + N_2\uparrow + 3H_2O$$

Reactions with electropositive metals. Ammonia gas reacts with strongly electropositive metals to form the amide, for example

$$2Na + 2NH_3 \rightarrow 2NaNH_2 + H_2$$

This reaction also occurs slowly when sodium is dissolved in liquid ammonia; initially a deep blue solution is formed which then decomposes giving hydrogen and sodium amide.

Liquid ammonia. This can be prepared by compressing ammonia gas. It has a boiling point of 240 K and is an excellent solvent for many inorganic and organic substances as well as for the alkali metals. Liquid ammonia is slightly ionized:

$$2NH_3 \rightleftharpoons NH_4^+ + NH_2^-$$

$$(\text{cf. } 2H_2O \rightleftharpoons H_3O^+ + OH^-)$$

Liquid ammonia, like water, is only a poor conductor of electricity. Ammonium salts dissolved in water behave as acids giving the ion NH_4^+, whilst amides which give the ion NH_2^- behave as bases. Thus the reaction:

$$NH_4Cl + KNH_2 \rightarrow KCl\downarrow + 2NH_3$$
$$\text{acid} \qquad \text{base} \qquad \text{salt} \qquad \text{solvent}$$

is a neutralization in liquid ammonia (p. 82).

Solutions of alkali metals in liquid ammonia are used in organic chemistry as reducing agents. The deep blue solutions effectively contain solvated electrons (p. 240), for example

$$Na \rightarrow Na^+ + e^-$$
$$e^- + yNH_3 \rightarrow [e(NH_3)_y]^-$$

Ammonium salts. Ammonium salts can be prepared by the direct neutralization of acid by ammonia. The salts are similar to alkali metals salts and are composed of discrete ions. Most ammonium salts are soluble in water. Since ammonia is volatile and readily oxidizable the behaviour of ammonium salts to heat is particularly interesting.

If the acid of the salt is also volatile, as in the chloride and the carbonate, dissociation occurs causing the salt to sublime:

$$NH_4Cl \rightleftharpoons NH_3 + HCl$$

The extent of dissociation at a given temperature can be determined by measuring the density of the vapour. Since anhydrous sulphuric acid is less volatile than hydrogen chloride, ammonium sulphate does not readily sublime on heating; some ammonia is evolved to leave the hydrogensulphate:

$$(NH_4)_2SO_4 \rightarrow NH_4HSO_4 + NH_3\uparrow$$

If the acid of the ammonium salt is an oxidizing agent, then on heating the salt, mutual oxidation and reduction occurs. The oxidation products can be nitrogen or one of its oxides and the reactions can be explosive, for example:

$$(NH_4)_2Cr_2O_7 \rightarrow N_2 + 4H_2O + Cr_2O_3$$
$$NH_4NO_3 \rightarrow N_2O + 2H_2O$$

Uses of ammonia and ammonium compounds. Most of the ammonia produced is used in the manufacture of nitrogenous fertilizers such as ammonium sulphate. Other uses include nitric acid and synthetic fibre and plastic manufacture.

Detection of ammonia and ammonium salts. All ammonium salts evolve ammonia on heating with alkali. Ammonia may be detected by (a) its smell, (b) its action in turning red litmus blue and (c) the orange-brown colour produced with Nessler's reagent. This is a very sensitive test.

Ammonia may be estimated by dissolving the gas in a known volume of standard acid and then back-titrating the excess of acid. In a method widely used for the determination of basic nitrogen in organic substances (the Kjeldahl method), the nitrogenous material is converted into ammonium sulphate by heating with concentrated sulphuric acid. The ammonia is then driven off by the action of alkali and absorbed in standard acid.

Ammonia present in very small quantities in solution may be estimated by comparing the intensity of colour produced with Nessler's reagent (p. 382) with standard colours, using a simple form of colorimeter called a 'nesslerizer'.

Hydroxylamine, NH_2OH

In the hydroxylamine molecule, one hydrogen atom of ammonia is replaced by a hydroxyl group. Hydroxylamine is prepared by the electrolytic reduction of nitric acid, using a lead cathode:

$$HNO_3 + 6H^+ + 6e^- \rightarrow NH_2OH + 2H_2O$$

Sulphuric acid is added to the electrolyte and the hydroxylamine is formed as *hydroxylammonium sulphate*, $(NH_3OH)_2SO_4$ [cf. $(NH_4)_2SO_4$]. Addition of barium chloride then precipitates barium sulphate and hydroxylammonium chloride, $(NH_3OH)Cl$, is obtained.

Pure hydroxylamine is a crystalline solid of low melting point (306 K) but is rarely prepared because it decomposes above 288 K and is very susceptible to explosive decomposition. Hence the properties studied are those of the hydroxylammonium salts, i.e. containing the ion NH_3OH^+, analogous to NH_4^+. These are strong reducing agents, for example they reduce iron(III) to iron(II) salts in acid solution:

$$4Fe^{3+} + 2NH_3OH^+ \rightarrow 4Fe^{2+} + N_2O + 6H^+ + H_2O$$

Note that dinitrogen oxide is the other product. In alkaline solution, however, hydroxylamine oxidizes iron(II) hydroxide to iron(III) hydroxide and is itself reduced to ammonia. This is an example of the effect of pH change on oxidation reduction behaviour (p. 92):

$$NH_2OH + 2Fe(OH)_2 + H_2O \rightarrow 2Fe(OH)_3 + NH_3$$

Hydroxylamine condenses with the carbonyl group of an aldehyde or ketone to form an oxime:

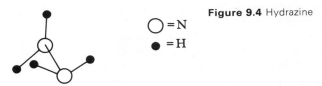

Hydrazine, N_2H_4

Hydrazine, like hydroxylamine, may be considered as a derivative of ammonia, one hydrogen atom being replaced by an —NH$_2$ group. The structure shown in *Figure 9.4* is such that the the lone pairs on one nitrogen are at maximum distance from those on the other.

○ = N
● = H

Figure 9.4 Hydrazine

Hydrazine is prepared, anhydrous and in good yield, by glow discharge electrolysis of liquid ammonia; a platinum cathode is immersed in the liquid and a platinum wire anode is mounted just above the surface (or it can be immersed if a high current density is used). The Raschig process — the reaction of ammonia with chloramine (p. 196) — gives lower yields and the hydrazine is not anhydrous.

Pure hydrazine is a colourless liquid, melting point 275 K, and boiling point 387 K. It is surprisingly stable for an endothermic compound ($\Delta H_f = +50.6 \text{ kJ mol}^{-1}$). Each nitrogen atom has a lone pair of electrons and either one or both nitrogen atoms are able to accept protons to give $N_2H_5^+$ and the less stable $N_2H_6^{2+}$. The base strength of hydrazine is, however, lower than that of ammonia. As might be expected, hydrazine is readily soluble in water from which the hydrate $N_2H_4.H_2O$ can be crystallized.

Hydrazine, unlike ammonia, will burn in air with evolution of much heat:

$$N_2H_4 + O_2 \rightarrow N_2 + 2H_2O$$

This reaction has been carefully studied with the aim of obtaining the enthalpy of combustion as electrical energy, and successful hydrazine–air fuel cells have been developed using potassium hydroxide as the electrolyte. The hydrazine fuel, however, has the disadvantage that it is expensive and poisonous.

In aqueous solution hydrazine can behave either as an oxidizing or reducing agent. Powerful reducing agents such as zinc reduce hydrazine to ammonia, while chlorine oxidizes it to give nitrogen:

$$N_2H_5^+ + Cl_2 \rightarrow N_2\uparrow + 5H^+ + 4Cl^-$$

Hydrazine and its alkylated derivatives are used as rocket fuels; in organic chemistry, substituted phenylhydrazines are important in the characterization of sugars and other compounds, for example aldehydes and ketones containing the carbonyl group $\sideset{}{}{\mathop{>}}C{=}O$.

Hydrogen azide (hydrazoic acid), HN_3

Hydrogen azide has no resemblance to either ammonia or hydrazine. It has a structure involving resonance between the forms

$$H{-}N{=}\overset{+}{N}{=}\bar{N} \qquad\qquad H{-}\bar{N}{-}\overset{+}{N}{\equiv}N$$

It is prepared by the oxidation of hydrazine in strongly acid solution; the oxidizing agent used is usually nitrous acid (i.e. sodium nitrite is added to the acid solution of hydrazine):

$$N_2H_5^+ + HNO_2 \rightarrow HN_3 + H_3O^+ + H_2O$$

Pure hydrogen azide is a colourless liquid, b.p. 310 K. It is very ready to detonate violently when subjected to even slight shock, and so is used in aqueous solution. It is a weak acid, reacting with alkali to give *azides*, which contain the ion N_3^-.

Hydrogen azide behaves as both an oxidizing and reducing agent in solution. Thus it will oxidize hydrochloric acid to chlorine, the main products being nitrogen and ammonium ions:

$$HN_3 + 3H^+ + 2Cl^- \rightarrow Cl_2\uparrow + NH_4^+ + N_2\uparrow$$

On the other hand, chloric(I) acid, for example, oxidizes hydrogen azide to nitrogen:

$$2HN_3 + OCl^- \rightarrow 3N_2\uparrow + Cl^- + H_2O$$

The *azides* are salts which resemble the chlorides in solubility behaviour; for example silver azide, AgN_3, is insoluble and sodium azide NaN_3, soluble in water. Sodium azide is prepared by passing dinitrogen oxide over molten sodamide:

$$2NaNH_2 + N_2O \rightarrow NaN_3 + NaOH + NH_3$$

All the azides are potentially dangerous, and liable to detonate on heating, but those of the alkali and alkaline earth metals can be heated with caution if pure; they then evolve pure nitrogen.

9.5.2   Hydrides of phosphorus

Phosphine

Phosphine can be prepared by the reaction of a strong alkali with white phosphorus; potassium, sodium and barium hydroxides may be used:

$$P_4 + 3KOH + 3H_2O \rightarrow 3KH_2PO_2 \qquad + \qquad PH_3\uparrow$$
$$ \text{potassium}$$
$$ \text{phosphinate}$$
$$ \text{(hypophosphite)}$$

This reaction gives an impure product containing hydrogen and another hydride, diphosphane, P_2H_4.

Pure phosphine can be prepared by the reduction of a solution of phosphorus trichloride in dry ether with lithium aluminium hydride:

$$4PCl_3 + 3LiAlH_4 \rightarrow 4PH_3\uparrow + 3LiCl + 3AlCl_3$$

The reaction of potassium hydroxide solution with phosphonium iodide also gives pure phosphine:

$$PH_4I + KOH \rightarrow KI + H_2O + PH_3\uparrow$$

Properties. Phosphine is a colourless gas at room temperature, boiling point 183 K, with an unpleasant odour; it is extremely poisonous. Like ammonia, phosphine has an essentially tetrahedral structure with one position occupied by a lone pair of electrons. Phosphorus, however, is a larger atom than nitrogen and the lone pair of electrons on the phosphorus are much less 'concentrated' in space. Thus phosphine has a very much smaller dipole moment than ammonia. Hence phosphine is not associated (like ammonia) in the liquid state (*see* data in *Table 9.2*) and it is only sparingly soluble in water.

Towards a simple Lewis base, for example the proton, phosphine is a poorer electron donor than ammonia, the larger phosphorus atom being less able to form a stable covalent bond with the acceptor atom or molecule. Phosphine is, therefore, a much weaker Lowry–Brønsted base than ammonia and there is no series of phosphonium salts corresponding to the ammonium salts; but phosphonium halides, PH_4X (X = Cl, Br, I) can be prepared by the direct combination of phosphine with the appropriate hydrogen halide. These compounds are much more easily dissociated than ammonium halides, the most stable being the iodide, but even this dissociates at 333 K:

$$PH_4I \rightleftharpoons PH_3 + HI$$

The other halides dissociate at lower temperatures and, if put into water, all are decomposed, the proton transferring to water which is a better electron pair donor:

$$PH_4X + H_2O \rightarrow PH_3 + H_3O^+ + X^-$$

Phosphine has a much lower thermal stability than ammonia and sparking decomposes it to red phosphorus and hydrogen, 2 volumes of phosphine giving 3 volumes of hydrogen. Not unexpectedly, therefore, phosphine is a more powerful reducing agent than ammonia. If passed into a solution of a salt of copper, silver or gold the metal phosphide is obtained but this decomposes to give the metal on standing or more quickly on boiling. Pure phosphine ignites in air at 423 K and burns to phosphoric(V) acid:

$$PH_3 + 2O_2 \rightarrow H_3PO_4$$

Replacement of the hydrogen atoms by methyl groups to give *trimethylphosphine* $(CH_3)_3P$, makes it a stronger base (as $[(CH_3)_3PH]OH$), and improves the donor power of the phosphorus as it does with nitrogen.

Towards some transition metal atoms or ions, trimethylphosphine is a stronger ligand than ammonia, i.e. forms more stable complexes. This is because the transition metal atom or ion can 'back-donate' electrons from its d orbitals into the vacant $3d$ oribtals of the phosphorus — this is not possible with ammonia which has no $2d$ orbitals.

Diphosphane, P_2H_4

This can be extracted from impure phosphine prepared by the action of sodium hydroxide on phosphorus. Unlike hydrazine, it has no basic properties. It is a powerful reducing agent and burns spontaneously in air, this reaction explaining why impure phosphine containing traces of diphosphane ignites spontaneously in air.

9.5.3   Hydrides of arsenic and antimony

Arsine, AsH_3, and *stibine*, SbH_3, are formed when arsenic and antimony compounds respectively are reduced by a process in which hydrogen is evolved. They are colourless, unpleasant smelling, poisonous gases. Stibine is less stable than arsine but both decompose readily on heating to form the element and hydrogen. Both arsine and stibine are covalent compounds and they have little power to donate electrons; although the arsonium ion, AsH_4^+, is known, this forms no stable compounds. The donor ability of arsine is enhanced when the hydrogen atoms are replaced by methyl groups (cf. phosphine, p. 201).

Diarsane, As_2H_4

Arsenic (but not antimony) forms a second hydride. This is extremely unstable, decomposing at very low temperatures. Replacement of the hydrogen atoms by methyl groups gives the more stable substance tetramethyldiarsane, *cacodyl*, $(CH_3)_2As$—$As(CH_3)_2$, a truly foul-smelling liquid.

Bismuthine

Very small quantities of bismuthine are obtained when a bismuth–magnesium alloy, Bi_2Mg_3, is dissolved in hydrochloric acid. As would be expected, it is extremely unstable, decomposing at room temperature to bismuth and hydrogen. Alkyl and aryl derivatives, for example trimethylbismuthine, $Bi(CH_3)_3$, are more stable.

9.6   Oxides of Group V elements

The principal oxides formed by Group V elements and their formal oxidation states are given in *Table 9.3*. Nitrogen is unusual in forming so many oxides. The acidity of the Group V oxides falls from phosphorus, whose oxides are acidic, through arsenic and antimony whose oxides are amphoteric, to the basic oxide bismuth. This change is in accordance with the change from the non-metallic element, phosphorus, to the essentially metallic element, bismuth. The $+5$ oxides are found, in each case, to be more acidic than the corresponding $+3$ oxides.

Table 9.3 Oxides of Group V elements

Element	N	P	As	Sb	Bi
Oxidation state					
+1	N_2O				
+2	NO				
+3	N_2O_3	P_4O_6	As_4O_6	Sb_4O_6	Bi_2O_3
+4	NO_2, N_2O_4				
+5	N_2O_5	P_4O_{10}	As_2O_5	Sb_2O_5	

9.6.1 Oxides of nitrogen

Dinotrogen oxide (nitrous oxide), N_2O

This can be prepared by the controlled reduction of a nitrite [nitrate(III)] or nitrate. Cautious heating of ammonium nitrate gives dinitrogen oxide by an 'internal' oxidation–reduction process:

$$NH_4NO_3 \rightarrow N_2O\uparrow + 2H_2O$$

Too rapid heating produces explosive decomposition. The reaction between hydroxylammonium chloride, NH_3OH^+, Cl^-, and sodium nitrite gives pure dinitrogen oxide:

$$NH_3OH^+ + NO_2^- \rightarrow N_2O\uparrow + 2H_2O$$

Dinitrogen oxide is a colourless gas; the molecule has the *geometric* structure N—N—O, and is a resonance hybrid of the two forms:

$$\overset{-}{N}=\overset{+}{N}=O \qquad\qquad N\equiv\overset{+}{N}-\overset{-}{O}$$

i.e. $\overset{x\ x}{\underset{x\ x}{\overset{x}{N}}}\overset{\bullet}{\underset{\bullet}{N}}\overset{x\ \bullet}{\underset{\bullet}{O}}\bullet$ and $\bullet\overset{\bullet}{\underset{\bullet}{N}}\overset{\bullet}{\underset{x}{N}}\overset{x\ \bullet\bullet}{\underset{\bullet\bullet}{O}}\bullet$

the molecule being linear; in this respect it resembles the isoelectronic molecule of carbon dioxide, $O=C=O$. There is also a resemblance in physical properties, but the dinitrogen oxide molecule possesses a small dipole moment, unlike that of carbon dioxide.

Table 9.3 Comparison of dinitrogen oxide with oxygen

Dinitrogen oxide	Oxygen
Slightly soluble in water (1 vol. in 1 vol. at 280 K)	Almost insoluble
No reaction with nitrogen monoxide	Brown fumes of nitrogen dioxide
Phosphorus burns leaving an equal volume of gas (nitrogen)	No gas left
Diamagnetic	Paramagnetic
Molecular mass 44	Molecular mass 32

It is slightly soluble in water, giving a neutral solution. It is chemically unreactive and is not easily oxidized or reduced and at room temperature it does not react with hydrogen, halogens, ozone (trioxygen) or alkali metals. However, it decomposes into its elements on heating, the decomposition being exothermic:

$$N_2O \rightarrow N_2 + \tfrac{1}{2}O_2 \qquad \Delta H^{\ominus} = -90.4 \text{ kJ mol}^{-1}$$

Once this reaction has been initiated, it supports the combustion of many substances since they can burn in the liberated oxygen. In this respect, it is hardly distinguishable from oxygen itself; but other properties serve to distinguish the two gases (*see Table 9.3*), in particular their magnetism.

Magnetic properties

A few substances such as iron and cobalt–nickel alloys are *ferromagnetic* i.e. are strongly attracted to the poles of a magnet. Most other substances are *diamagnetic*, i.e. are very weakly repelled from the field of a magnet. Some ions and molecules are, however, *paramagnetic*, i.e. are very weakly attracted by a magnet. Thus if we hang a tube containing liquid oxygen (i.e. highly 'concentrated' oxygen) just above the poles of a powerful electromagnet, the tube is pulled towards the magnet as shown in *Figure* 9.5.

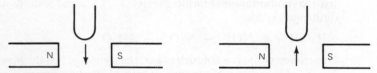

Figure 9.5 Paramagnetism (left) and diamagnetism (right)

Paramagnetism implies the presence of single, unpaired, electrons. Hence nitrogen monoxide is paramagnetic, and so is any other molecule or ion containing unpaired electrons. If the total number of electrons in an ion or molecule is odd, then it must be paramagnetic; but some molecules (e.g. O_2) and ions have an even number of electrons and yet are paramagnetic because some of them are unpaired.

Nitrogen monoxide (nitric oxide), NO

Nitrogen monoxide is the most stable of all the oxides of nitrogen. It can be prepared in small amounts by direct combination of the elements at high temperature or in the presence of an electric discharge (p. 190). It can be prepared in the laboratory by the reduction of nitric acid and solutions of nitrates and nitrites.

The reaction between copper and nitric acid, 1 part concentrated acid and 1 part water, gives impure nitrogen monoxide:

$$3Cu + 8HNO_3 \rightarrow 3Cu(NO_3)_2 + 4H_2O + 2NO\uparrow$$

The reduction of a nitrate, for example potassium nitrate, by iron(II) sulphate in the presence of concentrated sulphuric acid gives reasonably pure nitrogen monoxide. The mixture is warmed and at this temperature the nitrogen monoxide produced does not combine with unchanged iron(II) sulphate (*see* p. 205).

Industrially nitrogen monoxide is prepared by the catalytic oxidation of ammonia as an intermediate in the manufacture of nitric acid (p. 212). The molecule of nitrogen monoxide contains an odd number of electrons and can be represented as

$$\overset{x\,\,x}{\underset{x}{N}}\overset{\cdot}{\underset{\cdot}{:}}\overset{\cdot\,\cdot}{\underset{\cdot}{O}}\overset{\cdot}{:}$$

This shows the unpaired electron on the nitrogen atom; it is in fact 'shared' over the whole molecule. Molecules such as nitrogen monoxide which contain unpaired electrons are referred to as *odd electron molecules*. The presence of the odd electron can be detected by magnetic experiments when such substances are found to be paramagnetic, and they are attracted into a magnetic field (*see* note on p. 204). Molecules and ions containing unpaired electrons are very weakly attracted by a magnetic field. In some cases the total number of electrons may be even and yet the molecule may still be paramagnetic; this is because some of the electrons are unpaired; for example oxygen is paramagnetic. The presence of the unpaired electron explains why, chemically, nitrogen monoxide is more reactive than dinitrogen oxide. However, the properties of nitrogen monoxide differ significantly from other odd electron molecules. For example, the gaseous form is colourless although both the liquid and solid are blue. At room temperature it shows little tendency to dimerize, a process which would result in the pairing of the odd electron. However, loss of this odd electron gives the *nitrosonium* or *nitrosyl* ion, NO^+. A number of salts containing this ion are known, for example nitrosyl tetrafluoroborate, $(NO)^+(BF_4)^-$, and nitrosyl hydrogensulphate, $(NO)^+(HSO_4)^-$. (This last compound was formed in the lead chamber process for sulphuric acid manufacture.)

Nitrogen monoxide does show some ability to gain an electron and when passed into a solution of sodium in liquid ammonia, the unstable compound sodium dioxodinitrate(I) (hyponitrite). Na_2NO_2 [i.e. $Na_2^{2+}(NO^-)_2$] is formed. In addition to these reactions covalent bonds are formed by electron sharing and electron donation. Nitrogen monoxide, when it is absorbed by cold aqueous iron(II) sulphate, forms the brown ion $[Fe(NO)(H_2O)_5]^{2+}$ in which one ligand molecule of water has been replaced by nitrogen monoxide, the latter donating an electron pair.

Electrons are shared when nitrogen monoxide combines with oxygen, a spontaneous reaction, to give nitrogen dioxide

$$2NO + O_2 \rightarrow 2NO_2$$

(Although this reaction is exothermic, the gas does not burn in air or oxygen.)

A similar reaction occurs with chlorine, to give nitrosyl chloride

$$2NO + Cl_2 \rightarrow 2NOCl$$

As might be expected for a $+2$ oxide, nitrogen monoxide can act as both an oxidizing and reducing agent. Oxygen oxidizes it to NO_2 whilst more powerful oxidizing agents such as acidified potassium manganate(VII) solution oxidize it to nitric acid.

Reduction products vary depending on the reducing agent, for example dinitrogen oxide is obtained with sulphurous acid, nitrogen is obtained when the gas is passed over heated metals (e.g. copper and iron) and ammonia is produced when the gas reacts with aqueous chromium(II) salts.

Nitrogen dioxide, NO_2, and dinitrogen tetroxide, N_2O_4

The structure of nitrogen dioxide contains an unpaired (odd) electron and the molecule is consequently paramagnetic. The odd electron is not localized on any atom and the structure can be best represented as a resonance hybrid of the structures:

Both N—O bonds are of equal length.

Unlike nitrogen monoxide, nitrogen dioxide has properties more typical of an odd electron molecule. It is a coloured (brown), reactive gas which dimerizes to the diamagnetic colourless gas dinitrogen tetroxide, N_2O_4, in which the odd electron is paired. The structure of dinitrogen tetroxide can be represented as a resonance hybrid of:

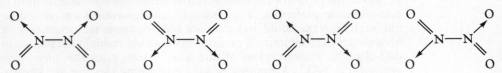

All the N—O bonds are of equal length.

The two oxides, NO_2 and N_2O_4, exist in equilibrium, the position of which depends very greatly on temperature:

$$N_2O_4(g) \rightleftharpoons 2NO_2(g) \qquad \Delta H = +57.2 \text{ kJ mol}^{-1}$$

Below 262 K the solid dimer N_2O_4 exists as a colourless solid. At 262 K colourless liquid N_2O_4 is produced but as the temperature is increased dissociation begins and the liquid becomes a dilute solution of brown NO_2 in liquid N_2O_4 and is pale brown in colour. The liquid boils at 294 K. As the temperature is further increased the gas gradually darkens in colour as more N_2O_4 dissociates, this being complete at 423 K when the gas is almost black in colour. Above 423 K further dissociation occurs into nitrogen monoxide and oxygen, both of which are colourless and hence the colour of the gas slowly diminishes.

N_2O_4	$\rightleftharpoons$	N_2O_4	$\rightleftharpoons$	$2NO_2$	$\rightleftharpoons$	$2NO + O_2$
(m.p. 262 K) colourless solid		(b.p. 294 K) pale yellow liquid		(100% at 423 K) dark brown gas		(100% at 870 K) colourless gases

Preparation. Nitrogen dioxide is commonly prepared by heating the nitrate of a heavy metal, usually that of lead(II). Lead is selected as it is the only common nitrate free from water of crystallization; evolved water would react with nitrogen dioxide.

$$2Pb(NO_3)_2 \rightarrow 2PbO + 4NO_2\uparrow + O_2\uparrow$$

If the mixture of oxygen and nitrogen dioxide is passed through a **U** tube in a freezing mixture the dioxide condenses mainly as N_2O_4 and the oxygen passes on.

Chemical properties. Nitrogen dioxide can be both oxidized and reduced. It is reduced by phosphorus, charcoal and sulphur which burn in it to form their oxides and nitrogen. Heated metals such as iron and copper also reduce it to nitrogen but other reducing agents such as hydrogen sulphide and aqueous iodide give nitrogen monoxide:

$$NO_2 + H_2S \rightarrow NO + H_2O + S\downarrow$$
$$NO_2 + 2I^- + H_2O \rightarrow NO + I_2 + 2OH^-$$

Strong oxidizing agents such as acidified potassium manganate(VII) oxidize NO_2 to the nitrate ion:

$$2MnO_4^- + 10NO_2 + 2H_2O \rightarrow 2Mn^{2+} + 4H^+ + 10NO_3^-$$

Nitrogen dioxide dissolves in water to give a mixture of nitrous and nitric acids:

$$2NO_2 + H_2O \rightarrow HNO_2 + HNO_3$$

The nitrous acid decomposes rapidly at room temperature, thus:

$$3HNO_2 \rightarrow HNO_3 + 2NO + H_2O$$

giving an overall reaction:

$$H_2O + 3NO_2 \rightarrow 2HNO_3 + NO\uparrow$$

If this reaction takes place in air, the evolved nitrogen monoxide is oxidized to the dioxide and this dissolves; hence virtually complete conversion of nitrogen dioxide into nitric acid can occur (*see* nitric acid, p. 211). With alkalis, a mixture of nitrite and nitrate is formed:

$$2OH^- + 2NO_2 \rightarrow NO_3^- + NO_2^- + H_2O$$

Dinitrogen tetroxide, N_2O_4, as a liquid, has some power as a solvent, and appears to dissociate slightly to give nitrosyl nitrate, thus:

$$N_2O_4 \rightleftharpoons NO^+ + NO_3^-$$

If metallic zinc is dissolved in this liquid, the following reaction occurs:

$$Zn + 2N_2O_4 \rightarrow Zn(NO_3)_2 + 2NO\uparrow$$
$$\text{i.e.}\quad Zn + 2NO^+ \rightarrow Zn^{2+} + 2NO\uparrow$$
$$(\text{cf.}\quad Zn + 2H^+ \rightarrow Zn^{2+} + H_2\uparrow)$$

Hence dinitrogen tetroxide (sometimes mixed with an organic solvent) can be used to prepare *anhydrous* metal nitrates (many heavy metal nitrates are hydrated when prepared in aqueous solution, and they cannot be dehydrated without decomposition).

Dinitrogen trioxide, N_2O_3

Dinitrogen trioxide, the anhydride of nitrous acid, is very unstable. At low temperature it dissociates thus:

$$2N_2O_3 \rightleftharpoons 2NO + N_2O_4$$

Dinitrogen pentoxide, N_2O_5

Dinitrogen pentoxide is the anhydride of nitric acid and is prepared by removing the water from pure nitric acid by means of phosphorus(V) oxide. It is a crystalline solid having the ionic structure of $(NO_2)^+(NO_3)^-$, *nitronium nitrate* (the nitronium ion is mentioned later). It decomposes above 273 K, thus:

$$2N_2O_5 \rightarrow 2N_2O_4 + O_2$$

9.6.2 Oxides of phosphorus

Phosphorus forms a number of oxides, the best established being phosphorus(III) oxide, P_4O_6, and phosphorus(V) oxide, P_4O_{10}. The $+5$ oxide is the more stable and the $+3$ oxide is easily oxidized.

Phosphorus(III) *oxide,* P_4O_6

Phosphorus(III) oxide is prepared by passing a slow (i.e. limited) stream of air over burning white phosphorus. A mixture of the two oxides P_4O_6 and P_4O_{10} is thereby formed; phosphorus(V) oxide can be condensed out of the emerging gas stream as a solid by passing through a U tube heated in a water bath to about 330 K; the more volatile phosphorus(III) oxide passes on and can be condensed in a second U trap surrounded by ice.

Phosphorus(III) oxide dissolves in several organic solvents, for example benzene or carbon disulphide; the relative molecular mass in these solvents corresponds to the formula P_4O_6, as does the density of the vapour, and the structure is as shown in *Figure 9.6*.

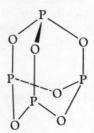

Figure 9.6 Structure of phosphorus(III) oxide

Phosphorus(III) oxide reacts slowly with oxygen at ordinary temperatures to give the pentoxide, P_4O_{10}. The reaction is rapid if the oxide is heated in air. It is oxidized vigorously by chlorine and bromine which form the oxidehalides, POX_3.

Phosphorus(III) oxide dissolves slowly in cold water to yield phosphonic acid, H_3PO_3 (phosphorous acid):

$$P_4O_6 + 6H_2O \rightarrow 4H_3PO_3$$

With hot water a vigorous but complex reaction occurs, the products including phosphine and phosphoric(V) acid. This disproportionation reaction can be approximately represented as:

$$P_4O_6 + 6H_2O \rightarrow PH_3 + 3H_3PO_4$$

Phosphorus(V) *oxide,* P_4O_{10}

This oxide was originally given the formula P_2O_5 and called 'phosphorus pentoxide'; but the vapour density and structure indicate the formula P_4O_{10}. It is prepared by burning phosphorus in a plentiful supply of air or oxygen:

$$P_4 + 5O_2 \rightarrow P_4O_{10}$$

It is a white, deliquescent solid, very powdery, which exhibits polymorphism; on heating, several different crystalline forms appear over definite ranges of temperature — ultimately, the P_4O_{10} unit in the crystal disappears and a polymerized glass is obtained, which melts to a clear liquid.

The most important property of phosphorus(V) oxide is its great tendency to react with water, either free or combined. It reacts with ordinary water with great vigour, and much heat is evolved; trioxophosphoric(V) acid is formed, but the local heating may convert some of this to tetraoxophosphoric(V) acid:

$$P_4O_{10} + 2H_2O \rightarrow 4HPO_3$$
$$HPO_3 + H_2O \rightarrow H_3PO_4$$

Phosphorus(V) oxide will remove water from acids to give the acid anhydride. For example, if nitric acid is distilled with it, dinitrogen pentoxide is formed:

$$P_4O_{10} + 4HNO_3 \rightarrow 2N_2O_5 + 4HPO_3$$

Phosphorus(V) oxide is an extremely effective desiccating agent, reducing the vapour pressure of water over it to a negligibly small value. However, in the presence of water vapour the fine powder soon becomes covered with a layer of glassy trioxophosphoric acid, and this reduces the rate at which drying can occur. For this reason, gases are better dried by passing them through loosely-packed 'pentoxide', rather than merely over the surface.

9.6.3   Oxides of arsenic

Arsenic forms two important oxides, As_4O_6 and As_4O_{10}.

Arsenic(III) *oxide,* As_4O_6

This is formed when arsenic burns in air (cf. phosphorus which gives P_4O_{10}). It can exist in two crystalline modifications; the stable one at room temperature, which also occurs naturally as *arsenolite*, has an octahedral form. Solid arsenic(III) oxide is easily reduced, for example by heating with charcoal, whereupon arsenic deposits as a black shiny solid on the cooler parts of the tube.

Arsenic(III) oxide is slightly soluble in water, giving a solution with a sweetish taste — but as little as 0.1 g can be a fatal dose! [The antidote is freshly-precipitated iron(III) hydroxide.] The solution has an acid reaction to litmus, owing to the formation of arsenic(III) acid:

$$As_4O_6 + 6H_2O \rightleftharpoons 4H_3AsO_3$$

Arsenic(III) acid is an extremely weak acid; in fact, the oxide is amphoteric, since the following equilibria occur:

$H_3AsO_3 \rightleftharpoons AsO_3^{3-} + 3H^+$

H_3AsO_3 [or $As(OH)_3$] $\rightleftharpoons$ $[As^{3+}] + 3OH^-$ (*see* p. 223)

Hence arsenic(III) oxide dissolves readily in alkalis to give *arsenates*(III), for example

$As_4O_6 + 6CO_3^{2-} \rightarrow 4AsO_3^{3-} + 6CO_2\uparrow$

but in strong acid solution tripositive arsenic ions may be formed. This reaction indicates very clearly the increased electropositive character of arsenic.

In aqueous solution arsenic(III) oxide is a reducing agent being oxidized to arsenate(V) by halogens, chlorate(I), nitric acid and even iron(III) chloride.

Arsenic(V) oxide, As_4O_{10}

Unlike phosphorus pentoxide, this oxide cannot be made directly. *Arsenic*(V) *acid*, H_3AsO_4 (strictly, tetraoxoarsenic acid), is first prepared by oxidizing arsenic(III) oxide with concentrated nitric acid or some other strong oxidizing agent:

$2H_3AsO_3 + 2HNO_3 \rightarrow 2H_3AsO_4 + NO\uparrow + NO_2\uparrow + H_2O$

When the solution is concentrated, a solid of formula $As_4O_{10}.8H_2O$ [which may be composed of hydrated arsenic(V) acid] is obtained, and this, on fairly prolonged heating to 800 K, loses water and leaves arsenic(V) oxide. No compound corresponding to the other acids of phosphorus is formed, but salts are known.

Arsenic(V) oxide is a white deliquescent solid, which liberates oxygen only on very strong heating, leaving arsenic(III) oxide:

$As_4O_{10} \rightarrow As_4O_6 + 2O_2$

It dissolves in water to give arsenic(V) acid, and in alkalis to form *arsenates*(V).

9.6.4   Oxides of antimony

Antimony forms both a +3 and a +5 oxide. The +3 oxide can be prepared by the direct combination of the elements or by the action of moderately concentrated nitric acid on antimony. It is an amphoteric oxide dissolving in alkalis to give antimonates(III) (for example sodium 'antimonite', $NaSbO_2$), and in some acids to form salts, for example with concentrated hydrochloric acid the trichloride, $SbCl_3$, is formed.

Antimony(V) oxide can be prepared by treating antimony with concentrated nitric acid. It is an oxidizing agent and when gently heated loses oxygen to form the trioxide. (The change in oxidation state stability shown by antimony should be noted since it corresponds to increasing metallic character.)

Unlike the amphoteric +3 oxide, the +5 oxide is acidic and dissolves only in alkalis to give hydroxoantimonates which contain the ion $[Sb(OH)_6]^-$. A third oxide, Sb_2O_4, is known but contains both antimony(III) and antimony(V), $Sb^{III}(Sb^VO_4)$, cf. Pb_3O_4.

9.6.5   Oxides of bismuth

Bismuth forms both $+3$ and $+5$ oxides. The $+3$ oxide, unlike the corresponding oxides of the other Group V elements, is insoluble in alkalis, and dissolves only in acids (when bismuth salts are formed), a clear indication of the more metallic nature of bismuth.

Bismuth(V) oxide is not easy to prepare; bismuth(III) oxide (or better a suspension of the hydroxide) must be oxidized with a strong oxidizing agent such as the peroxodisulphate ion. When this is carried out, the *bismuthate* ion, $[Bi^V(OH)_6]^-$, is formed. On evaporation, the sodium salt, for example, has the formula $NaBiO_3$. Addition of acid to a solution of a bismuthate precipitates bismuth(V) oxide, Bi_2O_5, but this loses oxygen rapidly and forms the trioxide. The bismuthate ion is an extremely strong oxidizing agent, for example the manganese(II) ion Mn^{2+} is oxidized to manganate(VII) MnO_4^-.

9.7   Oxoacids and their salts

9.7.1   Nitrogen

Nitric(V) *acid*, HNO_3

Nitric acid is prepared in the laboratory by distilling equal masses of potassium nitrate and concentrated sulphuric acid using an air condenser, the stem of which dips into a flask cooled by tap water. The reaction is:

$$H_2SO_4 + KNO_3 \rightarrow KHSO_4 + HNO_3$$

The temperature is kept as low as possible to avoid decomposition of the nitric acid to (brown) nitrogen dioxide. The nitric acid condenses out as a fuming liquid; it may be purified by redistillation with concentrated sulphuric acid. If the nitric acid is condensed at room temperature, it gives off dinitrogen pentoxide, N_2O_5 (which fumes with the atmospheric moisture), and so becomes diluted somewhat. Only if it is frozen out at 231 K (the melting point) does it form pure nitric acid, HNO_3. 'Concentrated' nitric acid contains about 67 per cent of the pure acid — this is the constant boiling mixture formed by distilling a solution of any concentration. Hence concentrated nitric acid is not pure nitric acid.

On the large scale, nitric acid is now made in large quantities by the catalytic oxidation of ammonia, employing the reaction:

$$4NH_3 + 5O_2 \rightarrow 4NO + 6H_2O \qquad \Delta H = -120 \text{ kJ mol}^{-1}$$

The process is as follows: ammonia gas (made by the Haber process) is liquefied under pressure, to freeze out any water, and the anhydrous gas is then passed together with dust-free air through a converter (*Figure 9.7*). This contains a gauze of platinum, or platinum–rhodium, heated at first electrically, then maintained at red heat by the exothermic reaction which takes place on it. The air–ammonia mixture must only remain in contact with the catalyst for a fraction of a second, otherwise the nitrogen monoxide decomposes to give nitrogen and oxygen. From this converter, the nitrogen monoxide is mixed with more air, to convert it into nitrogen dioxide. This reaction is also exothermic and the heat from it may be used to pre-heat the air stream entering the converter.

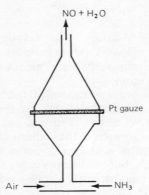

Figure 9.7 Catalytic oxidation of ammonia

The nitrogen dioxide is then passed up a water-cooled steel tower, fitted with baffles down which water flows. Here the nitrogen dioxide dissolves to give nitric acid and nitrogen monoxide; air is also passed up the tower to oxidize the latter to give more nitrogen dioxide, which is absorbed in turn, so that ultimately almost complete conversion of the nitrogen oxides to nitric acid is complete; the acid is collected, at a concentration of 50–65 per cent, at the base of the tower.

Properties. Pure nitric acid is a colourless liquid, density 1.52 g cm^{-3}, dissociating slightly above its melting point into dinitrogen pentoxide and water, as already mentioned: on boiling, more oxides of nitrogen are formed and the liquid obtained is then the constant boiling-point acid, density 1.41 g cm^{-3}; hence this latter acid ('concentrated nitric acid') is usually yellow owing to dissolved oxides formed during distillation. The colour deepens on exposure to daylight because nitrogen dioxide is formed in solution by the photochemical reaction:

$$4HNO_3 \xrightarrow{\text{light}} 4NO_2 + 2H_2O + O_2$$

A similar decomposition occurs if nitric acid is subject to a temperature above its boiling point.

The chemical properties of nitric acid require us to consider the structure first. The vapour of pure nitric acid (i.e. anhydrous) is probably composed of molecules of 'hydrogen nitrate', which structurally is a resonance hybrid of such forms as:

$$H-O-N\overset{\displaystyle O}{\underset{\displaystyle O}{}} \qquad\qquad H-O-N\overset{\displaystyle O}{\underset{\displaystyle O}{}}$$

In liquid nitric acid, hydrogen bonding gives a loose structure similar to that of hydrogencarbonate ions. However, although pure nitric acid does not attack metals readily and does not evolve carbon dioxide from a carbonate, it is a conducting liquid, and undergoes autoionization thus:

$$2HNO_3 \rightleftharpoons H_2NO_3^+ + NO_3^-$$

and

$$H_2NO_3^+ + HNO_3 \rightleftharpoons NO_2^+ + H_3O^+ + NO_3^-$$

The second equilibrium is the more important, giving rise to the *nitronium ion*, NO_2^+, already mentioned as a product of the dissociation of dinitrogen tetroxide. Several nitronium salts have been identified, for example nitronium chlorate(VII), $(NO_2)^+(ClO_4)^-$. If pure nitric acid is dissolved in concentrated sulphuric acid, the freezing point of the latter is depressed to an extent suggesting the formation of four ions, thus:

$$HNO_3 + 2H_2SO_4 \rightleftharpoons NO_2^+ + H_3O^+ + 2HSO_4^-$$

It is the nitronium ion which is responsible for nitrating actions in organic chemistry which are carried out in a mixture of nitric and sulphuric acids. When nitric acid is dissolved in water, its behaviour is that of a strong acid, i.e.

$$HNO_3 + H_2O \rightleftharpoons H_3O^+ + NO_3^-$$

because of the proton affinity of water. The majority of the reactions of nitric acid are oxidations due to the nitrate ion in the presence of hydrogen ions — and the corresponding reduction product (from the nitrate ion) depends upon the hydrogen ion concentration and upon the nature of the substance oxidized; it may be nitrogen dioxide, nitrogen monoxide, dinitrogen oxide, nitrogen, hydroxylamine (NH_2OH) or ammonia (as ammonium ion in acid solution). The following are some typical examples:

Non-metals. These are often oxidized to the corresponding oxoacid, and nitrogen monoxide is formed. For example, sulphur gives sulphuric acid with cold concentrated nitric acid:

$$S + 2HNO_3 \rightarrow H_2SO_4 + 2NO$$

Iodine gives iodic(V) acid with hot concentrated acid:

$$3I_2 + 10HNO_3 \rightarrow 6HIO_3 + 10NO + 2H_2O$$

Fluorine, however, gives the substance 'fluorine nitrate', $FONO_2$:

$$HNO_3 + F_2 \rightarrow FONO_2 + HF$$

Violet phosphorus is oxidized to phosphoric(V) acid.

Metals. Nitric acid reacts with all common metals except gold and platinum, but some are rendered passive by the concentrated acid, for example aluminium, iron, cobalt, nickel and chromium. With the very weakly electropositive metals such as arsenic, antimony and tin, the oxide of the metal in its higher oxidation state is obtained; for example antimony yields the oxide antimony(V) oxide, Sb_2O_5 (in hydrated form). With more electropositive metals the nitrate of the metal is always formed, and the other products vary greatly. Metals which do not liberate hydrogen from dilute acids form nitrogen monoxide or nitrogen dioxide, according to conditions. For example, copper in cold nitric acid (1:1) reacts thus:

$$3Cu + 8HNO_3 \rightarrow 3Cu(NO_3)_2 + 2NO\uparrow + 4H_2O$$

In concentrated nitric acid (when warmed) the reaction is:

$$Cu + 4HNO_3 \rightarrow Cu(NO_3)_2 + 2NO_2 + 2H_2O$$

Metals which do liberate hydrogen from dilute acids, for example zinc, magnesium, can react with nitric acid to give dinitrogen oxide, for example:

$$4Zn + 10HNO_3 \rightarrow 4Zn(NO_3)_2 + N_2O + 5H_2O$$

and if the hydrogen ion content of the nitric acid is further increased, by adding dilute sulphuric acid, hydroxylamine or ammonia is formed.

With very dilute nitric acid and magnesium, some hydrogen is evolved.

With a nitrate in *alkaline* solution, ammonia is evolved quantitatively by Devarda's alloy (Al, 45 per cent; Cu, 50 per cent; and Zn, 5 per cent). This reaction can be used to estimate nitrate in absence of ammonium ions (*see* p. 215):

$$NO_3^- + 4Zn + 15OH^- + 6H_2O \rightarrow NH_3\uparrow + 4Zn(OH)_6^{2-}$$

Cations. Some of these are oxidized to a higher state by nitric acid. For example, iron(II) (in presence of sulphuric acid) is quantitatively oxidized to iron(III):

$$3Fe^{2+} + NO_3^- + 4H^+ \rightarrow 3Fe^{3+} + NO\uparrow + 2H_2O$$

Tin(II) chloride, in presence of hydrochloric acid, is oxidized to tin(IV) chloride, the nitrate ion in this case being reduced to hydroxylamine and ammonia.

The noble metals such as gold and platinum, although almost insoluble in nitric acid, are very ready to form chloro-complexes; for example gold gives the $[AuCl_4]^-$ ion very readily. Hence they can be dissolved by *aqua regia*, a mixture of 3 volumes of concentrated hydrochloric acid and 1 volume of concentrated nitric acid. The latter oxidizes the gold to the auric [gold(III)] state (Au^{3+}), which then appears as the ion $[AuCl_4]^-$ (p. 375).

Nitrates

Hydrated nitrates, and anhydrous nitrates of very electropositive metals (for example Na, K), contain the ion NO_3^- which has the structure containing resonance hybrids:

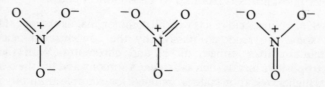

with the N—O distances identical. In other anhydrous metal nitrates, prepared as on p. 207, the nitrate groups may be bonded covalently to the metal, thus: M—ONO$_2$ [for example Cu(NO$_3$)$_2$, p. 360].

Nitrates are prepared by the action of nitric acid on a metal or its oxide, hydroxide or carbonate. All inorganic nitrates are soluble in water. On heating, the nitrates of the alkali metals yield oxygen and the nitrite:

$$2KNO_3 \rightarrow 2KNO_2 + O_2\uparrow$$

Ammonium nitrate gives dinitrogen oxide and steam:

$$NH_4NO_3 \rightarrow 2H_2O + N_2O\uparrow$$

The nitrates of other metals give nitrogen dioxide, oxygen and the metal oxide, unless the latter is unstable to heat, in which case the metal and oxygen are formed (for example from nitrates of silver and mercury):

$$2Cu(NO_3)_2 \rightarrow 2CuO + 4NO_2 + O_2$$
$$2AgNO_3 \rightarrow 2Ag + 2NO_2 + O_2$$

Nitrates are detected by:
1 The action of heat on the solid (above).
2 By the brown ring test with iron(II) sulphate and cold concentrated sulphuric acid.
3 By their oxidizing action; heating with copper and concentrated sulphuric acid yields brown fumes of nitrogen dioxide.
4 By the evolution of ammonia with Devarda's alloy in alkaline solution in absence of ammonium ions; this is used quantitatively, the ammonia being absorbed in excess of standard acid and the excess of acid back-titrated.

Nitrous acid [*nitric*(III) *acid*]
Nitrous acid, HNO_2, is known as a gas, but otherwise exists only in solution, in which it is a weak acid. Hence addition of a strong acid to a solution of a nitrite [nitrate(III)] produces the free nitrous acid in solution.

Nitrous acid is unstable, decomposing to give nitric acid and evolving nitrogen monoxide:

$$3HNO_2 \rightarrow NO_3^- + H_3O^+ + 2NO$$

It is an effective oxidizing agent and can oxidize iodide to iodine, and the ammonium ion to nitrogen. The reduction products of nitrous acid vary greatly with conditions. For example, nitrogen monoxide or ammonia may be formed when hydrogen sulphide is oxidized to sulphur, according to the acidity of the solution. Hydrazine is oxidized by nitrous acid to hydrogen azide. Nitrous acid can itself be oxidized to nitric acid, but only by strong oxidizing agents such as manganate(VII). Nitrous acid is important in organic chemistry for its ability to diazotize primary aromatic amines — an important step in the manufacture of dyestuffs.

Nitrites
These all contain the ion NO_2^-. They are much more stable than nitrous acid, and those of the alkali metals can be fused without decomposition. They are usually prepared by heating the alkali metal nitrate, alone or with lead as a reducing agent — the latter method being the one used in the manufacture of sodium nitrite for use in the dye industry. Lead will also reduce nitrate to nitrite if present as 'lead sponge':

e.g.

$$KNO_3 + Pb \rightarrow KNO_2 + PbO$$

The addition of even a weak acid (such as ethanoic acid) to a nitrite produces nitrous acid which readily decomposes as already indicated. Hence a nitrite is distinguished from a nitrate by the evolution of nitrous fumes when ethanoic acid is added to the solid at room temperature.

9.7.2 Phosphorus

Phosphorus forms a large number of oxoacids, many of which cannot be isolated but do form stable salts. In general ionizable hydrogen is bonded to the phosphorus through an oxygen atom; hydrogen atoms attached *directly* to phosphorus are *not* ionizable.

Acids containing phosphorus(III)
Two of these are important:

$H_2PO(OH)$ phosphinic (hypophosphorous) acid

and

$HPO(OH)_2$ phosphonic (orthophosphorous) acid

X-Ray diffraction studies of the oxoacid anions indicate the following probable arrangements for the acids:

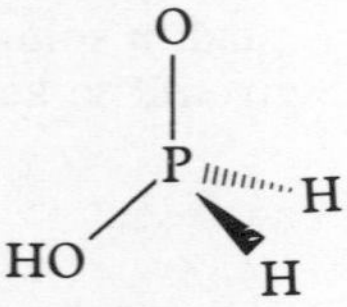

phosphinic
acid

and

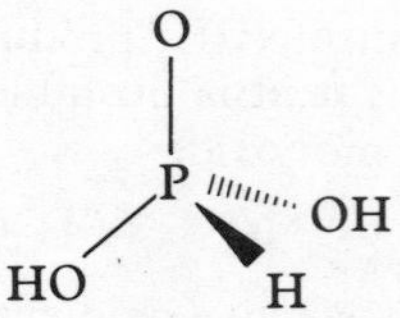

phosphonic
acid

In each case the P—O bonds have some multiple character. *Phosphinic acid* is a moderately strong monobasic acid. On being heated, the acid and its salts disproportionate evolving phosphine:

$$4H_2PO_2^- \rightarrow 2PH_3 + 2HPO_4^{2-}$$

Both the acid and its salts are powerful reducing agents. They reduce, for example, halogens to halides, and heavy metal cations to the metal. Copper(II) ion is reduced further to give copper(I) hydride, a red-brown precipitate:

$$3H_3PO_2 + 3H_2O + 2Cu^{2+} \rightarrow 2CuH\downarrow + 3H_3PO_3 + 7H^+$$

Phosphonic acid, H_3PO_3, often called just 'phosphorous acid', is prepared by the hydrolysis of phosphorus trichloride; a stream of air containing phosphorus trichloride vapour is passed into ice-cold water, and crystals of the solid acid separate:

$$PCl_3 + 3H_2O \rightarrow H_3PO_3 + 3HCl$$

The acid is dibasic (*see* structure p. 216). Like phosphinic acid it disproportionates when heated:

$$4H_3PO_3 \rightarrow PH_3 + 3H_3PO_4$$

and is a strong reducing agent. Also like phosphinic acid it reduces heavy metal ions to the metal, but copper(II) ions are not reduced to CuH.

Acids containing phosphorus (V)

The important phosphoric acids and their relation to the anhydride P_4O_{10} are:

$$P_4O_{10} \xrightarrow{\text{H}_2\text{O}} HPO_3 \underset{\text{heat}}{\overset{}{\rightleftharpoons}} H_4P_2O_7 \underset{\text{heat}}{\overset{\text{hot water}}{\rightleftharpoons}} H_3PO_4$$

$(P_4O_{10}, 2H_2O)$ $\qquad$ $(P_4O_{10}, 4H_2O)$ $\qquad$ $(P_4O_{10}, 6H_2O)$

(poly)trioxophosphoric $\qquad$ heptaoxodiphosphoric $\qquad$ tetraoxophosphoric

(meta) $\qquad\qquad\qquad$ (pyro) $\qquad\qquad\qquad$ (ortho)

(The formulae P_4O_{10}, xH_2O are merely to illustrate the interrelationship and have no structural meaning.)

Tetraoxophosphoric acid, H_3PO_4. This is prepared in the laboratory either by dissolving phosphorus(V) oxide in water (giving trioxophosphoric acid) and then heating to give the tetraoxo-acid; or by heating violet phosphorus with 33 per cent nitric acid, which oxidizes it thus:

$$4P + 10HNO_3 + H_2O \rightarrow 4H_3PO_4 + 5NO\uparrow + 5NO_2\uparrow$$

Caution is required in both methods. In the second case, in particular, gentle heating only is essential once the reaction starts. The solution obtained is evaporated somewhat, cooled in a vacuum desiccator and the crystals of the tetraoxo-acid filtered off; too drastic evaporation causes formation of the heptaoxodiphosphoric acid by loss of water.

Industrially, phosphoric(V) acid is manufactured by two processes. In one process phosphorus is burned in air and the phosphorus(V) oxide produced is dissolved in water. It is also manufactured by the action of dilute sulphuric acid on bone-ash or phosphorite, i.e. calcium tetraoxophosphate(V), $Ca_3(PO_4)_2$; the insoluble calcium sulphate is filtered off and the remaining solution concentrated. In this reaction, the calcium phosphate may be treated to convert it into the more soluble dihydrogenphosphate, $Ca(H_2PO_4)_2$. When mixed with the calcium sulphate this is used as a fertilizer under the name 'superphosphate'.

Tetraoxophosphoric acid is a colourless solid, very soluble in water; an 85 per cent solution is often used ('syrupy phosphoric acid'). It is tribasic, giving the ions:

$$H_2PO_4^- \quad \rightleftharpoons \quad HPO_4^{2-} \quad \rightleftharpoons \quad PO_4^{3-}$$

$\qquad\qquad\qquad\qquad\qquad\qquad\qquad\qquad$ (tetrahedral)

$\longrightarrow$

decreasing hydrogen ion concentration and decreasing solubility of salts

In anhydrous phosphoric(V) acid, tetrahedral PO_4^{3-} groups are connected by hydrogen bonds, a structure which can be represented as

The dotted lines represent the hydrogen bonds and it is these bonds which are responsible for the syrupy nature of the acid.

The *tetraoxophosphates*, except those of the alkali metals, sodium, potassium, rubidium, caesium (and ammonium), are insoluble in water but are brought into solution by the addition of acid which, as shown, effects a change from the ion PO_4^{3-} (with three negative charges) to the ion $H_2PO_4^-$ (with one); this change increases the solubility. Organic phosphates(V) are of great importance in biological processes, and chains of the type

occur in DNA and RNA.

Condensed phosphates(V)

In addition to the above acids and anions which contain only one phosphorus atom there are many other condensed phosphates(V) which contain more than one phosphorus atom and P—O—P bonds. Structures include both ring and chain forms. Separation of these complex anions can be achieved by ion exchange and chromatography.

Two examples of condensed phosphoric(V) acids are heptaoxodiphosphoric(V) (pyrophosphoric) and polytrioxophosphoric (metaphosphoric) acids.

Heptaoxodiphosphoric acid, $H_4P_2O_7$, as its old name suggests, is formed as one product when phosphoric(V) acid is heated (loss of water on heating leads to a mixture of acids). It forms two series of salts, the sodium salts, for example, have the formulae $Na_2H_2P_2O_7$ and $Na_4P_2O_7$.

In solution, both heptaoxodiphosphoric(V) acid and the heptaoxodiphosphates(V) (pyrophosphates) are slowly converted (more rapidly on heating) into phosphoric(V) acid or its salts, for example

$$H_4P_2O_7 + H_2O \rightarrow 2H_3PO_4$$

Polytrioxophosphoric(V) *acid,* $(HPO_3)_n$, is formed as a polymeric glassy solid when phosphoric(V) acid is heated for a long period. It may also be obtained in solution by passing sodium polytrioxophosphate(V) through a cation-exchange column. It is a monobasic acid, forming only one set of salts, but the simple formula, $NaPO_3$, for the sodium salt, is misleading since there are many polytrioxophosphates known of general formula $(NaPO_3)_n$, where n may be 3, 4 or a much larger number.

A salt originally called sodium hexametaphosphate, with n believed to be 6, is now thought to contain many much larger anion aggregates. It has the important property that it 'sequesters', i.e. removes, calcium ions from solution. Hence it is much used as a water-softener.

9.7.3   Arsenic

Acids containing arsenic(III)

Arsenic(III) (arsenious) acid, H_3AsO_3. When arsenic(III) oxide is dissolved in water the corresponding acid is formed:

$$As_4O_6 + 6H_2O \rightleftharpoons 4H_3AsO_3$$

It is an extremely weak acid but does form salts. Two kinds are known, trioxoarsenates(III), for example Na_3AsO_3, and dioxoarsenates(III), for example $Cu(AsO_2)_2$.

The arsenate(III) ion can be reduced by systems which generate hydrogen (for example metal/acid) to give arsine, for example

$$AsO_3^{3-} + 3Zn + 9H^+ \rightarrow AsH_3\uparrow + 3Zn^{2+} + 3H_2O$$

whilst other reducing agents give either arsenic or an arsenide.

Powerful oxidizing agents, for example $Cr_2O_7^{2-}$ and MnO_4^- ions, oxidize the arsenate(III) ion to arsenate(V). The reaction with iodine, however, is reversible depending on the conditions:

$$AsO_3^{3-} + I_2 + 2OH^- \rightleftharpoons AsO_4^{3-} + 2I^- + H_2O$$

Acids containing arsenic(V)

Arsenic(V) acid, H_3AsO_4 [strictly, tetraoxoarsenic(V) acid] is obtained when arsenic is oxidized with concentrated nitric acid or when arsenic(V) oxide is dissolved in water. It is a moderately strong acid which, like phosphoric(V) acid, is tribasic; arsenates(V) in general resemble phosphates(V) and are often isomorphous with them.

Arsenates(V) are more powerful oxidizing agents than phosphates(V) and will oxidize sulphite to sulphate, hydrogen sulphide (slowly) to sulphur and, depending on the conditions, iodide to iodine.

9.7.4   Antimony

No $+3$ acid is known for antimony but antimonates(III) (antimonites) formed by dissolving antimony(III) oxide in alkalis are known, for example sodium dioxoantimonate(III), $NaSbO_2$.

The $+5$ acid is known in solution and antimonates(V) can be obtained by dissolving antimony(V) oxide in alkalis. These salts contain the hexahydroxoantimonate(V) ion, $[Sb(OH)_6]^-$.

at all (since the electronegative fluorine atoms will attract the lone pair electrons), it forms a compound with nickel, $Ni(PF_3)_4$, very like nickel tetracarbonyl, $Ni(CO)_4$. This is explained by the fact that phosphorus can expand its valency shell of electrons and so receive electrons from the nickel by a kind of 'back-donation', i.e. each nickel–phosphorus bond is $Ni\!=\!PF_3$, not just $Ni\!\leftarrow\!PF_3$.

Phosphorus trichloride

Phosphorus and chlorine combine directly to form either the trichloride or the pentachloride depending on the relative amounts of phosphorus and chlorine used.

The trichloride is obtained as a liquid, boiling point 349 K, when a jet of chlorine burns in phosphorus vapour. Care must be taken to exclude both air and moisture from the apparatus since phosphorus trichloride reacts with oxygen and is vigorously hydrolysed by water, fuming strongly in moist air. The hydrolysis reaction is:

$$PCl_3 + 3H_2O \rightarrow H_3PO_3 + 3HCl$$
$$\text{phosphonic}$$
$$\text{acid}$$

Similar reactions occur with organic compounds which contain hydroxyl groups, thus

$$3CH_3C\overset{O}{\diagdown_{OH}} + PCl_3 \rightarrow 3CH_3C\overset{O}{\diagdown_{Cl}} + H_3PO_3$$

Hydrogen chloride is also evolved.

The reaction with oxygen converts phosphorus trichloride into phosphorus trichloride oxide (oxychloride). $POCl_3$; the trichloride is able to remove oxygen from some molecules, for example sulphur trioxide

$$PCl_3 + SO_3 \rightarrow O\!=\!\overset{\overset{\textstyle Cl}{|}}{\underset{\underset{\textstyle Cl}{|}}{P}}\!\!-\!\!Cl + SO_2$$

Phosphorus trichloride reacts with chlorine in excess to give phosphorus pentachloride, an equilibrium being set up:

$$PCl_3 + Cl_2 \rightleftharpoons PCl_5$$

9.8.3   Phosphorus(V) halides

The properties of the phosphorus trihalides given above indicate the ability of phosphorus to increase its valency above 3. In phosphorus pentafluoride, PF_5 (a gas), and the *vapour* of phosphorus pentachloride, PCl_5 (solid at ordinary temperatures), phosphorus is covalently bound to the halogen atoms by five equal bonds to give a trigonal bipyramid structure. However, the covalency can increase further to six; the acid, HPF_6, and its salts, for example $NaPF_6$, containing the octahedral PF_6^- ion (hexafluorophosphate) are well known and stable. Here again then, fluorine excites the maximum covalency and we can compare the ions AlF_6^{3-}, SiF_6^{2-}, PF_6^-.

However, phosphorus pentachloride in the *solid* state has an ionic lattice built up of $[PCl_4]^+$ and $[PCl_6]^-$ ions and these ions are believed to exist in certain solvents. Thus under these conditions the maximum covalency is reached with chlorine. In phosphorus pentabromide, PBr_5, the solid has the structure $[PBr_4]^+[Br]^-$.

Phosphorus pentachloride, PCl_5

Phosphorus pentachloride is prepared by the action of chlorine on phosphorus trichloride. To push the equilibrium over to the right, the temperature must be kept low and excess of chlorine must be present. Hence the liquid phosphorus trichloride is run dropwise into a flask cooled in ice through which a steady stream of dry chlorine is passed: the solid pentachloride deposits at the bottom of the flask.

Phosphorus pentachloride sublimes and then dissociates on heating, dissociation being complete at $600\,K$. It is attacked by water, yielding first phosphorus trichloride oxide, thus:

$$H_2O + PCl_5 \rightarrow O{=}PCl_3 + 2HCl$$

and then tetraoxophosphoric(V) acid:

$$3H_2O + POCl_3 \rightarrow H_3PO_4 + 3HCl$$

The replacement of the —OH group by a chlorine atom is a very general reaction of phosphorus pentachloride. For example, if concentrated sulphuric acid is written as $(HO)_2SO_2$ then its reaction with phosphorus pentachloride may be written:

$$(HO)_2SO_2 + 2PCl_5 \rightarrow 2O{=}PCl_3 + 2HCl + \begin{array}{c}Cl\\Cl\end{array}\!\!\diagdown\!\!\diagup SO_2$$

sulphur dichloride dioxide

The reaction of ethanoic acid and phosphorus pentachloride may be written:

$$CH_3COOH + PCl_5 \rightarrow O{=}PCl_3 + HCl\uparrow + CH_3COCl$$

ethanoyl chloride

The trichloride oxide is most readily obtained in the laboratory by distillation of a mixture of the pentachloride and anhydrous ethanedioic acid:

$$(COOH)_2 + PCl_5 \rightarrow O{=}PCl_3 + CO_2\uparrow + CO\uparrow + 2HCl\uparrow$$

[since $(COOCl)_2$ is unstable].

These reactions (and those of the trichloride) indicate the great tendency of (quinquevalent) phosphorus to unite with oxygen (cf. silicon).

9.8.4   Arsenic halides

Arsenic trihalides

Arsenic forms a volatile trifluoride, AsF_3, and a fairly volatile trichloride, $AsCl_3$, which fumes in air. The latter is prepared by passing dry hydrogen chloride over arsenic(III) oxide at 500 K:

$$As_4O_6 + 12HCl \rightarrow 4AsCl_3 + 6H_2O$$

Arsenic trichloride is not completely hydrolysed by water, and in solution the following equilibrium is set up:

$$AsCl_3 + 3H_2O \rightleftharpoons H_3AsO_3 \qquad\qquad + 3HCl$$
$$\text{arsenic(III) acid}$$

Hence addition of concentrated hydrochloric acid to a solution of arsenic(III) acid produces arsenic(III) chloride in solution. The above equilibrium may be written:

$$[As^{3+}] + 3H_2O \rightleftharpoons H_3AsO_3 + 3H^+$$

where '$[As^{3+}]$' represents the complex mixture of cationic arsenic species present. This behaviour of arsenic(III) chloride is in contrast to that of phosphorus trichloride where hydrolysis by water is complete.

Arsenic pentahalides

Arsenic forms only the pentafluoride AsF_5, a colourless liquid, b.p. 326 K. This resembles phosphorus pentafluoride.

9.8.5   Antimony(III) halides

Antimony(III) *fluoride* is a readily hydrolysable solid which finds use as a fluorinating agent. Antimony(III) chloride is a soft solid, m.p. 347 K. It dissolves in water, but on dilution partial hydrolysis occurs and antimony chloride oxide SbOCl is precipitated:

$$[Sb^{3+}] + Cl^- + H_2O \rightleftharpoons 2H^+ + O{=\!\!=}Sb{-\!\!-}Cl$$

(Here again the simple formulation $[Sb^{3+}]$ is used to represent all the cationic species present.) The hydrolysis is reversible and the precipitate dissolves in hydrochloric acid and the trichloride is re-formed. This reaction is in sharp contrast to the reactions of phosphorus(III) chloride.

Antimony(V) *fluoride* is a viscous liquid.

Antimony(V) *chloride* is a fuming liquid, colourless when pure, m.p. 276 K. It is a powerful chlorinating agent.

9.8.6   Bismuth halides

The trihalides closely resemble those of antimony. Bismuth(V) fluoride is known. It is a white solid, and a powerful oxidizing agent.

9.9 Tests for Group V elements

9.9.1 Nitrogen

For nitrogen gas, there is no positive chemical test. In a gas mixture, any residual gas which shows no chemical reaction with any reagent is assumed to be nitrogen (or one of the noble gases). If a mixture of nitrogen and the noble gases is passed over heated magnesium, the magnesium nitride formed can be identified by the ammonia evolved on addition of water.

Combined nitrogen is usually convertible either into ammonia by reduction or to a nitrate by oxidation. Hence tests, qualitative or quantitative, already described can be applied for these.

9.9.2 Phosphorus

Prolonged oxidation of any phosphorus compound, followed by standing in water, converts it into phosphate(V). This can then be detected by the formation of a yellow precipitate when heated with ammonium molybdate and nitric acid. Specific tests for various oxophosphates are known.

9.9.3 Arsenic

Because of its toxicity, it is often necessary to be able to detect arsenic when present only in small amounts in other substances.

Arsenic present only in traces (in any form) can be detected by reducing it to arsine and then applying tests for the latter. In Marsh's test, dilute sulphuric acid is added dropwise through a thistle funnel to some arsenic-free zinc in a flask; hydrogen is evolved and led out of the flask by a horizontal tube. The arsenic-containing compound is then added to the zinc–acid solution, and the delivery tube heated in the middle. If arsenic is present, it is reduced to arsine by the zinc–acid reaction, for example:

$$AsO_4^{3-} + 4Zn + 11H^+ \rightarrow AsH_3 + 4Zn^{2+} + 4H_2O$$

The evolved arsine is decomposed to arsenic and hydrogen at the heated zone of the delivery tube; hence arsenic deposits as a shiny black mirror beyond the heated zone.

9.9.4 Antimony and bismuth

As can be expected, antimony compounds resemble those of arsenic. In the Marsh test, antimony compounds again give a black deposit which, unlike that formed by arsenic compounds, is insoluble in sodium chlorate(I) solution.

Solutions of many antimony and bismuth salts hydrolyse when diluted; the cationic species then present will usually form a precipitate with any anion present. Addition of the appropriate acid suppresses the hydrolysis, reverses the reaction and the precipitate dissolves. This reaction indicates the presence of a bismuth or an antimony salt.

When hydrogen sulphide is bubbled into an acidic solution of an antimony or a bismuth salt an orange precipitate, Sb_2S_3, or a brown precipitate,

Table 9.4 Summary of the properties of Group V

Element	N	P	As	Sb	Bi
	N_2, gas				
Oxidation states	$(-3) +3 +5$		← Solids exhibiting allotropy		
			+3 becoming less reducing, $+5$ becoming more reducing →		
Reactions: +air	NO with electric discharge	P_4O_6 (limited) P_4O_{10} (excess)	← Oxides M_2O_3 on heating		
+acid	No reaction	Conc. HNO_3 leads to $+5$ oxoacid or $+5$ oxide			Conc. HNO_3 gives $Bi(NO_3)_2 \cdot 5H_2O$
+alkali	No reaction	PH_3	arsenate(III)	No reaction	No reaction
+halogens	No reaction		MX_3 and MX_5 →		
Compounds: hydrides	NH_3 N_2H_4 N_3H		← MH_3, decreasing stability		
oxides	N_2O NO NO_2 N_2O_3 N_2O_5 (acidic)	P_4O_6 acidic P_4O_{10} acidic	As_4O_6 acidic As_4O_{10} acidic	Sb_2O_3 amphoteric Sb_2O_5 acidic	Bi_2O_3 basic Bi_2O_5 unstable
oxoacids and salts	HNO_2 HNO_3	$+3$ numerous $+5$ numerous	$+3$ H_3AsO_3 $+5$ H_3AsO_4 oxidizing	$+3$ SbO_2^- $+5$ (H_3SbO_4) oxidizing	$[Bi^V(OH)_6]^-$ and BiO_3^-; oxidizing
halides	NF_3 unreactive NCl_3 very reactive	MX_3; MX_5		$MX_5 + X^- \rightarrow MX_6^-$	

Bi_2S_3, is obtained. Bismuth(III) sulphide, unlike antimony(III) sulphide, is insoluble in lithium hydroxide.

Summary

For a summary of Group V, *see Table 9.4.*

Questions

1   Give an account of the oxides and the chlorides of arsenic, antimony and bismuth, including an explanation of any major differences. Show how the increasing metallic character of the element is reflected in the chemical behaviour of these compounds. Suggest a reason for the non-existence of $AsCl_5$ and $BiCl_5$.

C,S

2   Outline the laboratory preparation of a sample of dinitrogen tetroxide. Describe and explain what happens when it is heated from 290 K to 900 K. Suggest electronic structures for dinitrogen tetroxide and the other nitrogen-containing molecules formed from it on heating to 900 K. Point out any unusual structural features.

3   For either Group IV or Group V: C,A
    (a) point out two general trends in the physical properties of the elements, and explain, as far as you can, why these trends occur;
    (b) give examples of the way in which the most stable oxidation number of the elements in their compounds tend to decrease by two towards the bottom of the group, and describe how this tendency is related to their oxidizing and reducing properties;
    (c) describe in outline how, starting from the element, you would prepare a pure sample of either an oxide or chloride of an element in the group, and state how you would, in principle, try to establish its empirical formula.

N, Phys. Sci. A

4   Compare and contrast the following pairs of compounds as regards (a) methods of preparation, (b) important properties including hydrolysis, (c) thermal stability:
    (i) NCl_3 and PCl_3,
    (ii) NH_3 and PH_3,
    (iii) N_2O_5 and P_4O_{10}
    As far as possible account for different behaviour in terms of the structures of the compounds and the nature of bonding present.

L,S

5   (a) What is meant by the statement that 'nitrogen dioxide, NO_2, is an odd-electron molecule'?

(b) When NO_2 dimerizes to form N_2O_4, the product is not an odd-electron molecule. What explanation can you offer for this fact?

(c) Give two properties which are characteristic of odd-electron molecules.

(d) Give the name and formula of a compound in which NO_2^- ions are bonded to a metal ion by the donation of electron pairs.

(e) By means of equations, and stating the appropriate conditions, show how a sample of nitrogen(IV) oxide (nitrogen dioxide) may be obtained in the laboratory.

JMB,A

Chapter 10
Group VI
Oxygen, sulphur, selenium, tellurium, polonium

The elements in this group have six electrons in their outer quantum level, and can thus achieve a noble gas configuration by acquiring two electrons.

10.1 Properties of the elements

Some of the more important physical properties of the elements are given in *Table 10.1*. At ordinary temperatures oxygen exists as the diatomic gas O_2; the other elements are solids.

Melting and boiling points increase with increasing atomic number from oxygen to tellurium, with oxygen showing the deviation typical of a group head element. The expected decrease in ionization energy with increase in atomic number and size of the atoms should be noted.

Although the electron affinities do not change regularly with increasing atomic number, the increasing ionic radii imply decreasing lattice and hydration enthalpies. Hence, although oxygen forms a large number of wholly or partly ionic oxides with metals, containing O^{2-}, sulphur forms ionic compounds only with the more electropositive elements such as sodium, and most of its compounds are partly or wholly covalent.

All the elements are able to share two electrons forming two covalent bonds. The two covalent bonds formed by oxygen can be separate bonds, for example

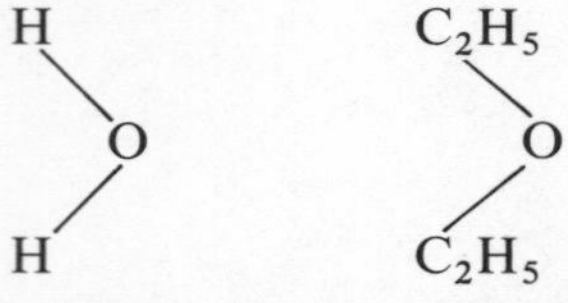

H
 \
  O
 /
H

C_2H_5
 \
  O
 /
C_2H_5

or a double bond, for example

$$O{=}C{=}O$$

$$CH_3{-}\overset{\displaystyle O}{\underset{\displaystyle H}{\overset{\|}{C}}}$$

The covalently bonded oxygen atom still has two lone pairs of electrons and can act as an electron pair donor. It rarely donates both pairs (to achieve 4-

Table 10.1 Selected properties of the elements

Element	Atomic number	Outer electrons	Atomic* radius nm	Radius/nm of X^{2-} ion	m.p./K	b.p./K	Electron affinity kJ mol^{-1}		First ionization energy kJ mol^{-1}	Electronegativity (Pauling)
							$X(g) \rightarrow X^{-}(g)$	$X(g) \rightarrow X^{2-}(g)$		
O	8	$2s^2 2p^4$	0.066	0.146	54	90	−141	+791	1310	3.5
S	16	$3s^2 3p^4$	0.104	0.190	392	718	−200	+649	999	2.5
Se	34	$3d^{10} 4s^2 4p^4$	0.114	0.202	490	958	−213	+702	941	2.4
Te	52	$4d^{10} 5s^2 5p^4$	0.132	0.222	723	1260	−222	+627	869	2.1
Po	84	$5d^{10} 6s^2 6p^4$	—	—	527	1235	—	—	813	—

*Covalent radius.

coordination) and usually only one donor bond is formed. A water molecule, for example, can donate to a proton, forming H_3O^+, and diethyl ether (ethoxyethane) can donate to an acceptor such as boron trifluoride:

$$
\begin{array}{c}
C_2H_5 \\
\diagdown \\
\quad O \rightarrow BF_3 \\
\diagup \\
C_2H_5
\end{array}
$$

Sulphur in hydrogen sulphide and its derivatives is a much less effective simple electron pair donor and the other Group VI elements show this property to a very minor extent. However, compounds based on bivalent sulphur [for example, dimethyl sulphide $(CH_3)_2S$] are often found to be effective ligands in transition metal complexes. Unlike oxygen, the remaining elements can increase their covalency to a maximum of six by utilizing the low energy $3d$ orbitals not available to oxygen, and hexacoordinate compounds (for example SF_6) are known. However, as the atomic number and size of the atoms increase from oxygen to polonium, the elements become more electropositive, the hydrides less stable and the stabilities of the higher oxidation states decrease. Only polonium can really be said to show weakly metallic properties, although tellurium oxides are amphoteric.

There are peculiarities associated with compounds containing oxygen and hydrogen where hydrogen bond formation gives rise to many properties which are not shown by the compounds of the other elements.

10.2 Occurrence and extraction of elements of Group VI

10.2.1 Oxygen

Oxygen occurs (as O_2) in the atmosphere (21 per cent by volume, 23 per cent by mass). The proportion is constant over the Earth's surface; it is also constant for many miles upwards, because the turbulence of the atmosphere prevents the tendency for the lighter gases, for example helium, to increase in amount at higher altitudes.

Water contains 89 per cent by mass of oxygen, and the outer crust of the Earth contains about 47 per cent; hence air, land and sea together contain about 50 per cent by mass of oxygen.

On the industrial scale oxygen is obtained by the fractional distillation of air. A common laboratory method for the preparation of oxygen is by the decomposition of hydrogen peroxide, H_2O_2, a reaction catalysed by manganese(IV) oxide:

$$2H_2O_2 \xrightarrow{\ MnO_2\ } 2H_2O + O_2\uparrow$$

A similar decomposition of the chlorate(I) (hypochlorite) ion, OCl^-, catalysed by both light and cobalt(II) ions, is less commonly used:

$$2ClO^- \rightarrow 2Cl^- + O_2\uparrow$$

Oxygen can also be prepared by the thermal decomposition of certain solid compounds containing it. These include oxides of the more noble metals, for example of mercury or silver:

$$2HgO \rightarrow 2Hg + O_2\uparrow$$

certain higher oxides, for example of lead(IV) and manganese(IV):

$$2PbO_2 \rightleftharpoons 2PbO + O_2\uparrow$$

peroxides, for example of barium:

$$2BaO_2 \rightleftharpoons 2BaO + O_2\uparrow$$

and certain oxosalts, notably the nitrates, chlorates(V), iodates(V) and manganates(VII) of alkali metals.

Pure oxygen is conveniently prepared by the thermal decomposition of potassium manganate(VII):

$$2KMnO_4 \rightarrow K_2MnO_4 + MnO_2 + O_2\uparrow$$

Oxygen can be produced by certain reactions in solution, for example the oxidation of hydrogen peroxide by potassium manganate(VII) acidified with sulphuric acid:

$$2MnO_4^- + 5H_2O_2 + 6H_3O^+ \rightarrow 2Mn^{2+} + 14H_2O + 5O_2\uparrow$$

10.2.2   Sulphur

Large deposits of free sulphur occur in America, Sicily and Japan. Combined sulphur occurs as sulphides, for example galena, PbS, zinc blende, ZnS, and iron pyrites, FeS_2, and as sulphates, notably as gypsum or anhydrite, $CaSO_4$.

In America, the sulphur deposits (mostly in Louisiana and Texas) are dome-shaped layers about 30 cm thick, between limestone above and anhydrite below. From these, the sulphur is extracted by the Frasch process. A metal tube, about 15 cm diameter and containing two concentric inner tubes (*Figure 10.1*) is sunk into the top of the deposit. Water, superheated to 450 K, is forced under pressure down the outer tube, and enters the sulphur layer through perforations. The sulphur melts (m.p. 388 K) and enters the inner pipe at the bottom, up which it flows for some distance. Compressed air is forced down the innermost pipe; this emulsifies the water and molten sulphur mixture, so lowering its density, and the emulsion rises to the top of the pipe, where it is run off into vats to solidify. The purity is usually 99.8 per cent.

Large quantities of sulphur are recovered from petroleum and natural gas. Naturally occurring hydrogen sulphide, H_2S, and that produced in the cracking and catalytic hydrogenation of petroleum is first removed by absorption and the regenerated gas is converted into sulphur by partial combustion with air, the overall reaction being

$$6H_2S + 3O_2 \rightarrow 6H_2O + 6S$$

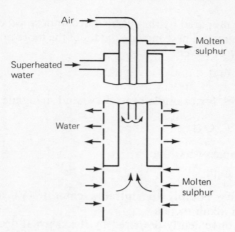

Figure 10.1 The Frasch pump

10.2.3   Selenium and tellurium

Selenium and tellurium occur naturally in sulphide ores, usually as an impurity in the sulphide of a heavy metal. They are recovered from the flue dust produced when the heavy metal sulphide is roasted.

10.2.4   Polonium

This is a radioactive element. It occurs in minute traces in barium and thorium minerals, but it can be produced by irradiation of bismuth in a nuclear reactor. (The study of its chemistry presents great difficulty because of its intense α radiation).

10.3   Allotropes

Oxygen, sulphur and selenium are known to exist in more than one allotropic form.

10.3.1   Oxygen

This exists in two allotropic forms, the usual form O_2 which may, if necessary, be called dioxygen, and ozone or trioxygen O_3.

   Oxygen is a colourless gas which condenses to a pale blue liquid, b.p. 90 K, which is markedly paramagnetic indicating the presence of unpaired electrons (p. 204). Simple valence bond theory (as used in this book) would indicate the structure

$$:\overset{..}{O}:\overset{..}{O}: \qquad \text{i.e.} \qquad O\!=\!\!=\!O$$

which accounts for the high oxygen–oxygen bond strength (bond dissociation energy, 498 kJ mol^{-1}), but does not explain the paramagnetism. The molecular orbital theory of bonding, however, suggests not only a doubly bonded structure but also two molecular orbitals (i.e. orbitals of the complete O_2 molecule) of equal energy each containing *one* electron, and this satisfactorily explains both the high bond strength and paramagnetism.

Oxygen, like nitrogen monoxide, NO, shows little tendency to dimerize although the presence of the unstable, weakly bonded species, tetratomic oxygen O_4, has been reported as a constituent of liquid oxygen.

Ozone, O_3, is found in trace quantities in the upper atmosphere where it is believed to be formed by the photochemical dissociation of oxygen molecules by the intense ultraviolet light from the Sun; absorption of this light in the process prevents it from reaching the surface of the Earth where it would destroy all living matter very rapidly.

Small quantities of ozone are produced when oxygen and air are subject to an electrical discharge and it is, therefore, found in the neighbourhood of working electrical machines. Probably a small quantity of atomic oxygen is initially produced; most of this recombines quickly to give oxygen, O_2, but a few atoms react to form ozone:

$$O_2 + O \rightarrow O_3$$

The ozone molecules also decompose by reaction with atomic oxygen, so that the actual concentration of ozone is small.

Ozone is formed in certain chemical reactions, including the action of fluorine on water (p. 282) and the thermal decomposition of iodic(VII) (periodic) acid. It is also formed when dilute (about 1M) sulphuric acid is electrolysed at high current density; at low temperatures the oxygen evolved at the anode can contain as much as 30 per cent ozone.

Ozone is normally produced by the use of a silent electrical discharge and a number of ozonizers have been produced. Brodie's apparatus is shown in outline in *Figure 10.2*.

With a potential of approximately 20 000 V the ozonized oxygen produced can contain up to 10 per cent ozone and pure ozone can be obtained by liquefaction of the mixture followed by fractional distillation (O_2, b.p. 90 K; O_3, b.p. 161 K).

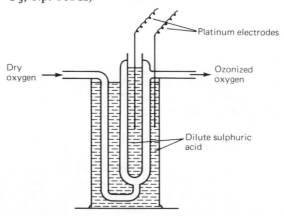

Figure 10.2 Preparation of ozone: Brodie's apparatus

At room temperature ozone is a pale blue diamagnetic gas which condenses to a deep blue liquid. It has a characteristic smell, and is toxic. Ozone is a very endothermic compound:

$$O_3 \rightarrow \tfrac{2}{3}O_2 \qquad \Delta H = -142 \text{ kJ mol}^{-1}$$

It decomposes exothermically to oxygen, a reaction which can be explosive. Even dilute ozone decomposes slowly at room temperature; the decomposition is catalysed by various substances [for example manganese(IV) oxide and soda-lime] and occurs more rapidly on heating.

Ozone is very much more reactive than oxygen and is a powerful oxidizing agent especially in acid solution (the redox potential varies with conditions but can be as high as $+2.0$ V). Some examples are:

1   The conversion of black lead(II) sulphide into white lead(II) sulphate (an example of oxidation by addition of oxygen):

$$PbS + 4O_3 \rightarrow PbSO_4 + 4O_2\uparrow$$

2   The oxidation of iron(II) to iron(III) in acid solution:

$$2Fe^{2+} + O_3 + 2H_3O^+ \rightarrow 2Fe^{3+} + O_2\uparrow + 3H_2O$$

The adherence of mercury to glass, i.e. 'tailing' in presence of ozone, is probably due to the formation of an oxide. The oxidation of the iodide ion to iodine in solution is used to determine ozone quantitatively:

$$2I^- + H_2O + O_3 \rightarrow 2OH^- + I_2 + O_2\uparrow$$

The liberated iodine is titrated with standard sodium thiosulphate(VI) solution after acidification to remove the hydroxide ions.

Addition compounds called *ozonides* are produced when alkenes react with ozone and reductive cleavage of these compounds is used extensively in preparative and diagnostic organic chemistry.

The molecular formula of ozone was determined by comparing its rate of diffusion with that of a known gas. The *geometric* structure of the molecule is angular with two equal O—O distances, which are slightly greater than in the oxygen molecule, and an O—O—O angle of 116°:

Ozone has long been used on a small scale for water purification since it destroys viruses as well as bacteria, and recent developments suggest that this use will increase in importance.

10.3.2   Sulphur

The structures of sulphur in solid, liquid and gaseous phases are complicated. *Rhombic* sulphur is the solid allotrope stable at room temperature. It is yellow, readily soluble in carbon disulphide, from which it can be crystallized, and has a density of 2.06 g cm^{-3}. Above 369 K, the transition temperature, rhombic sulphur is no longer stable, slowly changing to *monoclinic* sulphur, and if rhombic sulphur is melted, allowed to partly solidify, and the remaining molten sulphur is poured off, there remain long needle-like crystals (almost colourless) of monoclinic sulphur, density 1.96 g cm^{-3}. A good specimen of monoclinic sulphur can be prepared by crystallizing a concentrated solution of sulphur in xylene, taking care to keep the temperature above 368 K. On standing at room temperature, monoclinic sulphur slowly changes to the rhombic form. Both these allotropes contain S_8 molecules with rings of eight sulphur atoms, as shown in *Figure 10.3*.

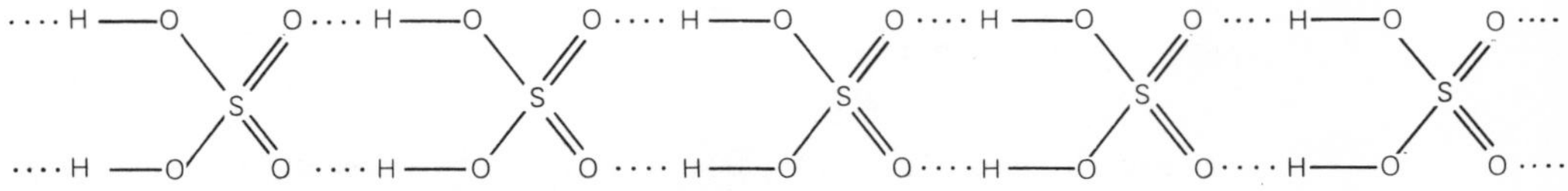

Figure 10.3 The sulphur molecule

When sulphur is melted viscosity changes occur as the temperature is raised. These changes are due to the formation of long-chain polymers (in very pure sulphur, chains containing about 100 000 atoms may be formed). The polymeric nature of molten sulphur can be recognized if molten sulphur is poured in a thin stream into cold water, when a plastic rubbery mass known as *plastic sulphur* is obtained. This is only slightly soluble in carbon disulphide, but on standing it loses its plasticity and reverts to the soluble rhombic form. If certain substances, for example iodine or oxides of arsenic, are incorporated into the plastic sulphur, the rubbery character can be preserved.

Colloidal sulphur is produced by careful addition of acid to sodium thiosulphate solution.

10.3.3　Selenium

Like sulphur, selenium exists in a number of allotropic forms. These include both crystalline (rhombic and monoclinic) modifications which almost certainly contain Se_8 ring structures. Selenium, however, also has a grey allotrope which is metallic in appearance. It is stable at room temperature and is made up of extended spiral chains of selenium atoms.

10.3.4　Tellurium

Only one form of tellurium is known with certainty. It has a silvery white metallic appearance.

10.4　Chemical reactivity

10.4.1　Reactions with air

At high temperatures oxygen reacts with the nitrogen in the air forming small amounts of nitrogen monoxide (p. 190). Sulphur burns with a blue flame when heated in air to form sulphur dioxide SO_2, and a little sulphur trioxide SO_3. Selenium and tellurium also burn with a blue flame when heated in air, but form only their dioxides, SeO_2 and TeO_2.

10.4.2   Reactions with acids

Oxygen
Oxygen is unaffected by aqueous acids unless they have powerful reducing properties, in which case the acid is oxidized*. For example

$$2HNO_2 + O_2 \rightarrow 2HNO_3$$
$$4HI + O_2 \rightarrow 2I_2 + 2H_2O$$

However, hydrogen chloride gas, obtained as a by-product in chlorination reactions, is commercially converted into chlorine by passing the hydrogen chloride mixed with air over a copper catalyst at a temperature of 600—670 K whereupon the following reaction occurs:

$$4HCl + O_2 \rightleftharpoons 2H_2O + 2Cl_2$$

This is a modification of the process originally devised by Deacon; further reference is made on p. 278.

Sulphur, selenium and tellurium
These elements are generally unaffected by non-oxidizing acids (behaviour expected for non-metallic elements) but they do react when heated with concentrated sulphuric and nitric acids, both powerful oxidizing agents. Sulphur is oxidized to sulphur dioxide by hot concentrated sulphuric acid.

$$S + 2H_2SO_4 \rightarrow 2H_2O + 3SO_2$$

and to sulphuric acid by hot concentrated nitric acid,

$$S + 6HNO_3 \rightarrow H_2SO_4 + 6NO_2\uparrow + 2H_2O$$

With concentrated nitric acid, selenium and tellurium form only their $+4$ oxoacids, H_2SeO_3 and H_2TeO_3 respectively, indicating a tendency for the higher oxidation states to become less stable as the atomic number of the element is increased (cf. Group V, Chapter 9).

Polonium
The more metallic nature of polonium is shown by the fact that it dissolves not only in concentrated nitric and sulphuric acids but also in hydrofluoric and hydrochloric acids.

---

*The redox half-reaction $O_2(g) + 4H_3O^+ + 4e^- \rightarrow 6H_2O$ has $E^\ominus = +1.23$ V suggesting that oxygen is a good oxidizing agent in acid solution. However, when oxygen gas is passed into a solution where oxidation might be expected, the reaction is often too slow to be observed — there is an adverse kinetic factor.

10.4.3   Reactions with alkalis

Oxygen does not react with alkalis. Sulphur dissolves slowly in strong alkalis to give a mixture of sulphite and sulphide initially:

$$3S + 6OH^- \rightarrow 2S^{2-} + SO_3^{2-} + 3H_2O$$

However, the sulphide ion can attach to itself further atoms of sulphur to give *polysulphide* ions, for example S_2^{2-}, S_3^{2-}, and so these are found in solution also. Further, the sulphite ion can add on a sulphur atom to give the thiosulphate ion, $S_2O_3^{2-}$ which is also found in the reaction mixture.

Selenium and tellurium react similarly, forming selenides and selenates(IV), and tellurides and tellurates(IV) respectively. Like the sulphide ion, S^{2-}, the ions Se^{2-} and Te^{2-} form polyanions but to a much lesser extent.

10.4.4   Reactions with elements

Oxygen is a very reactive element and many metals and non-metals burn in it to give oxides; these reactions are dealt with under the individual group headings.

Sulphur is less reactive than oxygen but still quite a reactive element and when heated it combines directly with the non-metallic elements, oxygen, hydrogen, the halogens (except iodine), carbon and phosphorus, and also with many metals to give sulphides. Selenium and tellurium are less reactive than sulphur but when heated combine directly with many metals and non-metals.

10.5   Uses of the elements

10.5.1   Oxygen

Very large quantities of oxygen are used in steel manufacture (p. 343). Other important uses include organic oxidation reactions; the oxidation of ethene to epoxyethane

$$H_2C{=\!\!=}CH_2 \quad\longrightarrow\quad H_2C\overset{\displaystyle{}}{\underset{\displaystyle O}{\diagdown\diagup}}CH_2$$

is of particular importance. The high temperature flames obtained when hydrocarbons burn in oxygen have many uses. The oxygen–ethyne (acetylene) flame, for example, is used in the cutting and welding of metals. All these products of complete hydrocarbon–oxygen combustion are gases and considerable expansion therefore occurs on reaction. The thrust produced is the basis of the internal combustion and many rocket engines.

10.5.2   Sulphur

Sulphur is used in the manufacture of matches and fireworks, as a dust insecticide and for vulcanizing rubber. Most of the world supply of sulphur, however, is used for the manufacture of sulphuric acid (p. 260).

10.5.3 Selenium

Like sulphur, selenium has been used in the vulcanization of rubber. It is also used in photoelectric cells.

10.6 Hydrides of Group VI elements

All Group VI elements form a hydride H_2X. With the notable exception of water, they are all poisonous gases with very unpleasant smells. *Table 10.2* gives some of their important physical properties. The properties of water are seen to differ greatly from the other hydrides; the deviations can be largely explained by the formation of hydrogen bonds between water molecules.

Table 10.2 Hydrides of Group VI elements

Property	H_2O	H_2S	H_2Se	H_2Te
Relative molecular mass	18.0	34.0	80.0	129.6
m.p./K	273	188	207	225
m.p./K	373	213	232	271
Enthalpy of formation ($\Delta H_f^{\ominus}$/kJ mol^{-1})	-285.9	-20.6	$+77.5$	$+143$
Enthalpy of vaporization ($\Delta H_v^{\ominus}$/kJ mol^{-1})	40.7	18.7	19.3	23.2
Mean thermochemical bond energy for M—H bond/kJ mol^{-1}	467	347	276	—

In addition to the hydrides of formula H_2X, oxygen forms the hydride H_2O_2, hydrogen peroxide, and sulphur forms a whole series of hydrides called sulphanes. These are yellow liquids which are thermodynamically unstable with respect to hydrogen sulphide and sulphur.

10.6.1 Water, H_2O

Physical properties

The fact that water is a liquid at room temperature with high enthalpies of fusion and vaporization can be attributed to hydrogen bond formation. The water molecule is shown in *Figure 10.4*.

Because of the presence of the lone pairs of electrons, the molecule has a dipole moment (and the liquid a high permittivity or dielectric constant). In ice, there is an infinite three-dimensional structure in which the oxygen atom of each water molecule is surrounded by four hydrogen atoms arranged

Figure 10.4 The water molecule

approximately tetrahedrally, two (in the molecule) attached by covalent bonds, and two from adjacent molecules by longer hydrogen bonds. As the temperature is increased hydrogen bonds begin to break and at 273 K there are insufficient to maintain the crystalline lattice and the solid melts. The liquid formed at 273 K has a quasi-crystalline structure. Between 273 K and 277 K the hydrogen bonds rearrange and the 'crystal' structure changes; the molecules pack more closely together so that the density increases. But above 277 K (where the density reaches a maximum value) the effect of thermal agitation of the 'molecules' becomes increasingly important and there is an overall expansion.

Solvent properties

The high permittivity (dielectric constant) makes water a highly effective solvent for ionic crystals, since the electrostatic attractive forces between oppositely charged ions are reduced when the crystal is placed in water. Moreover, since water is not composed of randomly arranged molecules but has some degree of 'structure', the introduction of charged ions which attract the polar water molecules, produces a new 'structure', and a fraction of the water molecules become associated with the ions — the process known as *hydration*. Energy is evolved in this process — hydration energy — and this assists the solution of both ionic and partly covalent substances: in the latter case *hydrolysis* may also occur (*see* p. 240). There are, however, many non-ionic substances for which water is a good solvent; this is because the molecules of such substances almost always contain hydrogen and oxygen atoms which can form hydrogen bonds with water molecules. Hence, for example, substances containing the —OH group, for example alcohols, carboxylic acids and some carbohydrates, are soluble in water, provided that the rest of the molecule is not too large.

Chemical properties

As expected from the enthalpy of formation, water is thermally very stable but when steam is heated to above 1300 K slight dissociation to the elements does occur. Pure water is almost a non-conductor of electricity but slight ionic dissociation occurs:

$$2H_2O \rightleftharpoons H_3O^+ + OH^- \qquad K_{298} = 10^{-14} \text{ mol}^2 \text{ l}^{-2}$$

Thus water can behave as an acid towards bases stronger than itself (p. 78), for example

$$H_2O + NH_3 \rightleftharpoons NH_4^+ + OH^-$$
$$H_2O + CO_3^{2-} \rightleftharpoons HCO_3^- + OH^-$$

and as a base to acids stronger than itself, for example

$$H_2O + HCl \rightleftharpoons H_3O^+ + Cl^-$$
$$H_2O + HNO_3 \rightleftharpoons H_3O^+ + NO_3^-$$

Water can also behave as both an oxidizing and a reducing agent:

$$2H_2O + 2e^- \rightarrow H_2(g) + 2OH^-(aq) \quad : \quad 2H_2O \rightarrow O_2 + 4e^- + 4H^+(aq)$$

Many metals are oxidized by water. At ordinary temperatures the more electropositive metals, for example, sodium, calcium (or their amalgams with mercury), react to give hydrogen, for example:

$$2Na + 2H_2O \rightarrow 2NaOH + H_2\uparrow$$

The reaction may be *visualized* as occurring thus:

$$Na(s) + nH_2O \rightarrow Na^+(aq) + e^-(aq)$$
$$e^-(aq) \rightarrow OH^-(aq) + \tfrac{1}{2}H_2$$

Evidence for the 'solvated electron' $e^-(aq)$ can be obtained; reaction of sodium vapour with ice in the complete absence of air at 273 K gives a blue colour (cf. the reaction of sodium with liquid ammonia, p. 197). Magnesium, zinc and iron react with steam at elevated temperatures to yield hydrogen, and a few metals, in the presence of air, form a surface layer of oxide or hydroxide, for example iron, lead and aluminium. These reactions are more fully considered under the respective metals.

Water is not easily oxidized but fluorine and chlorine are both capable of liberating oxygen:

$$2F_2 + 2H_2O \rightarrow O_2 + 4HF$$
$$2Cl_2 + 2H_2O \xrightarrow{\text{sunlight}} O_2 + 4HCl$$

Hydrolysis

The term hydrolysis is used widely to mean (a) the direct reaction of water with a substance, for example the hydrolysis of an ion:

$$CH_3COO^- + H_2O \rightleftharpoons CH_3COOH + OH^-$$
$$H^- + H_2O \rightarrow OH^- + H_2\uparrow$$

or the hydrolysis of a molecule:

$$PCl_3 + 3H_2O \rightarrow H_3PO_3 + 3HCl$$
$$CH_3CN + H_2O \rightarrow CH_3CONH_2$$
$$CH_3CONH_2 + H_2O \rightarrow CH_3COONH_4$$

(b) the dissociation of water co-ordinated to a cation to yield hydroxonium ions, for example

$$[Fe(H_2O)_6]^{3+} + H_2O \rightleftharpoons [Fe(H_2O)_5(OH)]^{2+} + H_3O^+$$

This topic has been dealt with in depth previously, and it should be particularly noted that in each type of hydrolysis the initial electrostatic attraction of the water molecule is followed by covalent bond formation and (in contrast to hydration) the water molecule is broken up.

Water as a catalyst

Water appears to act as a catalyst in many chemical and physical changes; but because a minute trace of water is often all that is necessary to produce such a change, it is often very difficult to decide whether water is used up in the process (i.e. is or is not a true catalyst) and by what mechanism the 'catalysis' is accomplished. Thus, it was once believed that ammonium chloride, vigorously dried, did not undergo dissociation on heating into ammonia and hydrogen chloride. In fact, presence of a trace of water assists the volatilization of the solid, which can occur much more rapidly in the presence of water than when dry; the dissociation occurs with or without water. Again, boron trifluoride, BF_3 (Chapter 7), is known to be a very efficient catalyst for the polymerization of unsaturated organic compounds to form large polymer molecules; but catalysis only occurs if a minute trace of water is present — hence water here is called a 'cocatalyst'.

Other examples of water as an apparent catalyst are: (a) carbon monoxide will not burn in oxygen unless a trace of water is present, (b) sodium can be melted in dry chlorine without reaction; in the presence of a trace of moisture, violent reaction occurs.

Natural water

Because of its excellent solvent properties naturally-occurring water is never pure. During its passage through the air, rain water absorbs carbon dioxide, small amounts of oxygen and nitrogen, and in urban areas, small quantities of other gaseous oxides such as those of sulphur. On reaching the ground it can absorb more carbon dioxide from decaying animals and vegetable material and dissolve any soluble salts. The dissolved carbon dioxide can attack limestone or other rock containing the carbonates of calcium and magnesium:

$$CaCO_3(s) + CO_2(aq) + H_2O \rightarrow Ca^{2+}(aq) + 2HCO_3^-(aq)$$

Such water, and also that containing salts of multipositive metals (usually sulphates), is said to be *hard* since it does not readily produce a lather with soap. Experiments with alkali metal salts can be performed to verify that the hardness is due to the presence of the multipositive metal ions and not to any of the anions present. The hardness due to calcium and magnesium hydrogencarbonates is said to be *temporary* since it can be removed by boiling:

$$Ca^{2+} + 2HCO_3^- \xrightarrow{\text{heat}} CaCO_3\downarrow + CO_2\uparrow + H_2O$$

whilst that due to other salts is called *permanent* hardness and is unaffected by boiling. Soap, essentially sodium stearate $C_{17}H_{35}COO^-Na^+$, gives stearate and sodium ions in solution. The metal ions causing hardness form insoluble stearates which appear as scum, using up soap needed to 'solubilize' the fats and oils mainly responsible for 'dirt'. The metal stearate precipitates — scum — may be slightly coloured, and water for washing and laundering must be softened, or a detergent used as an alternative to soap.

Detergents are made by, for example, treating petroleum hydrocarbons with sulphuric acid, yielding sulphonated products which are water soluble. These can also 'solubilize' fats and oils since, like the stearate ions, they have an oil-miscible hydrocarbon chain and a water-soluble ionic end. The calcium salts of these substances, however, are soluble in water and, therefore, remove hardness without scum formation.

However, the deposition of salts from temporarily hard water in boilers, and so on (for example the 'fur' found in kettles) makes it desirable to soften such water for domestic and industrial use. Very soft water has the disadvantage that it attacks lead piping to give the hydroxide, $Pb(OH)_2$, which is slightly soluble and may give rise to lead poisoning, which is cumulative.

Methods for removing the metal ions responsible for hardness in water

Temporary hardness only may be removed:

(1) By boiling, as explained above; a method too expensive for use on a large scale.
(2) By addition of slaked lime, in calculated quantity for the particular degree of hardness (Clark's method):

$$Ca(HCO_3)_2 + Ca(OH)_2 \rightarrow 2CaCO_3\downarrow + 2H_2O$$

For temporary hardness due to magnesium hydrogencarbonate, more lime is required, since the magnesium precipitates as the hydroxide (less soluble than the carbonate):

$$Mg(HCO_3)_2 + 2Ca(OH)_2 \rightarrow Mg(OH)_2\downarrow + 2CaCO_3 + 2H_2O$$

It is thus important to determine the relative amounts of calcium and magnesium, for addition of too much lime means that calcium ions are reintroduced into the water, i.e. it becomes hard again, this hardness being *permanent*.

Temporary or permanent hardness may be removed:

(1) By addition of sodium carbonate, for example.

$$Ca(HCO_3)_2 + Na_2CO_3 \rightarrow CaCO_3\downarrow + 2NaHCO_3$$
$$CaSO_4 + Na_2CO_3 \rightarrow CaCO_3\downarrow + Na_2SO_4$$

(2) By the use of an ion-exchanger.

An ion-exchanger can be a naturally-occurring aluminosilicate, called a zeolite, or its synthetic equivalent known by a trade name, for example 'Permutit'. Such exchangers have large, open three-dimensional structured anions with the negative charges at intervals, and balancing cations capable of free movement throughout the open structure.

Alternatively the ion exchanger may be a synthetic polymer, for example a sulphonated polystyrene, where the negative charges are carried on the $-SO_3$ ends, and the interlocking structure is built up by cross-linking between the carbon atoms of the chain. The important property of any such solid is that the negative charge is static — a part of the solid — whilst the positive ions can move from their positions. Suppose, for example, that the positive ions are sodium ions. If we shake up the solid ion-exchanger with hard water, the sodium ions are replaced, i.e. *exchanged*, with ions of greater charge, for example those of calcium and magnesium, and hence the water is softened.

In practice, the exchanger is used in granules packed in a vertical column, through which the water flows. The capacity for exchange is considerable but when the column is exhaused i.e. 'filled' with calcium and magnesium ions, it can be regenerated by passing a concentrated solution of a sodium salt, for example sodium chloride, through it, the exchange equilibrium now favouring replacement of the calcium and magnesium by sodium ions since the latter are present in a much higher concentration.

Pure water

The type of exchanger used to soften water is more correctly called a *cation-exchanger* but it is also possible to make synthetic *anion-exchangers* in which negative ions are mobile and can be exchanged. By using hydrogen ions instead of sodium ions on the cation-exchanger (i.e. by regenerating it with hydrochloric acid instead of sodium chloride) and a hydroxyl ion anion-exchanger, the cations and anions present in water can be replaced by hydrogen and hydroxyl ions respectively. These ions unite to form un-ionized water. Thus any soluble salts can be removed completely from water by using two exchangers in series (or mixed in one column). Hence this is a method of obtaining pure water and can be used instead of distillation.

Pure water for use in the laboratory can be obtained from tap water (hard or soft) by distillation; if water of great purity is required, distillation must be carried out in special apparatus, usually made of quartz, not glass or metal; precautions must be taken to avoid any spray getting into the distillate. Water which is sufficiently pure for most laboratory purposes can, however, be obtained by passing tap water through cation-exchangers and anion-exchangers as described above, when the water is 'deionized'.

The estimation of water

In a substance such as a salt hydrate (for example $BaCl_2.2H_2O$) water can be determined by heating until it is all driven off. Provided that only water is evolved on heating, the difference in mass gives the water content. If water is mixed with other decomposition products, then the substance is heated in a current of dry nitrogen, and the evolved water absorbed in a **U** tube containing, say, calcium chloride, which is weighed before and after the experiment. (Dumas' experiment on the composition of water made use of this method.)

A method of estimating small amounts of water in organic liquids (and also in some inorganic salts) is that of Karl Fischer. The substance is titrated with a mixture of iodine, sulphur dioxide and pyridine dissolved in methanol. The essential reaction is:

$$H_2O + I_2 + SO_2 + CH_3OH \rightarrow 2HI + CH_3HSO_4$$

The base pyridine removes the hydriodic acid formed. The end-point occurs when the brown colour of free iodine is seen, i.e. when all the water has been used up. This method is widely used.

10.6.2   Heavy water, deuterium oxide, D_2O

Heavy water is obtained as a residue after prolonged electrolysis of ordinary water. Heavy water, as its name indicates, has a higher density than ordinary water (1.11 as against 1.00 g cm^{-3}), a slightly higher boiling point (374.6 K) and slightly different physical properties in general. Chemically, heavy water behaves like ordinary water in the kinds of reaction which it undergoes, but the rate of reaction is often different and the properties of the products may differ also. Thus, deuterium oxide adds on to anhydrous salts to form *deuterates* analogous to hydrates, for example the deuterate of copper(II) sulphate, $CuSO_4.5D_2O$, which has a slightly lower vapour pressure than the pentahydrate at the same temperature. Hydrolysis of aluminium tricarbide to give methane is a rapid reaction; deuterium oxide yields deuteriomethane, CD_4, only slowly. The fermentation of glucose proceeds more slowly in heavy water than in ordinary water.

Deuterium oxide has been used in the laboratory:

(1) For exchange experiments; in these, some hydrogen-containing compound is mixed with deuterium oxide, and the rate and extent of exchange between the two are studied. It is found that compounds containing 'labile' hydrogen (i.e. hydrogen atoms which are rapidly replaceable) exchange readily; others with fixed hydrogen do not. Examples of labile hydrogen atoms are those in the ammonium ion, NH_4^+, and in hydroxy compounds such as alcohols and sugars; non-labile hydrogen atoms are found in benzene, and in the phosphinate ion, $H_2PO_2^-$. The non-labile atoms in the phosphinate ion support the view that the hydrogen atoms are directly attached to the phosphorus and are not present as hydroxyl, —OH, groups (p. 216).

(2) As a starting material for other deuterio-compounds. For example deuterium oxide, on magnesium nitride, gives deuterioammonia, ND_3; with calcium dicarbide, deuterioethyne, C_2D_2, is obtained.

On a larger scale, deuterium oxide has been used as a 'moderator' in nuclear reactors, having some advantages over graphite.

10.6.3   Hydrogen peroxide, H_2O_2

Hydrogen peroxide is probably unique in the very large number of reactions by which it is formed. Some of these may be mentioned:

(1) From hydrogen and oxygen, by
    (a) Burning hydrogen in oxygen and cooling the flame rapidly, by directing against ice.
    (b) By exposing hydrogen and oxygen to intense ultraviolet light.
    (c) By exposure to certain radioactive rays, for example neutrons or electrons.
(2) By passage of a glow discharge through water vapour. This can produce good yields of highly concentrated hydrogen peroxide (cf. preparation of hydrazine).
(3) By oxidation processes, for example oxidation of hydrocarbons, fatty acids and even some metals.
(4) By electrolytic oxidation (*see* below).

In many of the processes, it is believed that hydroxyl radicals, OH·, are formed and that some of these unite to form hydrogen peroxide:

$$OH\cdot\ +\ OH\cdot\ \rightarrow\ HO{:}OH$$

In the laboratory, hydrogen peroxide can be *prepared* in dilute aqueous solution by adding barium peroxide to ice-cold dilute sulphuric acid:

$$BaO_2 + H_2SO_4 \rightarrow BaSO_4\downarrow + H_2O_2$$

The formation of an insoluble film of barium sulphate soon causes the reaction to cease, but addition of a little hydrochloric acid or better phosphoric(V) acid to the sulphuric acid allows the reaction to continue.

Alternatively an ice-cold dilute solution of sodium peroxide is passed through a column containing a cation-exchanger of the synthetic type (p. 243) where the cation is hydrogen (i.e. H_3O^+), then exchange occurs:

$$Na_2O_2 + 2H_3O^+ \rightarrow H_2O_2 + 2Na^+ + 2H_2O$$
$$\text{(on exchanger)} \qquad\qquad \text{(on exchanger)}$$

Hydrogen peroxide is obtained in aqueous solution at the bottom of the column. This is a good method of preparation.

On a large scale, hydrogen peroxide is produced by the electrolysis of ammonium hydrogensulphate, using a platinum anode and a lead cathode separated by a diaphragm. The essential process occurring is:

$$2NH_4HSO_4 \rightarrow (NH_4)_2S_2O_8 + H_2\uparrow$$

i.e.

$$2HSO_4^- \rightarrow S_2O_8^{2-} + 2H^+ + 2e^-$$

and

$$2H^+ + 2e^- \rightarrow H_2\uparrow$$

This is a process of anodic oxidation. The ammonium peroxodisulphate formed is then hydrolysed and the solution distilled *in vacuo*:

$$(NH_4)_2S_2O_8 + 2H_2O \rightarrow 2NH_4HSO_4 + H_2O_2$$

The ammonium hydrogensulphate is returned to the electrolytic cell. A process such as this yields an aqueous solution containing about 30 per cent hydrogen peroxide. The solution can be further concentrated, ultimately yielding pure hydrogen peroxide, by fractional distillation; but the heating of concentrated hydrogen peroxide solutions requires care (*see* below).

The above method has now been largely replaced by a newer process, in which the substance 2-ethylanthraquinone is reduced by hydrogen in presence of a catalyst to 2-ethylanthraquinol; when this substance is oxidized by air, hydrogen peroxide is formed and the original anthraquinone is recovered:

2-ethylanthraquinone   + H_2O_2 $\xleftarrow{\text{air}}$ 2-ethylanthraquinol

Properties

Pure hydrogen peroxide is a colourless, viscous liquid, m.p. 272.5 K, density 1.4 g cm^{-3}. On heating at atmospheric pressure it decomposes before the boiling point is reached; and a sudden increase of temperature may produce explosive decomposition, since the decomposition reaction is strongly exothermic:

$$H_2O_2(l) \rightarrow H_2O(l) + \tfrac{1}{2}O_2(g) \qquad \Delta H = -98.3 \text{ kJ mol}^{-1}$$

This is a disproportionation reaction, and is strongly catalysed by light and by a wide variety of materials, including many metals (for example copper and iron) especially if these materials have a large surface area. Some of these can induce explosive decomposition. Pure hydrogen peroxide can be kept in glass vessels in the dark, or in stone jars or in vessels made of pure aluminium with a smooth surface.

The structure of hydrogen peroxide is given in *Figure 10.5*. Rotation about the O—O bond is relatively easy. Hydrogen bonding causes even more association of liquid hydrogen peroxide than occurs in water (and hence hydrogen peroxide is more viscous).

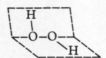

Figure 10.5 The hydrogen peroxide molecule

Aqueous solutions of hydrogen peroxide

Because of the instability of pure and concentrated aqueous solutions of hydrogen peroxide, it is usually used in dilute solution. The concentration of such solutions is often expressed in terms of the volume of oxygen evolved when the solution decomposes:

$$2H_2O_2 \rightarrow 2H_2O + O_2\uparrow$$

Thus a '10 volume' solution is such that 1 cm^3 yields 10 cm^3 of oxygen at s.t.p. From the above equation we see that 2 moles H_2O_2 give 22.4 l of oxygen at s.t.p. and using this fact the concentration of any solution can be calculated.

Aqueous solutions of hydrogen peroxide decompose slowly; the decomposition is catalysed by alkalis, by light and by heterogeneous catalysts, for example dust, platinum black and manganese(IV) oxide, the latter being used in the common laboratory preparation of oxygen from hydrogen peroxide (p. 230).

Acidity

Hydrogen peroxide in aqueous solution is a weak dibasic acid:

$$H_2O_2 \rightleftharpoons H^+ + HO_2^- \qquad K_a = 2.4 \times 10^{-12} \text{ mol l}^{-1}$$

The salts, known as peroxides (e.g. Na_2O_2) yield hydrogen peroxide on acidification and this reaction provides a useful method of differentiating between *peroxides* which contain the O—O linkage, and dioxides.

Oxidizing and reducing properties

Hydrogen peroxide has both oxidizing properties (when it is converted into water) and reducing properties (when it is converted into oxygen); relevant data for the half-reactions are:

oxidation $H_2O_2(aq) + 2H_3O^+ + 2e^- \rightarrow 4H_2O$ $E^\ominus = +1.77$ V
reduction $O_2(g) + 2H_3O^+ + 2e^- \rightarrow 2H_2O_2(aq)$ $E^\ominus = +0.69$ V

The following reactions are examples of hydrogen peroxide used as an oxidizing agent:

(1) Lead(II) sulphide is oxidized to lead(II) sulphate; this reaction has been used in the restoration of old pictures where the white lead pigment has become blackened by conversion into lead sulphide due to hydrogen sulphide in urban air:

$$PbS + 4H_2O_2 \rightarrow PbSO_4 + 4H_2O$$
black   white

(2) Iron(II) is oxidized to iron(III) in acid solutions:

$$2Fe^{2+} + H_2O_2 + 2H^+ \rightarrow 2Fe^{3+} + 2H_2O$$

(3) Iodide ions are oxidized to iodine in acid solution:

$$2I^- + 2H^+ + H_2O_2 \rightarrow I_2 + 2H_2O$$

As the above redox potentials indicate, only in the presence of very powerful oxidizing agents does hydrogen peroxide behave as a reducing agent. For example:

(1) Chlorine water (p. 283) is reduced to hydrochloric acid:

$$HClO + H_2O_2 \rightarrow H_2O + HCl + O_2\uparrow$$

(2) The hexacyanoferrate(III) ion is reduced in alkaline solution to hexacyanoferrate(II):

$$[Fe(CN)_6]^{3-} + H_2O_2 + 2OH^- \rightarrow [Fe(CN)_6]^{4-} + 2H_2O + O_2\uparrow$$

[Compare this reaction with (2) of the oxidizing examples, where iron(II) is oxidized to iron(III) in acid solution; change of pH, and complex formation by the iron, cause the *complexed* iron(III) to be reduced.]

(3) Manganate(VII) is reduced to manganese(II) ion in acid solution (usually sulphuric acid):

$$2MnO_4^- + 6H^+ + 5H_2O_2 \rightarrow 2Mn^{2+} + 8H_2O + 5O_2\uparrow$$

It has been shown in this reaction that all the evolved oxygen comes from the hydrogen peroxide and none from the manganate(VII) or water, by using $H_2{}^{18}O_2$ and determining the ^{18}O isotope in the evolved gas.

The reaction with acidified potassium manganate(VII) is used in the quantitative estimation of hydrogen peroxide.

Two tests for hydrogen peroxide
(1) The oxidation of black lead(II) sulphide to the white sulphate is a very sensitive test if the black sulphide is used as a stain on filter paper.
(2) Addition of dilute potassium dichromate(VI) solution, $K_2Cr_2O_7$, to a solution of hydrogen peroxide produces an unstable blue coloration; on adding a little ether and shaking this compound transfers to the organic layer in which it is rather more stable.

Uses
Pure hydrogen peroxide (or highly concentrated solution) is used together with oil as an under-water fuel. The fuel is ignited by inducing the strongly exothermic decomposition reaction by spraying it with a finely-divided solid catalyst. Mixtures of hydrazine (p. 199) and hydrogen peroxide are used for rocket propulsion.

Hydrogen peroxide in aqueous solution has many uses, because the products from its reaction are either water or oxygen, which are generally innocuous. The chief use is bleaching of textiles, both natural and synthetic, and of wood pulp for paper. Other uses are the oxidation of dyestuffs, in photography and in the production of porous concrete and foam rubber where the evolved oxygen 'leavens' the product. Hydrogen peroxide is a useful antiseptic (for example, in toothpaste). It is increasingly used to prepare organic *peroxo*-compounds, which are used as catalysts in, for example, polymerization reactions, and to prepare *epoxy*-compounds (where an oxygen atom adds on across a carbon–carbon double bond); these are used as plasticizers.

10.6.4   Hydrogen sulphide H_2S

Sulphur can be reduced directly to hydrogen sulphide by passing hydrogen through molten sulphur; the reversible reaction

$$H_2 + S \rightleftharpoons H_2S$$

occurs. In the laboratory the gas is most conveniently prepared by the action of an acid on a metal sulphide, iron(II) and dilute hydrochloric acid commonly being used:

$$FeS + 2HCl \rightarrow FeCl_2 + H_2S\uparrow$$

The gas is washed with water to remove any hydrogen chloride. Since iron(II) sulphide is a non-stoichiometric compound and always contains some free iron, the hydrogen sulphide always contains some hydrogen, liberated by the action of the iron on the acid. A sample of hydrogen sulphide of better purity can be obtained if antimony(III) sulphide (stibnite), Sb_2S_3, is warmed with concentrated hydrochloric acid:

$$Sb_2S_3 + 6HCl \rightarrow 2SbCl_3 + 3H_2S\uparrow$$

Alternatively pure hydrogen sulphide is obtained by the hydrolysis of aluminium(III) sulphide:

$$Al_2S_3 + 6H_2O \rightarrow 2Al(OH)_3 + 3H_2S\uparrow$$

Properties

Hydrogen sulphide is a colourless gas, b.p. 213 K, with a most unpleasant odour; the gas is very toxic, but the intense odour fortunately permits very minute concentrations of the gas to be detected. It is found in small amounts in some natural springs and certain oil fields.

Hydrogen sulphide burns in air with a blue flame yielding sulphur dioxide, but if the air supply is limited, preferential combustion to form sulphur occurs:

$$2H_2S + 3O_2 \rightarrow 2SO_2 + 2H_2O$$
$$2H_2S + O_2 \rightarrow 2S\downarrow + 2H_2O$$

Hydrogen sulphide is slightly soluble in water, giving an approximately 0.1 M solution under 1 atmosphere pressure; it can be removed from the solution by boiling. The solution is weakly acidic and dissolves in alkalis to give sulphides and hydrogensulphides. The equilibrium constants

$$H_2S + H_2O \rightleftharpoons H_3O^+ + HS^- \qquad K_a = 8.9 \times 10^{-8} \text{ mol l}^{-1} \text{ at 298 K}$$
$$HS^- + H_2O \rightleftharpoons H_3O^+ + S^{2-} \qquad K_a = 1.2 \times 10^{-13} \text{ mol l}^{-1} \text{ at 298 K}$$

indicate that both normal and acid salts will be hydrolysed.

Hydrogen sulphide is a reducing agent in both acid and alkaline solution as shown by the following examples:

(1) Its aqueous solution oxidizes slowly on standing in air depositing sulphur.

(2) It reduces the halogen elements in aqueous solution depositing sulphur:

$$Cl_2 + H_2S \rightarrow 2HCl + S\downarrow$$

(3) It reduces sulphur dioxide, in aqueous solution:

$$2H_2S + SO_3^{2-} + 2H^+ \rightarrow 3H_2O + 3S\downarrow$$

(4) In acid solution, dichromates(VI) [and also chromates(VI) which are converted into dichromates] are reduced to chromium(III) salts:

$$Cr_2O_7^{2-} + 8H^+ + 3H_2S \rightarrow 2Cr^{3+} + 7H_2O + 3S\downarrow$$

[Hence the orange colour of a dichromate is changed to the green colour of the hydrated chromium(III) ion, Cr^{3+}, and sulphur is precipitated when hydrogen sulphide is passed through an acid solution.]

(5) In acid solution, the manganate(VII) ion is reduced to the manganese(II) ion with decolorization:

$$2MnO_4^- + 5H_2S + 6H^+ \rightarrow 5S\downarrow + 8H_2O + 2Mn^{2+}$$

(6) Iron(III) is reduced to iron(II):

$$2Fe^{3+} + H_2S \rightarrow 2Fe^{2+} + 2H^+ + S\downarrow$$

Hydrogen sulphide reacts slowly with many metals (more rapidly if they are heated) to yield the sulphide of the metal and (usually) hydrogen, for example causing the tarnishing of silver.

Since most metallic sulphides are insoluble, many are precipitated when hydrogen sulphide is passed through solutions containing ions of the metals.

Some are precipitated in acid, and others in alkaline solution, making the reactions valuable in the detection of metal cations in aqueous solution.

Tests for hydrogen sulphide
(1) It smells of rotten eggs.
(2) The blackening of filter paper, moistened with a soluble lead(II) salt (e.g. the ethanoate or nitrate), by the formation of lead(II) sulphide.

10.6.5   Hydrogen polysulphides or sulphanes

Compounds of hydrogen and sulphur, with a higher proportion of sulphur than in hydrogen sulphide, have been obtained as yellow oils by adding acids to the polysulphides of metals. They are unstable, decomposing into sulphur and hydrogen sulphide and thus making analysis difficult; however, sulphanes H_2S_x (x = 3 to 6) have been obtained in a pure state.

10.6.6   Hydrogen selenide (selenium hydride), H_2Se, and hydrogen telluride (tellurium hydride), H_2Te

These two gases can readily by prepared by the action of acids on selenides and tellurides respectively, the reactions being analogous to that for the preparation of hydrogen sulphide.

These gases have lower thermal stabilities than hydrogen sulphide as expected from their enthalpies of formation (*Table 10.2*) and they are consequently more powerful reducing agents than hydrogen sulphide.

Since the hydrogen–element bond energy decreases from sulphur to tellurium they are stronger acids than hydrogen sulphide in aqueous solution but are still classified as weak acids — similar change in acid strength is observed for Group VII hydrides.

Many of the reactions of these acids, however, closely resemble those of hydrogen sulphide, the main difference being one of degree.

10.6.7   Polonium hydride, H_2Po

This has been made in trace quantities by the action of dilute hydrochloric acid on magnesium plated with polonium. As expected, it is extremely unstable and decomposes even at 100 K.

10.7   Binary compounds

The elements (X) in this group are two electrons short of a noble gas structure which they can achieve either by gaining or sharing electrons. The formation of the X^{2-} ion may require considerable amounts of energy; thus for oxygen 650 kJ must be supplied for the reaction

$$O(g) + 2e^- \rightarrow O^{2-}(g) \qquad \Delta H = +650 \text{ kJ mol}^{-1}$$

Despite this energy requirement, many solid ionic oxides are known because, in their formation, a high lattice energy results from the combination of a metal cation with the small, double-charged O^{2-} ion, and this provides the energy required. [In aqueous solution, many ionic oxides are insoluble; if the oxide is soluble, then since O^{2-} is a very strong base (p. 80) it reacts with the water to give hydroxide ions OH^-.] In contrast to the oxide ion, the larger ions S^{2-}, Se^{2-} and Te^{2-} produce smaller lattice energies with cations in solids, and only the most electropositive metals yield ionic solids containing these anions; the other elements give essentially covalent compounds.

Oxygen bonds covalently to many non-metals, and in many oxides, both with metals and non-metals, the other element achieves a high oxidation state, for example Cr, +6 in CrO_3; S, +6 in SO_3; Cl, +7 in Cl_2O_7. (This ability to bring out high oxidation states is exhibited also by fluorine; it is to be attributed to the high electronegativities of oxygen and fluorine.)

10.7.1 Oxides

Oxygen will unite with, i.e. *oxidize* (in the simplest sense), most elements other than the noble gases, forming oxides. With strongly electropositive metals, for example sodium or calcium, the oxides formed are *ionic*, for example sodium gives the oxide Na_2O, containing the ion O^{2-}. Such oxides are *basic*, reacting with acids to give salts and water only; many examples are given in this book. With less electropositive metals or elements, for example aluminium, zinc and lead, the bond between element and oxygen may assume a partly covalent character, and the oxide becomes *amphoteric*, dissolving in both acids and bases, for example

$$Al_2O_3 + 6H^+ + 9H_2O \rightarrow 2[Al(H_2O)_6]^{3+}$$
$$\text{hydrated}$$
$$Al_2O_3 + 6OH^- + 3H_2O \rightarrow 2[Al(OH)_6]^{3-}$$

Notice that the acidic character is associated with the ability of aluminium to increase its covalency from three in the oxide to six in the hydroxoaluminate ion, $[Al(OH)_6]^{3-}$; the same ability to increase covalency is found in other metals whose oxides are amphoteric, for example

$$ZnO \rightarrow [Zn(OH)_4]^{2-} \text{ or } [Zn(OH)_6]^{4-}$$
$$PbO \rightarrow [Pb(OH)_4]^{2-} \text{ or } [Pb(OH)_6]^{4-}$$

10.7.2 Higher oxides

Variable oxidation state is also exhibited in the oxides themselves among metals in this region of electronegativity. Thus lead, for example, forms the monoxide PbO (+2) and the dioxide PbO_2 (+4) (the compound Pb_3O_4 is not a simple oxide but is sometimes called a 'compound' oxide). Similarly, manganese gives the oxides MnO and MnO_2.

Although the dioxides are oxidizing agents, for example

$$PbO_2 + 4HCl \rightarrow PbCl_2 + 2H_2O + Cl_2 \uparrow$$

the oxidizing power lies in the higher valency or oxidation state of the metal, not in the presence of more oxygen (distinction from peroxides, see p. 252).

The more noble metals (for example copper, mercury and silver can form oxides, and exhibit variable oxidation state in such compounds (for example Cu_2O, CuO), but it is not easy to prepare such oxides by direct action of oxygen on the metal, and elevated temperatures are necessary. Moreover, in the case of silver and mercury, loss of oxygen from the oxide by heating is easy. The oxides are, moreover, basic [for example $Ag_2O \rightarrow Ag^+(aq)$, $CuO \rightarrow Cu^{2+}(aq)$ in acids].

10.7.3 Acidic oxides

The other more electronegative elements are non-metals and form oxides which are entirely covalent and usually *acidic*. For example, sulphur yields the oxides SO_2 and SO_3, dissolving in bases to form the ions SO_3^{2-} and SO_4^{2-} respectively. A few non-metallic oxides are often described as *neutral* (for example carbon monoxide and dinitrogen oxide) because no directly related acid anion is known to exist.

The two oxides formed with hydrogen, H_2O and H_2O_2, have already been discussed, but it should be emphasized that hydrogen peroxide and the peroxides formed from it contain the —O—O— linkage. The oxidizing power of these peroxides lies in the oxygen of the peroxo-group, unlike the dioxides (*see* p. 251).

10.7.4 Sulphides

The alkali metal sulphides
These are ionic solids and can exist as the anhydrous salts (prepared by heating together sulphur with excess of the alkali metal) or as hydrates, for example $Na_2S.9H_2O$. Since hydrogen sulphide is a weak acid these salts are hydrolysed in water,

$$S^{2-} + H_2O \rightarrow HS^- + OH^-$$
$$HS^- + H_2O \rightarrow H_2S + OH^-$$

and smell of hydrogen sulphide. Aqueous solutions of these salts are conveniently prepared by the action of hydrogen sulphide on the alkali metal hydroxide; if excess of hydrogen sulphide is used the hydrogensulphide is formed, for example $NaHS$. Solutions of these sulphides can dissolve sulphur to give coloured polysulphides, for example Na_2S_4 containing anionic sulphur chains.

The sulphides of alkaline earth metals
These are similar to those of the alkali metals but are rather less soluble in water. However, calcium sulphide, for example, is not precipitated by addition of sulphide ions to a solution of a calcium salt, since in acid solution the equilibrium position

$$H_2S + Ca^{2+} \rightleftharpoons CaS + 2H^+$$

is very much to the left and in neutral, or alkaline solution the soluble hydrogensulphide is formed, for example

$$CaS + H_2O \rightarrow Ca^{2+} + HS^- + OH^-$$

The sulphides of aluminium and chromium

These can be prepared by the direct combination of the elements. They are rapidly hydrolysed by water and the hydrolysis of solid aluminium sulphide can be used to prepare hydrogen sulphide:

$$Al_2S_3 + 6H_2O \rightarrow 2Al(OH)_3 + 3H_2S\uparrow$$

Consequently they cannot be prepared by the addition of sulphide ions to a solution of the metal salt, the hydrated metal ions being so strongly acidic that the following reaction occurs, for example

$$2[Al(H_2O)_6]^{3+} + 3S^{2-} \rightarrow 2[Al(OH)_3(H_2O)_3]\downarrow + 3H_2S\uparrow$$

The sulphides of most other metals

These are practically insoluble in water, are not hydrolysed, and so may be prepared by addition of a sufficient concentration of sulphide ion to exceed the solubility product of the particular sulphide. Some sulphides, for example those of lead(II), copper(I) and silver(I), have low solubility products and are precipitated by the small concentration of sulphide ions produced by passing hydrogen sulphide through an acid solution of the metal salts; others for example those of zinc(II), iron(II), nickel(II) and cobalt(II) are only precipitated when sulphide ions are available in reasonable concentrations, as they are when hydrogen sulphide is passed into an alkaline solution.

Many of these sulphides occur naturally, for example iron(II) sulphide, FeS (magnetic pyrites), and antimony(III) sulphide, Sb_2S_3 (stibnite). They can usually be prepared by the direct combination of the elements, effected by heating, but this rarely produces a pure stoichiometric compound and the product often contains a slight excess of the metal, or of sulphur.

10.7.5   Selenides and tellurides

These closely resemble the corresponding sulphides. The alkali metal selenides and tellurides are colourless solids, and are powerful reducing agents in aqueous solution, being oxidized by air to the elements selenium and tellurium respectively (cf. the reducing power of the hydrides).

10.8   Oxides and oxoacids of sulphur and their salts

The elements, sulphur, selenium and tellurium form both di- and tri-oxides. The dioxides reflect the increasing metallic character of the elements. At room temperature, sulphur dioxide is a gas, boiling point 263 K, selenium dioxide is a volatile solid which sublimes at 588 K under 1 atmosphere pressure, and tellurium dioxide is a colourless, apparently ionic, crystalline dimorphic solid.

10.8.1   Sulphur dioxide, SO_2

Sulphur dioxide is formed together with a little of the trioxide when sulphur burns in air:

$$S + O_2 \rightarrow SO_2$$
$$2S + 3O_2 \rightarrow 2SO_3$$

It can be prepared by the reduction of hot concentrated sulphuric acid by a metal. Copper is used since it does not also liberate hydrogen from the acid:

$$Cu + 2H_2SO_4 \rightarrow CuSO_4 + 2H_2O + SO_2\uparrow$$

The equation is not strictly representative of the reaction for the acid is reduced further and a black deposit consisting of copper(I) and copper(II) sulphides is also produced.

Sulphur dioxide is also produced by the action of an acid (usually concentrated sulphuric since it is involatile) on a sulphite or hydrogensulphite for example

$$2HSO_3^- + H_2SO_4 \rightarrow SO_4^{2-} + 2H_2O + 2SO_2\uparrow$$

On the industrial scale it is produced in large quantities for the manufacture of sulphuric acid and the production methods are dealt with later. It has been estimated that more than 4 000 000 tonnes of sulphur dioxide a year enter the atmosphere of Britain from the burning of coal and oil.

The molecule of sulphur dioxide has a bent structure. Both S—O distances are equal and short and since sulphur can expand its outer quantum level beyond eight, double bonds between the atoms are likely; i.e.

Liquid sulphur dioxide as a solvent

Liquid sulphur dioxide is a solvent for a number of substances, for example iodine, sulphur, some sulphites, potassium iodide and sulphur dichloride oxide, $SOCl_2$ (see p. 268). The liquid can be *assumed* to ionize slightly, thus:

$$2SO_2 \rightleftharpoons SO^{2+} + SO_3^{2-}$$
$$2H_2O \rightleftharpoons H_3O^+ + OH^-$$

Hence, for example, sulphur dichloride oxide behaves as an 'acid' and a sulphite as a 'base' thus:

$$\underbrace{SOCl_2}_{\underbrace{SO^{2+} + 2Cl^-}_{\text{acid}}} + \underbrace{Na_2SO_3}_{\underbrace{2Na^+ + SO_3^{2-}}_{\text{base}}} \rightarrow \underbrace{2NaCl\downarrow}_{\substack{\text{salt} \\ \text{(insoluble)}}} + \underbrace{2SO_2}_{\text{solvent}}$$

Properties of sulphur dioxide

Sulphur dioxide is oxidized by chlorine in the presence of charcoal or camphor to give *sulphur dichloride dioxide (sulphuryl chlorde)*, SO_2Cl_2:

$$SO_2 + Cl_2 \rightarrow SO_2Cl_2$$

Dioxides and peroxides oxidize SO_2 to yield sulphates:

$$PbO_2 + SO_2 \rightarrow PbSO_4$$
$$Na_2O_2 + SO_2 \rightarrow Na_2SO_4$$

Sulphur dioxide is an acidic oxide and dissolves readily in water, and in alkalis with which it forms salts:

$$NaOH + SO_2 \rightarrow NaHSO_3$$
sodium hydrogensulphite
$$2NaOH + SO_2 \rightarrow Na_2SO_3 + H_2O$$
sodium sulphite

Although sulphur dioxide, as a gas, is a reducing agent in the sense that it unites with oxygen, free or combined (for example in dioxides or peroxides) most of its reducing reactions in aqueous solution are better regarded as reactions of 'sulphurous acid' (in acid solution), or the sulphite ion (in alkaline solution).

10.8.2   'Sulphurous acid'

The solution obtained when sulphur dioxide dissolves in water has long been thought to contain un-ionized sulphurous acid, H_2SO_3, but more probably contains hydrated sulphur dioxide (cf. NH_3 solution, p. 194). The solution behaves as a dibasic acid, i.e.

$$SO_2(aq) + 2H_2O \rightleftharpoons H_3O^+ + HSO_3^- \qquad K_a = 1.6 \times 10^{-2} \text{ mol l}^{-1} \text{ at } 298\text{ K}.$$
$$HSO_3^- + H_2O \rightleftharpoons H_3O^+ + SO_3^{2-} \qquad K_a = 6.2 \times 10^{-8} \text{ mol l}^{-1} \text{ at } 298\text{ K}.$$

The sulphite ion, SO_3^{2-}, has a pyramidal structure and the short S—O bond length suggests the presence of double bonding, i.e.

Two important redox potentials for reduction by sulphur dioxide in aqueous solution are:

acid $SO_4^{2-}(aq) + 4H_3O^+ + 2e^- \rightarrow H_2SO_3(aq) + 5H_2O \qquad E^{\ominus} = +0.17 \text{ V}$

alkali $SO_4^{2-}(aq) + H_2O + 2e^- \rightarrow SO_3^{2-}(aq) + 2OH^-(aq) \qquad E^{\ominus} = -0.93 \text{ V}$

Some important reducing reactions are given below; for simplicity, the reducing entity is taken to be SO_3^{2-} in all cases.
(1) Sulphites react with molecular oxygen (or air) to give sulphates, a

reaction catalysed by certain ions [for example Fe^{2+}, Cu^{2+}, arsenate(III) ion, AsO_3^{3-}] and inhibited by, for example, phenol, glycerol and tin(II) ions, Sn^{2+}:

$$2SO_3^{2-} + O_2 \rightarrow 2SO_4^{2-}$$

(2) Sulphites react with oxidizing agents, for example manganate(VII) and dichromate(VI):

$$\underset{\text{purple}}{2MnO_4^-} + 5SO_3^{2-} + 6H^+ \rightarrow \underset{\text{colourless}}{2Mn^{2+}} + 5SO_4^{2-} + 3H_2O$$

$$\underset{\text{orange}}{Cr_2O_7^{2-}} + 3SO_3^{2-} + 8H^+ \rightarrow \underset{\text{green}}{2Cr^{3+}} + 3SO_4^{2-} + 4H_2O$$

This reaction is a useful test for a sulphite or for moist sulphur dioxide, which turns 'dichromate paper' (filter paper soaked in potassium dichromate) from yellow to green.

(3) Sulphites are oxidized by chlorine water and solutions containing chloric(I) (hypochlorous) acid or the chlorate(I) (hypochlorite) ion

$$Cl_2 + SO_3^{2-} + H_2O \rightarrow 2Cl^- + SO_4^{2-} + 2H^+$$

or

$$OCl^- + SO_3^{2-} \rightarrow Cl^- + SO_4^{2-}$$

(4) Iron(III) is reduced to iron(II) by sulphites:

$$2Fe^{3+} + SO_3^{2-} + H_2O \rightarrow 2Fe^{2+} + 2H^+ + SO_4^{2-}$$

In the presence of strong reducing agents the sulphite ion acts as an oxidizing agent; some examples are:

(1) The oxidation of hydrogen sulphide to sulphur:

$$2H_2S + SO_3^{2-} + 2H^+ \rightarrow 3H_2O + 3S\downarrow$$

(2) In strongly acid solution, substances which are normally reducing agents reduce sulphur dioxide solution or sulphites, for example iron(II) and zinc:

$$4Fe^{2+} + SO_3^{2-} + 6H^+ \rightarrow 4Fe^{3+} + S\downarrow + 3H_2O$$

$$2SO_3^{2-} + \underset{\text{(dust)}}{Zn} + 4H^+ \rightarrow \underset{\text{(dithionite)}}{S_2O_4^{2-}} + Zn^{2+} + 2H_2O$$

If a *solid* sulphite is heated with zinc dust (or carbon) the sulphite is reduced to sulphide:

$$Na_2SO_3 + 3Zn \rightarrow Na_2S + 3ZnO$$

Uses

The reducing action of sulphurous acid and sulphites in solution leads to their uses as mild bleaching agents (for example magenta and some natural dyes, such as indigo, and the yellow dye in wool and straw are bleached). They are also used as a preservative for fruit and other foodstuffs for this reason. Other uses are to remove chlorine from fabrics after bleaching and in photography.

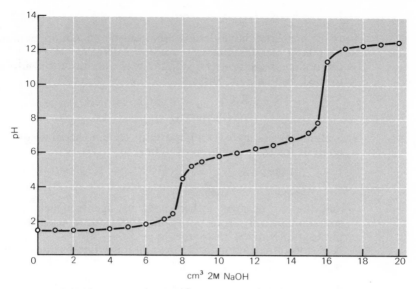

Figure 10.6 Titration of 25 cm^3 of saturated aqueous sulphur dioxide with 2M sodium hydroxide at 298 K

10.8.3 Sulphites and hydrogensulphites

When a saturated solution of sulphur dioxide is titrated against 2M sodium hydroxide solution the pH curve shown in *Figure 10.6* is obtained. The reaction completed on addition of 7.9 cm^3 is

$$SO_2(aq) + NaOH \rightarrow NaHSO_3$$
sodium
hydrogensulphite

and after 15.8 cm^3

$$SO_2(aq) + 2NaOH \rightarrow Na_2SO_3 \quad + H_2O$$
sodium sulphite

Evaporation and crystallization of the sodium sulphite solutions gives crystals of the heptahydrate $Na_2SO_3.7H_2O$. However, on evaporation of the hydrogensulphite solution, the solid obtained is chiefly sodium pentaoxodisulphate(IV) ('metabisulphite') $Na_2S_2O_5$, and contains little if any of the hydrogensulphite. However, the hydrogen sulphite ion is obtained when the solid redissolves in water:

$$Na_2S_2O_5 + H_2O \rightarrow 2Na^+ + 2HSO_3^-$$

Alternatively these salts can be prepared by first saturating a known volume of alkali with sulphur dioxide, giving a solution of the hydrogensulphite, from which sulphite can be prepared by the addition of a second equal volume of alkali.

Properties

The redox properties have already been considered. A number of reactions of soluble (alkali metal) sulphites are noteworthy:

(1) On boiling a solution of a sulphite with sulphur a thiosulphate(VI)* is formed, and sulphur 'dissolves':

$$SO_3^{2-} + S \rightarrow S_2O_3^{2-} \qquad \text{(e.g. Na}_2\text{S}_2\text{O}_3\text{)}$$
$$\text{thiosulphate(VI)}$$

Sodium thiosulphate is an important reducing agent used in volumetric analysis for the estimation of iodine:

$$I_2 + 2S_2O_3^{2-} \rightarrow 2I^- + S_4O_6^{2-}$$
$$\text{tetrathionate ion}$$

and thereby of many other oxidizing agents which liberate iodine stoichiometrically from potassium iodide. It is used as the 'fixer' in photography under the name 'hypo'.

(2) Addition of barium chloride precipitates white barium sulphite:

$$Ba^{2+} + SO_3^{2-} \rightarrow BaSO_3\downarrow$$

Barium sulphite is soluble in dilute hydrochloric acid unlike barium sulphate which is insoluble. Hence this reaction, and the evolution of sulphur dioxide on addition of an acid, distinguishes a sulphite from a sulphate.

(3) Sodium hydrogensulphite, when freshly prepared, reacts with aldehydes to form crystalline addition compounds, for example

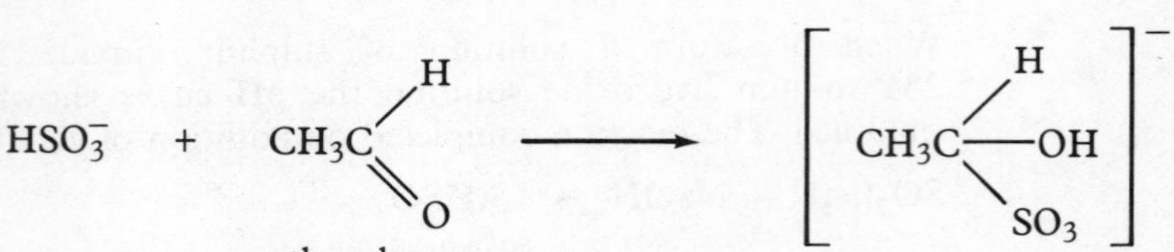

ethanal
(acetaldehyde)

This reaction is used in organic chemistry to separate an aldehyde from, for example, an ester.

10.8.4 Sulphur trioxide [sulphur(VI) oxide]

Sulphur trioxide was first prepared by heating iron(III) sulphate:

$$Fe_2(SO_4)_3 \rightarrow Fe_2O_3 + 3SO_3$$

It is also obtained by the dehydration of concentrated sulphuric acid with phosphorus(V) oxide:

$$2H_2SO_4 + P_4O_{10} \rightarrow 4HPO_3 + 2SO_3$$

*The thiosulphate ion has the structure $[S{=}SO_3]^{2-}$; the oxidation state of the *central* sulphur atom is $+6$.

and the thermal decomposition of iron(II) sulphate:

$2FeSO_4 \rightarrow Fe_2O_3 + SO_2 + SO_3$
iron(II)   iron(III)
sulphate   oxide

In the laboratory it is commonly prepared by the reaction between sulphur dioxide and oxygen at high temperature in the presence of a platinum catalyst:

$2SO_2 + O_2 \rightleftharpoons 2SO_3$

(This is the basis of the industrial manufacture of sulphuric acid and is dealt with on p. 260).

Sulphur trioxide can be collected as a white solid in a receiver surrounded by a freezing mixture of ice and salt.

Properties

In the vapour state, sulphur trioxide has the formula SO_3. The molecule is planar with all the S—O bonds short and of equal length. The structure can be represented simply as

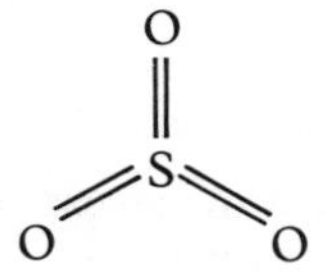

but is probably a resonance hybrid of several forms. Solid sulphur trioxide exists in at least two modifications, the α and β forms. The α-form is an ice-like transparent solid consisting of rings of formula S_3O_9 (shown *geometrically in Figure 10.7*). This form melts at 290 K, and boils at 318 K. The β-form, obtained when the α-form is allowed to stand for a long time at a temperature below 298 K, exists as asbestos-like, felted needles and has a structure consisting of SO_4 tetrahedra linked together in long chains.

Solid sulphur trioxide reacts explosively with liquid water:

$SO_3 + H_2O \rightarrow H_2SO_4 \qquad \Delta H = -88 \text{ kJ mol}^{-1}$

and it fumes strongly in moist air. The gas sulphur trioxide does not readily dissolve in water, but it reacts with concentrated sulphuric acid, thus:

$H_2SO_4 + SO_3 \rightarrow H_2S_2O_7$
$H_2S_2O_7 + SO_3 \rightarrow H_2S_3O_{10}$

and so on.

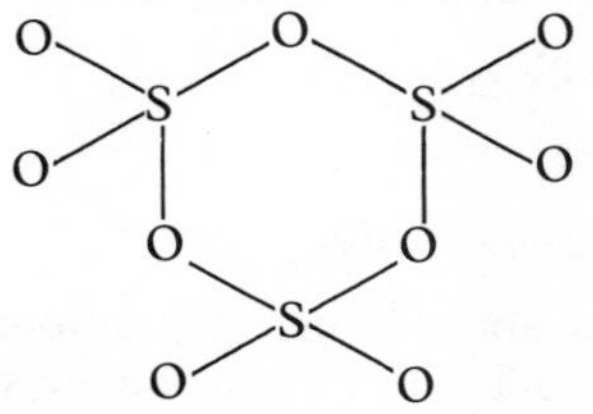

Figure 10.7 Geometrical shape of the α-form of solid sulphur(VI) oxide

Sulphur trioxide unites exothermically with basic oxides to give sulphates, for example

$$CaO + SO_3 \rightarrow CaSO_4$$

Sulphur trioxide is used on an industrial scale for sulphonating organic compounds.

10.8.5 Sulphuric acid, H_2SO_4

Sulphuric acid is probably the most important chemical substance not found naturally. Its manufacture is therefore important; the total world production is about 25 000 000 tonnes per year.

Manufacture
The different methods of manufacturing sulphuric acid are essentially the same in principle and consist of three distinct processes:
(1) Production of sulphur dioxide.
(2) Conversion of sulphur dioxide into sulphur trioxide.
(3) Conversion of sulphur trioxide into sulphuric acid.

(1) Sulphur dioxide is obtained in the following three ways:
   (a) By burning elemental sulphur (imported):

$$S + O_2 \rightarrow SO_2$$

   (b) As a by-product of the roasting process in the extraction of certain metals from their sulphide ores, for example

$$2ZnS + 3O_2 \rightarrow 2ZnO + 2SO_2\uparrow$$
$$2PbS + 3O_2 \rightarrow 2PbO + 2SO_2\uparrow$$
$$4FeS_2 + 11O_2 \rightarrow 2Fe_2O_3 + 8SO_2\uparrow$$

Since arsenic is often found in nature associated with sulphide ores, sulphur dioxide obtained by this method may contain some arsenic(III) oxide as impurity, and in certain processes this is a distinct disadvantage.
   (c) From *anhydrite*, $CaSO_4$ (the only sulphur compound found in large quantities in Great Britain).

Anhydrite, shale (SiO_2) and coke are finely powdered, intimately mixed and compressed into pellets which are fired in a reverberatory furnace at a temperature of about 1700 K.
The carbon reduces a quarter of the anhydrite to the sulphide:

$$CaSO_4 + 2C \rightarrow CaS + 2CO_2$$

The sulphide then reacts with the remaining anhydrite:

$$CaS + 3CaSO_4 \rightarrow 4CaO + 4SO_2$$

Thus the overall reaction is:

$$2CaSO_4 + C \rightarrow 2CaO + CO_2 + 2SO_2$$

The gases from the kiln contain about 9 per cent sulphur dioxide. (The calcium oxide combines with the silica to form a silicate slag which, when cool, is crushed and mixed with some anhydrite to give *cement*, a valuable by-product.)

In all the above methods, the sulphur dioxide obtained is impure. Dust is removed by first allowing the gases to expand, when some dust settles, then by passage through electrostatic precipitators and finally by washing with water. Water is removed by concentrated sulphuric acid which is kept in use until its concentration falls to 94 per cent.

(2) The combination of sulphur dioxide and oxygen to form the trioxide is slow and does not proceed to completion:

$$2SO_2 + O_2 \rightleftharpoons 2SO_3 \qquad \Delta H = -94 \text{ kJ mol}^{-1}$$

2 vol.   1 vol.   2 vol.

3 vol.

Although the left-to-right reaction is exothermic, hence giving a better equilibrium yield of sulphur trioxide at low temperatures, the reaction is carried out industrially at about 670–720 K. Furthermore, a better yield would be obtained at high pressure, but extra cost of plant does not apparently justify this. Thus the conditions are based on economic rather than theoretical grounds (cf. Haber process).

There are two processes using different catalysts:

(a) In the *Contact process* the catalyst now used is vanadium pentoxide, V_2O_5 promoted by potassium sulphate on a silica support. Platinum was a more efficient catalyst than vanadium pentoxide but was far more expensive and rendered inactive or poisoned by the presence of arsenic, which has no inhibiting effect on vanadium pentoxide, and, consequently, platinum is no longer used.

The catalyst is carried on perforated shelves inside cylindrical steel vessels called converters. The gas enters these at 670–720 K at atmospheric pressure.

(b) In the older *Lead Chamber process* (so called because the chamber was lined with lead, on which cold sulphuric acid has little action), the catalyst was *nitrogen monoxide*. This process is now only of historical industrial interest.

(3) The conversion of sulphur trioxide into sulphuric acid arises as a separate reaction in the Contact process.

Sulphur trioxide reacts violently with water, forming a fog of dilute sulphuric acid; it is however readily soluble in concentrated sulphuric acid.

In the manufacture of sulphuric acid the sulphur trioxide from the Contact chamber is passed into concentrated sulphuric acid, to which water is added at the required rate:

$$SO_3 + H_2SO_4 \rightarrow H_2S_2O_7$$
$$H_2S_2O_7 + H_2O \rightarrow 2H_2SO_4$$

The 94 per cent acid from the sulphur dioxide drying towers (above) is used here and its strength brought up to 98 per cent. This is 'concentrated' sulphuric acid. Stronger acid up to '106 per cent' may also be made. This concentration is suitable for the sulphonating in, for example, the detergent industry.

Uses

The production of 'superphosphate' (calcium hydrogen-phosphate + calcium sulphate) for fertilizers is the biggest use of sulphuric acid. Second to this is the manufacture of ammonium sulphate from ammonia (by the Haber process). This is also a fertilizer. Other uses are: conversion of viscose to cellulose in the manufacture of artificial silk, and so on; 'pickling' (removal of oxide) of metals before galvanizing or electroplating; manufacture of explosives, pigments and dyestuffs , as well as many other chemicals, for example hydrochloric acid; refining of petroleum and sulphonation of oils to make detergents; and in accumulators.

Properties

Pure sulphuric acid is a colourless, strongly hydrogen-bonded and therefore viscous and rather heavy liquid (density 1.84 g cm^{-3}). On heating, it decomposes near its boiling point, forming sulphur trioxide and a constant boiling (603 K) mixture of water and sulphuric acid containing 98 per cent of the latter. This is 'concentrated' sulphuric acid, which is usually used. Further heating gives complete dissociation into water and sulphur trioxide.

Affinity for water

Concentrated sulphuric acid has a strong affinity for water and great heat is evolved on mixing; hence *the acid must be added to water* to dilute it. Because of this affinity, the acid can be used to dry gases with which it does not react, for example oxygen, chlorine, sulphur dioxide, and was once used in desiccators. It will remove water of crystallization from some compounds, for example

$$CuSO_4.5H_2O \rightarrow CuSO_4 + 5H_2O$$

and also 'combined' water, for example in sugars and other organic compounds:

$$C_{12}H_{22}O_{11} \rightarrow 12C + 11H_2O$$

$$\rightarrow CO\uparrow + CO_2\uparrow + H_2O$$

ethanedioic acid
(oxalic acid)

Oxidizing properties

Concentrated sulphuric acid is an oxidizing agent, particularly when hot, but the oxidizing power of sulphuric acid decreases rapidly with dilution. The hot concentrated acid will oxidize non-metals, for example carbon, sulphur and phosphorus to give, respectively, carbon dioxide, sulphur dioxide and phosphoric(V) acid. It also oxidizes many metals to give their sulphates; cast iron, however, is not affected. The mechanisms of these reactions are complex and the acid gives a number of reduction products.

Hot concentrated sulphuric acid is a useful reagent for differentiating between chloride, bromide and iodide salts, since it is able to oxidize (a) iodide, giving iodine (purple) and the reduction products, hydrogen sulphide, sulphur and sulphur dioxide together with a little hydrogen iodide; (b) bromide, giving bromine (red-brown) and the reduction product sulphur dioxide together with hydrogen bromide. It is unable to oxidize the chloride ion and steamy fumes of hydrogen chloride are evolved.

Acidic properties

Concentrated sulphuric acid displaces more volatile acids from their salts, for example hydrogen chloride from chlorides (*see* above) and nitric acid from nitrates. The dilute acid is a good conductor of electricity. It behaves as a strong dibasic acid:

$$H_2SO_4 + H_2O \rightleftharpoons H_3O^+ + HSO_4^- \qquad K_a = 4 \times 10 \ mol \ l^{-1} \ at \ 298 \ K$$

$$HSO_4^- + H_2O \rightleftharpoons H_3O^+ + SO_4^{2-} \qquad K_a = 1.0 \times 10^{-2} \ mol \ l^{-1} \ at \ 298 \ K$$

the value of K_a for the first dissociation indicating that this reaction goes virtually to completion in dilute solution. The acid exhibits all the properties of the hydrogen ion, i.e. neutralizing bases, giving hydrogen with many metals and so on. Dilute sulphuric acid attacks iron, but lead very soon becomes resistant owing to the formation of a superficial layer of insoluble lead sulphate.

10.8.6   Fuming sulphuric acid (oleum)

When sulphur trioxide is dissolved in concentrated sulphuric acid the pure 100 per cent acid is first formed; then a further molecule of the trioxide adds on:

$$H_2SO_4 + SO_3 \rightarrow H_2S_2O_7$$
heptaoxodisulphuric(VI) acid
pyrosulphuric acid
or oleum
or fuming sulphuric acid

The formation of other polysulphuric acids $H_2O(SO_3)_n$ (general formula) by the addition of more sulphur trioxide, has been reported.

Pure sulphuric acid is a true acid. In dilute aqueous solution, sulphuric acid is an acid because the solvent water has an affinity for the proton:

$$H_2SO_4 + H_2O \rightleftharpoons H_3O^+ + HSO_4^-$$

In the pure acid the 'dihydrogen sulphate' has a proton affinity, so that

$$H_2SO_4 + H_2SO_4 \rightleftharpoons H_3SO_4^+ + HSO_4^-$$

If some polysulphuric acid is present, this can lose a proton more easily, for example

$$H_2SO_4 + H_2S_2O_7 \rightleftharpoons H_3SO_4^+ + HS_2O_7^-$$

Hence the strength of the acid goes up as sulphur trioxide is dissolved in it*. The acidity of pure and fuming sulphuric acids is not so apparent as in ordinary aqueous acids because it is masked by the oxidizing and other properties; moreover, the conductivity is very low because the large $H_3SO_4^+$ and HSO_4^- ions can move only slowly through the viscous acid in an electric field. An acid–base indicator sufficiently resistant to the oxidizing and sulphonating action of the concentrated acid to be used in it is now available; this indicator shows the acid to be quite strong.

10.8.7 The sulphates and hydrogensulphates

The hydrogensulphates (or bisulphates) containing the ion HSO_4^-, are only known in the solid state for the alkali metals and ammonium. Sodium hydrogensulphate is formed when sodium chloride is treated with cold concentrated sulphuric acid:

$$NaCl + H_2SO_4 \rightarrow NaHSO_4 + HCl\uparrow$$

It may also be obtained by crystallizing sodium sulphate from a dilute sulphuric acid solution:

$$Na_2SO_4 + H_2SO_4 \rightarrow 2NaHSO_4$$

The hydrogensulphate ion dissociates into hydrogen and sulphate ions in solution; hence hydrogensulphates behave as acids.

When solid sodium hydrogensulphate is heated, sodium 'pyrosulphate' is formed; further heating gives sodium sulphate and sulphur trioxide:

$$2NaHSO_4 \rightarrow Na_2S_2O_7 + H_2O\uparrow$$
$$Na_2S_2O_7 \rightarrow Na_2SO_4 + SO_3\uparrow$$

Electrolysis of the hydrogensulphate of potassium or ammonium can yield a *peroxodisulphate* and thence hydrogen peroxide.

The *sulphates* of many metals are soluble in water, but those of barium, lead, mercury(I), calcium and strontium are insoluble or only sparingly soluble. Soluble sulphates often crystallize out as hydrates, for example the *vitriols* such as, $FeSO_4.7H_2O$; $NiSO_4.7H_2O$; $CuSO_4.5H_2O$ and *double salts*, for example $FeSO_4.(NH_4)_2SO_4.6H_2O$ and the *alums*, for example $KAl(SO_4)_2.12H_2O$. In these salts, most of the water molecules are attached to the cation; the remaining water molecules are connected by hydrogen bonds partly to the sulphate ions and partly to the cationic water molecules (for example $CuSO_4.5H_2O$, *see* p. 359).

The sulphates of the alkali and alkaline earth metals and manganese(II) are stable to heat; those of heavier metals decompose on heating, evolving

---

*Actually, the pure acid H_2SO_4 always contains some $H_2S_2O_7$, because there is an equilibrium:

$$2H_2SO_4 \rightleftharpoons H_2S_2O_7 + H_2O$$

Thus water is available to take the proton, and $H_2S_2O_7$ to lose it, even in the 'pure' acid H_2SO_4.

sulphur trioxide and leaving the oxide or the metal:

$$Fe_2(SO_4)_3 \rightarrow Fe_2O_3 + 3SO_3\uparrow$$
$$2Ag_2SO_4 \rightarrow 4Ag + 2SO_3\uparrow + O_2\uparrow$$

The sulphate ion is detected by addition of barium chloride in the presence of hydrochloric acid; a white precipitate of barium sulphate is obtained. The same test can be used to estimate sulphate, the barium sulphate being filtered off, dried and weighed.

In the sulphate ion, the four oxygen atoms are tetrahedrally arranged round the sulphur atom, at equal distances; hence all the S—O bonds are identical, and their short length suggests that they are double bonds (as in SO_2, SO_3, and SO_3^{2-}):

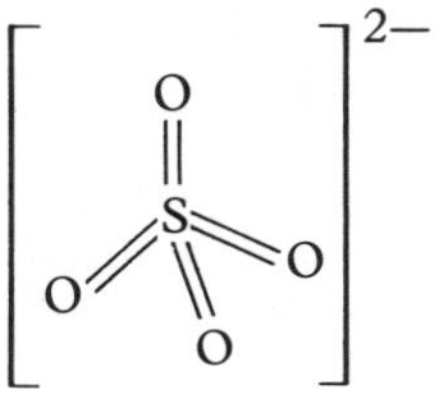

This structure is perhaps best visualized by regarding it as built up from a sulphur trioxide molecule and an oxide ion (this happens in practice).

In pure sulphuric acid, two of the S⋯O distances are somewhat longer, and it is believed that the structure is as shown in *Figure 10.8*. The dotted lines represent hydrogen bonds. The high boiling point and viscosity of the pure acid indicate strong intermolecular forces of this kind.

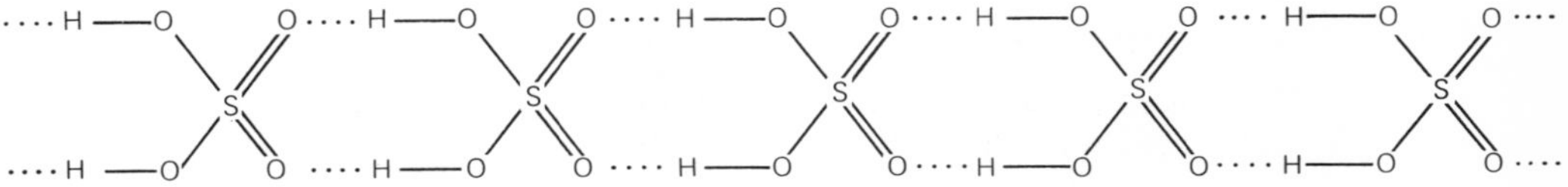

Figure 10.8 Hydrogen bonding in sulphuric acid

10.8.8 Other acids

In addition to the simple acids discussed above, sulphur forms two *peroxosulphuric acids* containing the —O—O— linkage and a number of thionic acids containing more than one sulphur atom.

10.9 Oxides and oxoacids of selenium and tellurium

10.9.1 Selenium

Selenium dioxide is a volatile solid obtained when selenium is burnt in air or oxygen. It is very soluble in water, forming a solution of selenic(IV) (selenious) acid H_2SeO_3, a dibasic acid forming two series of salts. Both the acid and its salts are fairly good oxidizing agents, oxidizing (for example) sulphur dioxide and hydrogen iodide.

Selenium trioxide, SeO_3, is a white deliquescent solid which has never been obtained completely pure. When selenic(VI) acid H_2SeO_4, is dehydrated a mixture of selenium dioxide and trioxide is obtained and oxygen is evolved. Selenic(VI) acid H_2SeO_4 is formed when selenium trioxide is dissolved in water and is a strong dibasic acid. It is a more powerful oxidizing agent than sulphuric acid and will, for example, oxidize hydrochloric acid evolving chlorine.

10.9.2 Tellurium

Tellurium dioxide, TeO_2, is a white non-volatile solid obtained when tellurium is burnt in air. It is only slightly soluble in water but dissolves in alkalis to form salts.

Tellurium trioxide, TeO_3, is an orange yellow powder made by thermal decomposition of telluric(VI) acid $Te(OH)_6$. It is a strong oxidizing agent which will, like H_2SeO_4, oxidize hydrogen chloride to chlorine. It dissolves in hot water to give telluric(VI) acid. This is a weak acid and quite different from sulphuric and selenic acids. Two series of salts are known.

10.10 Halides

Oxygen halides are dealt with in Chapter 11, p. 291. Sulphur, selenium and tellurium form many halides, and only a brief introduction to the subject is given here.

10.10.1 Fluorides

All three elements form gaseous hexafluorides by the direct combination of the elements. They all have octahedral structures.

$X = S, Se, or Te$

Sulphur hexafluoride, SF_6, is chemically unreactive, resembling nitrogen, and is unaffected by heat, water, fused alkalis, and many heated metals. This stability is attributed to the high S—F bond strength and to the inability of attacking reagents, such as water, to coordinate to the covalently saturated sulphur (cf. SF_4 p. 267). It finds a use as a high-voltage gaseous insulator.

Both selenium hexafluoride and tellurium hexafluoride are more reactive than sulphur hexafluoride. Tellurium hexafluoride is slowly hydrolysed by water to telluric(VI) acid and on heating it decomposes to fluorine and the tetrafluoride.

The tetrafluorides of the elements can be prepared. They are all less stable than the corresponding hexafluorides and are hydrolysed readily by water. They can all be used as fluorinating agents and sulphur tetrafluoride is extensively used for this purpose, for example the fluorination of organic carbonyl groups:

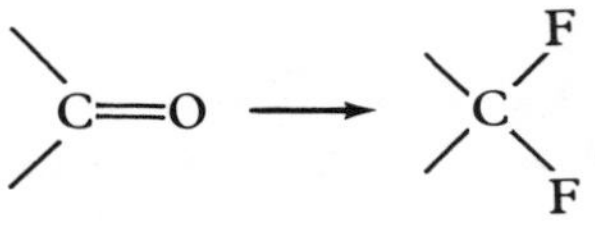

The structure of sulphur tetrafluoride, and probably also SeF_4 and TeF_4, is trigonal bipyramidal with one position occupied by a lone pair of electrons:

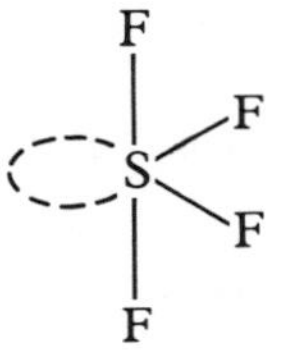

10.10.2   Chlorides

Sulphur and selenium form the chlorides disulphur dichloride S_2Cl_2 and diselenium dichloride Se_2Cl_2. They are made by the direct combination of the elements. Both are covalent, yellow liquids which are readily hydrolysed by water:

$$S_2Cl_2 + 3H_2O \rightarrow 2HCl + H_2S + SO_3^{2-} + 2H^+$$

(Further reaction between hydrogen sulphide and the sulphite ion yields sulphur together with thionic acids):

$$2Se_2Cl_2 + 3H_2O \rightarrow H_2SeO_3 + 3Se + 4HCl$$

Diselenium dichloride acts as a solvent for selenium. Similarly disulphur dichloride is a solvent for sulphur and also many other covalent compounds, such as iodine. S_2Cl_2 attacks rubber in such a way that sulphur atoms are introduced into the polymer chains of the rubber, so hardening it. This product is known as vulcanized rubber. The structure of these dichlorides is given in *Figure 10.9* (cf. H_2O_2, *Figure 10.5*).

Sulphur and tellurium form a chloride of formula XCl_2. Sulphur dichloride SCl_2 is a red liquid at room temperature whilst the corresponding tellurium compound is a black solid.

A number of bromides and iodides are known but there are no sulphur iodides.

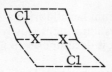

Figure 10.9 Structure of selenium and sulphur dichlorides

10.10.3   Halide oxides

A number of halide oxides are formed by sulphur and selenium but only one is considered here.

Sulphur dichloride oxide, thionyl chloride, SOCl$_2$

This is an important laboratory reagent and has the structure shown below:

It is prepared by heating together phosphorus pentachloride and a sulphite, for example calcium sulphite:

$$2PCl_5 + CaSO_3 \rightarrow 2POCl_3 + CaCl_2 + SOCl_2$$

The oxide dichloride, b.p. 351 K, is separated from the less volatile phosphorus oxychloride by a fractional distillation.

Sulphur oxide dichloride is a colourless liquid which fumes in moist air. It is hydrolysed by water to give a mixture of sulphurous and hydrochloric acids:

$$SOCl_2 + 2H_2O \rightarrow 4H^+ + SO_3^{2-} + 2Cl^-$$

Hence on warming, sulphur dioxide is evolved.

Sulphur oxide dichloride is used as a chlorinating agent in organic chemistry, for example in the preparation of acid chlorides:

$$CH_3COOH + SOCl_2 \rightarrow CH_3COCl + SO_2\uparrow + HCl\uparrow$$

The advantage of the method, readily seen from the equation, is that the other products of the reaction are gaseous and escape. Hence equimolar quantities of reactants are used.

A somewhat similar reaction is the power of sulphur oxide dichloride to remove water or crystallization from hydrated chlorides, the hydroxyl groups of the water molecule reacting as do those in the acid molecules in the above reaction.

The action is a general one and may be written thus:

$$MCl_n.xH_2O + xSOCl_2 \rightarrow MCl_n + xSO_2\uparrow + 2xHCl\uparrow$$

The reaction provides a valuable method of *preparing anhydrous chlorides of metals.* It has been used to prepare the anhydrous chlorides of copper(II), zinc, cadmium, chromium(III), iron(III), cobalt(II) and nickel.

Table 10.3 Summary of the properties of Group VI

	O	S	Se, Te, (Po)
Element	O_2 gas O_3 gas	Sn solid (allotropy)	solids (allotropy)
Oxidation states	-2	-2 $+2$ $+4$ $+6$	-3 $+4$ $+6$
Reactions: +air	Gives NO at high temperatures only	SO_2 SO_3	MO_2 only
+acids	oxidizes reducing acids	──────oxidized by concentrated HNO_3 to oxoacids or oxides──────	
+alkalis		SO_3^{2-} S_n^{2-} $S_2O_3^{2-}$	MO_3^{2-} M_n^{2-}
			──────H_2M, stability decreasing──────→
Compounds:hydrides	H_2O: hydrogen-bonded liquid, acid-base behaviour	H_2S: gas, precipitates insoluble sulphides of many metal cations	
oxides	(ozone)	$SO_2(g) \rightarrow H_2SO_3(aq)$ $SO_3(s) \rightarrow H_2SO_4(l), (aq)$	MO_2 and MO_3, strongly oxidizing
oxoacids		H_2SO_3 and salts, reducing $H_2SO_4(l)$ oxidizing	H_2SeO_3 oxidizing H_2SeO_4 strongly oxidizing Telluric acid is $Te(OH)_6$
halides	*see* halogens	SF_2, SF_4, SF_6 unreactive S_2Cl_2 some halide oxides, e.g. $SOCl_2$	not considered

In both reactions above, the oxide dichloride is refluxed with the acid or the hydrated chloride; the sulphur dioxide and hydrogen chloride pass off and any unused sulphur oxide dichloride is distilled off *in vacuo*.

10.11 Tests for sulphur

Oxidation of a sulphur compound with concentrated nitric acid yields sulphuric acid or a sulphate, which can be tested for with barium chloride. This can be used to estimate the sulphur.

Summary

For a summary *see Table 10.3*.

Questions

1   How would you obtain a sample of pure ozone? Account for the conditions used in your method of preparation. What is the arrangement of oxygen atoms in an ozonide and what evidence would you cite in support of the structure you suggest?

L,A

2   Comment on and, where you are able, suggest reasons for the following observations
(a) Na_2O dissolves in water to give an alkaline solution: Cl_2O dissolves in water to give an acidic solution.
(b) Cl_2O is a gaseous oxide, its molecule being V-shaped: Na_2O is an ionic compound which has an infinite 3-dimensional lattice structure.
(c) Al_2O_3 forms a hydrated oxide which is basic, but the addition of alkali produces a solution containing the aluminate anion, AlO_2^-.
(d) SiO_2 and CO_2 are both acidic oxides, SiO_2 is a solid of high melting-point, whereas CO_2 is a gas.
(e) N_2O is a gaseous, neutral oxide, its molecule being linear.

C,A

3   Give an explanation of the following observations:
(a) An aqueous solution of sodium sulphide smells of hydrogen sulphide.
(b) When hydrogen sulphide is bubbled through an acidified solution of a cobalt(II) salt, no precipitate is formed, but a black precipitate is produced when the solution is made slightly alkaline.
(c) When hydrogen sulphide is bubbled through an aqueous solution of an aluminium(III) salt, a white precipitate of aluminium(III) hydroxide is obtained.
(d) Hydrogen sulphide (formula weight 34) is a gas, water (formula weight 18) is a liquid.

4   Describe one laboratory method for the preparation of a dilute solution of
     hydrogen peroxide.
         In what way does a solution of hydrogen peroxide react with (a) chlorine
     water, (b) potassium permanganate solution, (c) potassium dichromate
     solution, (d) hydrogen sulphide? 50 cm^3 of an aqueous solution of hydrogen
     peroxide were treated with an excess of potassium iodide and dilute sulphuric
     acid; the liberated iodine was titrated with 0.1M sodium thiosulphate
     solution and 20.0 cm^3 were required. Calculate the concentration of the
     hydrogen peroxide solution in g l^{-1}.

                                                                                     JMB,A

Chapter 11
Group VII: the halogens
Fluorine, chlorine, bromine, iodine

11.1 Physical properties

Table 11.1 and *Table 11.2* (p. 274) give some of the physical properties of the common halogens. *Figure 11.1* shows graphically some of the properties given in *Table 11.1*, together with enthalpies of atomization. All the elements exist as diatomic molecules X_2.

It can be seen that many properties change regularly with increasing atomic number, the changes being approximately linear in the case of the three elements chlorine, bromine and iodine, but a discontinuity almost always occurs for fluorine. This behaviour is typical for a group head element, which in addition tends to display properties not shown by other members of the group; a greater disparity in properties occurs between the first and second elements in a group than between any other two adjacent group elements.

11.1.1 Oxidation states

The electronic configuration of each halogen is one electron less than that of a noble gas, and it is not surprising therefore, that a halogen atom can accept an electron to form X^-. Indeed, the reactions $X(g) + e^- \rightarrow X^-(g)$ are all exothermic and the values (*see Table 11.1*), though small relative to the ionization energies, are all larger than the electron affinity of any other atom.

Numerous ionic compounds with halogens are known but a noble gas configuration can also be achieved by the formation of a covalent bond, for example in halogen molecules, X_2, and hydrogen halides, HX. When the fluorine atom acquires one additional electron the second quantum level is completed, and further gain of electrons is not energetically possible under normal circumstances, i.e. promotion to $3s$ requires too much energy. Thus fluorine is normally confined to a valency of 1 although in some solid fluorides bridge structures M—F—M are known in which fluorine acquires a covalency of 2.

All the remaining halogens have unfilled d orbitals available and the covalency of the element can be increased. Compounds and complex ions are formed both with other halogens and with oxygen in which the halogen can achieve a formal oxidation state as high as $+7$; for example chlorine has formal oxidation states of $+1$ in the chlorate(I) anion ClO^-; $+5$ in the chlorate(V) anion ClO_3^-, and $+7$ in the chlorate(VII) anion ClO_4^-.

Table 11.1 Selected properties of the elements

Element	Atomic number	Outer electrons	Atomic radius* nm	Radius/nm of ion X⁻	m.p./K	b.p./K	First ionization energy kJ mol⁻¹	Electron affinity kJ mol⁻¹	Electro-negativity (Pauling)
F	9	$2s^2 2p^5$	0.064	0.133	50	86	1680	−333	4.0
Cl	17	$3s^2 3p^5$	0.099	0.181	171	238	1255	−364	3.0
Br	35	$4s^2 4p^5$	0.111	0.196	266	332	1142	−342	2.8
I	53	$5s^2 5p^5$	0.130	0.219	387	456	1010	−295	2.5

*Covalent radius.

Table 11.2 Enthalpy data for halide ion formation in aqueous solution (kJ mol^{-1} unless specified)

	F	Cl	Br	I
$\frac{1}{2}X_2(s,l,g) \rightarrow \frac{1}{2}X_2(g)$	0	0	+15	+31
$\frac{1}{2}X_2(g) \rightarrow X(g)$	+79	+121	+97	+75
$X(g) + e^- \rightarrow X^-(g)$	−333	−364	−342	−295
$X^-(g) \rightarrow X^-(aq)$	−515	−381	−347	−305
$\frac{1}{2}X_2(g) + e^- \rightarrow X^-(aq)$	−769	−624	−577	−494
$E^{\ominus}/V$	+2.80	+1.36	+1.07	+0.54

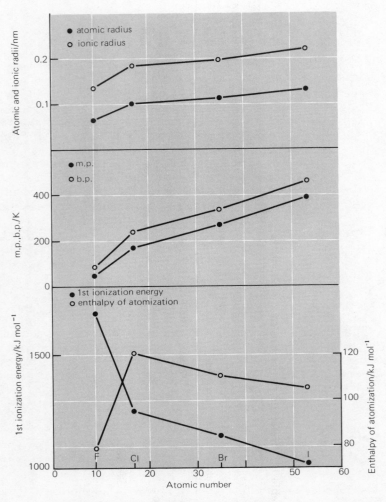

Figure 11.1 Properties of Group VII elements

11.1.2   Electrode potentials and reactivity of the halogens

One surprising physical property of fluorine is its electron affinity which, at -333 kJ mol^{-1}, is lower than that of chlorine, -364 kJ mol^{-1}, indicating that the reaction $X(g) + e^- \rightarrow X^-(g)$ is more exothermic for chlorine atoms. In view of the greater reactivity of fluorine a much higher electron affinity might reasonably have been expected. The explanation of this anomaly is found when the steps involved in a complete reaction are considered. For example, with a Group I metal ion $M^+(g)$ the steps to form a crystalline solid are,

(1) $\frac{1}{2}X_2(g) \rightarrow X(g)$ Bond dissociation enthalpy
(2) $X(g) + e^- \rightarrow X^-(g)$ Electron affinity
(3) $X^-(g) + M^+(g) \rightarrow M^+X^-(s)$ Lattice enthalpy

the overall reaction being

$$e^- + \frac{1}{2}X_2(g) + M^+(g) \rightarrow M^+X^-(s)$$

The enthalpies for the reactions of chlorine and fluorine are shown graphically in *Figure 11.2* as the relevant parts of a Born–Haber cycle. Also included on the graph are the hydration energies of the two halogen ions and hence the enthalpy changes involved in the reactions

$$\frac{1}{2}X_2(g) + e^- \xrightarrow{\;H_2O\;} X^-(aq)$$

The very low bond dissociation enthalpy of fluorine is an important factor contributing to the greater reactivity of fluorine. (This low energy may be due to repulsion between non-bonding electrons on the two adjacent fluorine atoms.) The higher hydration and lattice enthalpies of the fluoride ion are due to the smaller size of this ion.

Electron affinity and hydration energy decrease with increasing atomic number of the halogen and in spite of the slight fall in bond dissociation enthalpy from chlorine to iodine the enthalpy changes in the reactions

(1) $\frac{1}{2}X_2(g) + M^+(g) + e^- \rightarrow M^+X^-(s)$

(2) $\frac{1}{2}X_2(g) + e^- \xrightarrow{\;H_2O\;} X^-(aq)$

both decrease and the reaction becomes less exothermic. Hence the reactivity and the electrode potential (which is closely related to reaction (2) and indeed defined by it under standard conditions) decrease from fluorine to iodine. *Table 11.2* gives the enthalpy change (kJ mol^{-1}) for each halogen in reaction (2).

11.1.3   Electronegativity

The large value for fluorine, and the marked decrease from fluorine to iodine, are points to be noted. The high value for fluorine means that the bond between an element M and fluorine is likely to be more ionic (more polar) than a bond formed by M with any other elements. The low value for iodine

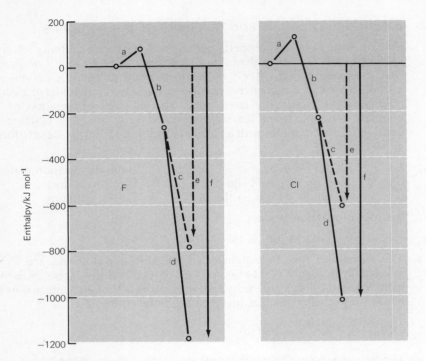

Figure 11.2 Formation of fluoride and chloride ions from the elements. The steps are

a $\frac{1}{2}X_2(g) \rightarrow X(g)$ bond dissociation energy
b $X(g) \rightarrow X^-(g)$ electron affinity
c $X^-(g) \rightarrow X^-(aq)$ hydration energy
d $X^-(g) + Na^+(g) \rightarrow Na^+X^-(s)$ lattice energy

Also shown are

e $\frac{1}{2}X_2(g) + aq + e^- \rightarrow X^-(aq)$ ΔH_f of $X^-(aq)$
f $\frac{1}{2}X_2(g) + Na^+(g) \rightarrow Na^+X^-(s)$ —

indicates the possibility that iodine may be electropositive in some of its compounds.

11.1.4   Oxidizing properties

For fluorine, the reaction

$$\tfrac{1}{2}X_2 + e^- \rightarrow X^-$$

is energetically highly favourable for the formation both of $X^-(g)$ and of $X^-(aq)$. Hence gaseous fluorine is highly reactive towards metals, giving essentially ionic fluorides; and in solution (as its high electrode potential indicates) it is one of the most powerful oxidizing agents, oxidizing water very readily (p. 90). Hence the fluoride ion cannot be converted into fluorine in aqueous solution; electrolysis of a fused fluoride must be used. In contrast, iodide ions in solution are readily oxidized even by air (*Table 4.9*) (p. 90).

11.1.5   Halogens as ligands

The small fluoride ion shows a great tendency to act as a ligand and form complex ions, for example $[AlF_6]^{3-}$, $[PF_6]^-$, $[FeF_6]^{3-}$ in which the central atom exhibits a high coordination number. The other larger halide ions show this tendency to a greatly diminished extent and the complexes formed are usually less stable, although certain metals (e.g. mercury) form iodo-complexes, for example $[HgI_4]^{2-}$ which are more stable than fluoro- or chloro-complexes. In certain cases there is insufficient space around the atom for as many iodine atoms as for other halogens, for example phosphorus forms pentahalides with fluorine, chlorine and bromine (and in the case of fluorine the ion $[PF_6]^-$), but no pentaiodide. The large size of iodine also accounts for the fact that there are few complexes with more than four iodine ligands.

An important reason for low coordination of iodide ions is that high coordination implies a high oxidation state of the central atom, which often (but not always) means high oxidizing power — and this means oxidation of the easily oxidized iodide ligands. Thus the non-existence of, for example, phosphorus(V) pentaiodide is to be explained by the oxidation of the iodide ligands and reduction of phosphorus to the $+3$ state, giving only PI_3, not PI_5.

11.2   Occurrence and extraction

11.2.1   Fluorine

Fluorine occurs widely in nature as insoluble fluorides. Calcium fluoride occurs as *fluorspar* or *fluorite*, for example in Derbyshire where it is coloured blue and called 'bluejohn'. Other important minerals are *cryolite* Na_3AlF_6 (p. 130) and *fluorapatite* $CaF_2.3Ca_3(PO_4)_2$. Bones and teeth contain fluorides and some natural water contains traces.

Fluorine cannot be prepared directly by chemical methods. It is prepared in the laboratory and on an industrial scale by electrolysis. Two methods are employed: (a) using fused potassium hydrogenfluoride, KHF_2, in a cell heated electrically to 520—570 K or (b) using fused electrolyte, of composition KF:HF = 1:2, in a cell at 340–370 K which can be electrically or steam heated. Moissan, who first isolated fluorine in 1886, used a method very similar to (b) and it is this process which is commonly used in the laboratory and on an industrial scale today. There have been many cell designs but the cell is usually made from steel, or a copper–nickel alloy ('Monel' metal). Steel or copper cathodes and specially made amorphous carbon anodes (to minimize attack by fluorine) are used. Hydrogen is formed at the cathode and fluorine at the anode, and the hydrogen fluoride content of the fused electrolyte is maintained by passing in hydrogen fluoride periodically. The fluorine obtained is almost pure, containing only a little hydrogen fluoride, which is removed by passage of the gas over sodium fluoride:

$$NaF + HF \rightarrow NaHF_2$$

Fluorine boils at 85 K to give a greenish-yellow diatomic gas.

11.2.2   Chlorine

The most common compound of chlorine is sodium chloride, NaCl, and this occurs widely in nature. Large deposits are found in Cheshire and these are extracted by the use of water although some is mined as rock salt. In many parts of the world sodium chloride is obtained from sea water. Other chlorides are found in small quantities both in rocks and sea water, for example *carnallite* $KCl.MgCl_2.6H_2O$ in the Stassfurt deposits. Chlorine, unlike fluorine, can be prepared by chemical oxidation of the chloride ion and this is the method usually used in the laboratory. Strong oxidizing agents are required for the oxidation and amongst those commonly used are manganese(IV) oxide, MnO_2, potassium dichromate(VI), $K_2Cr_2O_7$, both of which need to be heated with concentrated hydrochloric acid, and potassium manganate(VII), $KMnO_4$, which evolves chlorine at room temperature when treated with concentrated hydrochloric acid:

$$MnO_2 + 4HCl \rightarrow MnCl_2 + Cl_2 + 2H_2O$$
$$14H^+ + Cr_2O_7^{2-} + 6Cl^- \rightarrow 2Cr^{3+} + 7H_2O + 3Cl_2$$
$$16H^+ + 2MnO_4^- + 10Cl^- \rightarrow 2Mn^{2+} + 8H_2O + 5Cl_2$$

Alternatively a mixture of almost any solid chloride and manganese(IV) oxide will yield chlorine when warmed with concentrated sulphuric acid. These are the most common laboratory methods but there are many others.

On a large scale chlorine is obtained in several ways.

(1)   By the electrolysis of concentrated sodium chloride solution; this process was initially used primarily for the production of sodium hydroxide but the demand for chlorine is now so great that the chlorine is a primary and not a by-product.

(2)   By the electrolysis of fused magnesium chloride or fused sodium chloride.

(3)   By the oxidation of hydrogen chloride. A mixture of hydrogen chloride with air or oxygen is passed over a catalyst of copper(II) chloride containing one or more chlorides of rare-earth metals on a silica support at a temperature of 600–670 K; the reaction is exothermic:

$$4HCl + O_2 \rightleftharpoons 2H_2O + Cl_2$$

The equilibrium constant for this reaction decreases with increase in temperature but the higher temperature is required to achieve a reasonable rate of conversion. Hydrogen chloride is now being produced in increasing quantities as a by-product in organic chlorination reactions and it is economic to reconvert this to chlorine.

Chlorine has a boiling point of 238 K and is a greenish-yellow diatomic gas at room temperature. It can be liquefied by cooling or by a pressure of a few atmospheres at room temperature.

11.2.3   Bromine

Bromides of sodium, potassium, magnesium and calcium occur in sea water (about 0.07 per cent bromine) but the Dead Sea contains much more (5 per cent bromine). Salt deposits (e.g. at Stassfurt) also contain these bromides. Silver bromide, AgBr, is found in South America.

In the laboratory, bromine is prepared by oxidation of bromide ion; the oxidation is carried out by mixing solid potassium bromide with manganese(IV) oxide and distilling with concentrated sulphuric acid:

$$2KBr + MnO_2 + 3H_2SO_4 \rightarrow Br_2 + 2KHSO_4 + MnSO_4 + 2H_2O$$

The bromine is condensed and collected in a water-cooled receiver as a dark-red liquid.

On the industrial scale, bromine is obtained from sea water by using the displacement reaction with chlorine (the reaction by which bromine was discovered):

$$2Br^- + Cl_2 \rightarrow 2Cl^- + Br_2$$

The sea water is first treated with chlorine in acid solution (sulphuric acid is added) and very dilute bromine is obtained by blowing air through the solution. This is mixed with sulphur dioxide and the gases passed up a tower down which water trickles:

$$SO_2 + Br_2 + 2H_2O \rightarrow 2HBr + H_2SO_4$$

The mixture of the two acids (now much richer in bromine than the sea water) is then treated with chlorine again, and bromine obtained. The bromine may be freed from chlorine by bubbling it through iron(III) bromide solution, which retains the chlorine. Last traces of bromine from the process can be removed by passage over moist iron filings. Bromine is a dark-red heavy liquid, boiling point 332 K, appreciably volatile at ordinary temperatures. It is soluble in organic solvents, for example chloroform, and they can be used to extract bromine from aqueous solutions (*see* Tests, p. 303). Liquid bromide is extremely toxic and corrosive.

11.2.4   Iodine

Iodine occurs to a minute extent (less than 0.001 per cent) in sea water, but is found in greater concentration, combined in organic form, in certain seaweeds, in oysters and in cod livers. Crude Chile saltpetre, or *caliche* contains small amounts of sodium iodate, $NaIO_3$, from which iodine can be obtained (*see* below). Some insoluble iodides, for example those of silver and mercury(II), occur in Mexico. Iodine is found in the human body in the compound *thyroxin* in the thyroid gland; deficiency of iodine in diet causes enlargement of this gland (goitre).

Iodine is rarely prepared in the laboratory; one method used is the oxidation of an iodide by manganese(IV) oxide and sulphuric acid, for example with sodium iodide:

$$2NaI + MnO_2 + 3H_2SO_4 \rightarrow MnSO_4 + 2NaHSO_4 + I_2 + 2H_2O$$

The iodine distils off and can be collected on a cooled surface. It may be purified by sublimation *in vacuo*.

This reaction is also used on a large scale, to obtain iodine from seaweed. The ash from burnt seaweed ('kelp') is extracted with water, concentrated, and the salts other than iodides (sulphates and chlorides) crystallize out. The more soluble iodides remain and the liquor is mixed with sulphuric acid and manganese dioxide added; the evolved iodine distils off and is condensed.

Most iodine produced commercially comes from the sodium iodate(V) remaining after sodium nitrate has been crystallized from Chile saltpetre. The iodate(V) is first reduced to iodide by blowing sulphur dioxide into the solution (or by addition of sodium sulphite):

$$IO_3^- + 3SO_3^{2-} \rightarrow I^- + 3SO_4^{2-}$$

More iodate is then added, and with the sulphuric acid formed (or added if sodium sulphite is used), iodine is liberated:

$$IO_3^- + 5I^- + 6H^+ \rightarrow 3I_2 + 3H_2O$$

Alternatively, the iodide is precipitated as copper(I) iodide by addition of copper(II) sulphate, in presence of sulphite, thus:

$$2I^- + 2Cu^{2+} + SO_3^{2-} + H_2O \rightarrow 2CuI + SO_4^{2-} + 2H^+$$

The iodine is then liberated by heating the copper(I) iodide with sulphuric acid and iron(III) oxide:

$$2CuI + 6H_2SO_4 + 2Fe_2O_3 \rightarrow 2CuSO_4 + 4FeSO_4 + 6H_2O + I_2$$

The copper(II) sulphate is recovered and used to precipitate more copper(I) iodide. Iodine and its compounds are, relative to the other halogens, costly substances.

Iodine forms molecular crystals made up of I_2 molecules held together by van der Waals forces (p. 23); the crystals are dark-coloured with a glittering appearance. It is easily sublimed to form a bluish vapour *in vacuo*, but in air, the vapour is brownish-violet. Since it has a small vapour pressure at ordinary temperatures, iodine slowly sublimes if left in an open vessel; for the same reason, iodine is best weighed in a stoppered bottle containing some potassium iodide solution, in which the iodine dissolves to form potassium tri-iodide. The vapour of iodine is composed of I_2 molecules up to about 1000 K; above this temperature, dissociation into iodine atoms becomes appreciable.

Like bromine, iodine is soluble in organic solvents, for example chloroform, which can be used to extract it from an aqueous solution. The iodine imparts a characteristic purple colour to the organic layer; this is used as a test for iodine (p. 304). Brown solutions are formed when iodine dissolves in ether, alcohol, and acetone. In chloroform and benzene a purple solution is formed, whilst a violet solution is produced in carbon disulphide and some hydrocarbons. These colours arise owing to charge transfer (p. 52) between the iodine and the solvent organic molecules.

11.3 Characteristic reactions of the halogens

11.3.1 With hydrogen

All the halogens combine directly with hydrogen, the reaction generally occurring with decreasing vigour in the sequence F_2, Cl_2, Br_2, I_2.

The rate of reaction between fluorine and hydrogen varies a great deal with conditions. Solid fluorine and liquid hydrogen explode even at 21 K but mixing of the gases at room temperature in the dark may preclude any reaction; however a reaction can occur with explosive violence. A chain mechanism is likely for the reaction.

Mixtures of chlorine and hydrogen react only slowly in the dark but the reaction proceeds with explosive violence in light. A suggested mechanism for the photochemical chain reaction is:

$$Cl_2 + hv \rightarrow 2Cl\cdot$$
$$Cl\cdot + H_2 \rightarrow HCl + H\cdot$$
$$H\cdot + Cl^2 \rightarrow HCl + Cl\cdot \text{ and so on}$$

In the presence of charcoal, chlorine and hydrogen combine rapidly, but without explosion, in the dark. A jet of hydrogen will burn in chlorine with a silvery flame and vice versa.

The affinity of chlorine for hydrogen is so great that chlorine will react with many compounds containing this element, for example hydrocarbons (a wax taper burns in chlorine).

Chlorine substitutes the hydrogen of methane giving successively the chlorides CH_3Cl, CH_2Cl_2, $CHCl_3$ and CCl_4. It is to be noted that if a hydrocarbon is unsaturated, chlorine atoms will first *add* to the double or triple bond after which *substitution* may occur.

Chlorine will also remove hydrogen from hydrogen sulphide, liberating sulphur, and from ammonia, liberating nitrogen:

$$H_2S + Cl_2 \rightarrow 2HCl + S$$
$$8NH_3 + 3Cl_2 \rightarrow 6NH_4Cl + N_2$$

Bromine, like chlorine, also undergoes a photochemical chain reaction with hydrogen. The reaction with bromine, however, evolves less energy and is not explosive.

Like chlorine, bromine can displace hydrogen from saturated hydrocarbons, though not as readily, and adds on to unsaturated ones.

Iodine and hydrogen react reversibly to give hydrogen iodide:

$$H_2 + I_2 \rightleftarrows 2HI$$

This equilibrium has been extensively studied by Bodenstein. Unlike the other halogen–hydrogen reactions, it is not a chain reaction but a second order, bimolecular, combination.

Iodine does not replace hydrogen from saturated hydrocarbons directly, as do both chlorine and bromine.

11.3.2   With elements other than hydrogen

Fluorine is exceedingly reactive and combines vigorously with most elements. Some ignite spontaneously in gaseous fluorine at room temperature, for example K, B, Si, P, S, I. Other elements ignite when gently warmed in the gas, for example Ag and Zn, and even gold, platinum and xenon are attacked if heated strongly. Graphite is attacked slowly — hence the use of special electrodes in the extraction of fluorine —and diamond only above 950 K. Some metals, for example copper and nickel alloys, become coated with a superficial layer of fluoride. This prevents further reaction and hence vessels of these materials are used for the preparation and storage of fluorine. Oxygen and nitrogen do not combine directly with fluorine.

Chlorine reacts with most elements, both metals and non-metals, except carbon, oxygen and nitrogen, forming chlorides. Sometimes the reaction is catalysed by a trace of water (such as in the case of copper and zinc). If the element attacked exhibits several oxidation states, chlorine, like fluorine, forms compounds of high oxidation state, for example iron forms iron(III) chloride and tin forms tin(IV) chloride. Phosphorus, however, forms first the trichloride, PCl_3, and (if excess of chlorine is present) the pentachloride PCl_5.

Bromine has a lower electron affinity (and electrode potential) than chlorine but is still a very reactive element. It combines violently with alkali metals and reacts spontaneously with phosphorus, arsenic and antimony. When heated it reacts with many other elements, including gold, but it does not attack platinum, and silver forms a protective film of silver bromide. Because of the strong oxidizing properties, bromine, like fluorine and chlorine, tends to form compounds with the electropositive element in a high oxidation state.

Iodine, though generally less reactive than bromine, combines directly with many elements, for example silver, gold and aluminium, forming iodides. Mercury is also attacked and mercury(I) iodide, Hg_2I_2, is first formed but in the presence of excess of iodine this is oxidized to mercury(II) iodide, HgI_2. Iodine and phosphorus (red and white) react in the presence of water to form first phosphorus(III) iodide, PI_3, which is then hydrolysed to yield hydrogen iodide (p. 290). Iodine reacts with the other halogens to form interhalogen compounds (p. 301).

11.3.3   With compounds

The reactions with water

The oxidizing power of fluorine is seen in its reaction with water: in the liquid phase, water reacts to give hydrogen peroxide and some oxygen difluoride (p. 291); in the gas phase ozone and oxygen are produced:

$$3H_2O + 3F_2 \rightarrow 6HF + O_3$$

Recent work indicates the existence of *fluoric*(I) *acid*, HFO, formed by the reaction of fluorine and water at 273 K. The acid forms colourless crystals, m.p. 156 K, is very unstable, and has, as expected, very strong oxidizing properties.

Chlorine and bromine are both moderately soluble in water, and on crystallization these solutions give solid hydrates with the halogen molecules occupying cavities within a modified ice lattice. Iodine is only slightly soluble in water in which it forms a brown solution (brown solutions are also formed in ether, alcohol and acetone). The aqueous solutions of chlorine and bromine are good oxidizing agents. Chlorine, and to a lesser extent bromine, reacts reversibly with water to give a mixture of acids, for example:

$$Cl_2 + H_2O \rightleftharpoons HClO \qquad + HCl$$
$$\text{i.e. chloric(I)} \qquad \text{hydrochloric}$$
$$\text{acid} \qquad\qquad \text{acid}$$

The presence of chloric(I) acid makes the properties of 'chlorine water' different from those of gaseous chlorine, just as aqueous sulphur dioxide is very different from the gas. Chloric(I) acid is a strong oxidizing agent, and in acid solution will even oxidize sulphur to sulphuric acid; however, the concentration of free chloric(I) acid in 'chlorine water' is often low and oxidation reactions are not always complete. Nevertheless when 'chlorine' bleaches moist litmus, it is the chloric(I) acid which is formed that produces the bleaching. The reaction of chlorine gas with aqueous bromide or iodide ions which causes displacement of bromine or iodine (see below) may also involve the reaction

$$2I^- + HClO + HCl \rightarrow 2Cl^- + I_2 + H_2O$$

since water is present to produce the two acids. Chlorine water loses its efficiency as an oxidizing agent on standing because the chloric(I) acid decomposes. There are two possible ways of decomposition:

$$3HClO \rightarrow 2HCl + HClO_3$$
$$\text{chloric(V)}$$
$$\text{acid}$$

or

$$2HClO \rightarrow 2HCl + O_2$$

The second reaction is favoured by sunlight and by catalysts such as platinum black or metallic oxides (cf. the decomposition of aqueous hydrogen peroxide). Bromine water undergoes a similar decomposition in sunlight and oxygen is evolved but in general it is more stable than chlorine water and the equilibrium.

$$Br_2 + H_2O \rightleftharpoons HBr + HBrO$$

lies further to the left.

If 'chlorine water' is boiled the chloric(I) acid decomposes as above, but a little may break down into steam and the acid anhydride, dichlorine monoxide:

$$2HClO \rightleftharpoons Cl_2O + H_2O$$

The smell of chlorine water, somewhat different from that of gaseous chlorine, may be due to minute amounts of evolved dichlorine monoxide.

The reactions with alkalis

Oxygen difluoride, OF_2, is obtained when gaseous fluorine is passed through very dilute (2 per cent) sodium hydroxide solution:

$$2F_2 + 2NaOH \rightarrow 2NaF + OF_2 + H_2O$$

but with more concentrated alkali, oxygen is formed:

$$2F_2 + 4NaOH \rightarrow 4NaF + 2H_2O + O_2$$

The reactions of the other halogens can be summarized in the two equations:

(1) $X_2 + 2OH^- \rightarrow X^- + XO^- + H_2O$
(2) $3XO^- \rightarrow 2X^- + XO_3^-$

Reaction (1) is favoured by using dilute alkali and low temperature; with more alkali or higher temperatures the disproportionation reaction (2) occurs and the overall reaction becomes

$$3X_2 + 6OH^- \rightarrow 5X^- + XO_3^- + 3H_2O$$

The stability of the halate(I) anion, XO^-, decreases from chlorine to iodine and the iodate(I) ion disproportionates very rapidly even at room temperature.

The formation of halate(V) and halide ions by reaction (2) is favoured by the use of hot concentrated solutions of alkali and an excess of the halogen.

When chlorine is passed over molten sodium or potassium hydroxide, oxygen is evolved, the high temperature causing the chlorate(V) ion to decompose:

$$2ClO_3^- \rightarrow 2Cl^- + 3O_2$$

11.3.4   Other displacement and oxidation reactions

Many of the reactions of halogens can be considered as either oxidation or displacement reactions; the redox potentials (*Table 11.2*) give a clear indication of their relative oxidizing power in aqueous solution. Fluorine, chlorine and bromine have the ability to displace hydrogen from hydrocarbons, but in addition each halogen is able to displace other elements which are less electronegative than itself. Thus fluorine can displace all the other halogens from both ionic and covalent compounds, for example

$$2NaCl + F_2 \rightarrow 2NaF + Cl_2$$

$$2 \overset{\mid}{\underset{\mid}{-C}}{-}Cl + F_2 \rightarrow 2 \overset{\mid}{\underset{\mid}{-C}}{-}F + Cl_2$$

and oxygen from water and silica:

$$SiO_2 + 2F_2 \rightarrow SiF_4 + O_2$$

The reaction with silica explains why fluorine reacts with glass and quartz, but if these are rigorously freed from adsorbed water, the reaction is very slow; hence dry fluorine can be manipulated in dry glass apparatus but all glass taps must be lubricated with fluorocarbon grease since hydrocarbon greases would be attacked. The very strong oxidizing properties of fluorine in aqueous systems are seen in reactions such as the conversion of chlorate(V) into chlorate(VII), chromium(III) to dichromate(VI) and the oxidation of the hydrogensulphate ion, HSO_4^-, to peroxodisulphate:

$$2HSO_4^- + F_2 \rightarrow S_2O_8^{2-} + 2HF$$

Also, in anhydrous conditions, silver reacts with fluorine and forms silver difluoride AgF_2 and cobalt gives cobalt(III) fluoride, CoF_3, these metals showing higher oxidation states than is usual in their simple salts.

Chlorine has a lower electrode potential and electronegativity than fluorine but will displace bromine and iodine from aqueous solutions of bromide and iodide ions respectively:

$$Cl_2 + 2Br^- \rightarrow 2Cl^- + Br_2$$

Chlorine reacts directly with carbon monoxide to give carbonyl chloride (phosgene):

$$CO + Cl_2 \rightarrow COCl_2$$

and sulphur dioxide to give sulphur dichloride dioxide:

$$SO_2 + Cl_2 \rightarrow SO_2Cl_2$$

In aqueous solution sulphur dioxide (sulphurous acid) is oxidized to sulphuric acid:

$$SO_2 + Cl_2 + 2H_2O \rightarrow H_2SO_4 + 2HCl$$

Chlorine reacts with some metallic oxides to yield chlorides, for example

$$2Fe_2O_3 + 6Cl_2 \rightarrow 4FeCl_3 + 3O_2$$

Bromine has many oxidizing reactions ($E^{\ominus} = +1.07$ V) and like chlorine it will oxidize sulphur dioxide in aqueous solution to sulphuric acid, and hydrogen sulphide to sulphur.

Iodine has the lowest standard electrode potential of any of the common halogens ($E^{\ominus} = +0.54$ V) and is consequently the least powerful oxidizing agent. Indeed, the iodide ion can be oxidized to iodine by many reagents including air which will oxidize an acidified solution of iodide ions. However, iodine will oxidize arsenate(III) to arsenate(V) in alkaline solution (the presence of sodium carbonate makes the solution sufficiently alkaline) but the reaction is reversible, for example by removal of iodine,

$$\underset{\text{arsenate(III)}}{AsO_3^{3-}} + I_2 + 2OH^- \rightleftharpoons \underset{\text{arsenate(V)}}{AsO_4^{3-}} + 2I^- + H_2O$$

The oxidation of the thiosulphate ion $S_2O_3^{2-}$ to tetrathionate ion, $S_4O_6^{2-}$, is used to estimate iodine:

$$2S_2O_3^{2-} + I_2 \rightarrow S_4O_6^{2-} + 2I^-$$

The disappearance of iodine at the end point is detected by the addition of fresh starch solution which gives a blue complex as long as iodine is present.

11.4 The hydrides (hydrogen halides)

11.4.1 Physical properties

All the halogens form hydrides by direct combination of the elements. The hydrogen halides formed are covalently bonded, and when pure are colourless gases at room temperature. Some important physical properties of the hydrogen halides are given in *Table 11.3*. The data in *Table 11.3* clearly reveal unexpected properties for hydrogen fluoride. A graph of atomic number of the halogen against b.p. for the hydrogen halides has been given on p. 274. The abnormal behaviour is attributed to hydrogen bonding which causes association of hydrogen fluoride molecules. In the solid state hydrogen fluoride exists as an infinite zig-zag chain of molecules. Association

Table 11.3 Properties of the hydrogen halides

	HF	HCl	HBr	HI
m.p./K	190	159	186	222
b.p./K	293	188	206	238
Enthalpy of formation/kJ mol^{-1}	-269	-92.3	-36.2	$+26.0$
Bond dissociation energy/kJ mol^{-1}	566	431	366	299
Relative permittivity of liquid	66	9	6	3

also occurs in the liquid and gaseous phases and in the latter phase, investigations indicate the presence of $(HF)_2$ molecules and also more highly associated forms existing not only as chains but also as rings, for example $(HF)_6$.

The ability to form hydrogen bonds explains the formation of complex ions such as HF_2^- and $H_2F_3^-$ when a fluoride salt, for example potassium fluoride, is dissolved in aqueous hydrofluoric acid:

$$KF + HF \rightleftharpoons KHF_2 \qquad \text{(i.e. } K^+F^-\ldots H\text{—}F\text{)}$$

This reaction can be reversed by heating and is a convenient method of obtaining anhydrous hydrogen fluoride from an aqueous solution.

The dipole moments of the hydrogen halides decrease with increasing atomic number of the halogen, the largest difference occurring between HF and HCl, and association of molecules is not an important factor in the properties of HCl, HBr and HI. This change in dipole moment is reflected in the diminishing permittivity (dielectric constant) values from HF to HI.

Thermal stability of hydrogen halides

The enthalpies of formation and hydrogen–halogen bond strengths are given in *Table 11.3*. The formation of hydrogen fluoride from its elements occurs with explosive violence; the hydrogen–fluorine bond produced is extremely strong (H—F $= 566$ kJ mol^{-1}, cf. C—C in diamond 356 kJ mol^{-1}) and stable to heat up to very high temperatures. Both chlorine and bromine undergo a photochemical chain reaction with hydrogen. The hydrogen–halide bond strength correctly indicates the high thermal stability of hydrogen chloride, with hydrogen bromide being rather less stable. Unlike the hydrogen halides so far discussed, hydrogen iodide is an endothermic compound, and reference has been made to the equilibrium

$$H_2 + I_2 \rightleftharpoons 2HI$$

This equilibrium is established when hydrogen iodide is heated, hydrogen–iodine bonds being broken.

Acidity of hydrogen halides

All the hydrogen halides are freely soluble in water and react according to the general equation

$$HX + H_2O \rightleftharpoons H_3O^+ + X^-$$

The steps involved are given on p. 79. When HX is HCl, HBr or HI, all three are strong acids in water with acid strength increasing from HCl to HI.

The bond dissociation energy of the hydrogen–fluorine bond in HF is so great that the above equilibrium lies to the left and hydrogen fluoride is a weak acid in dilute aqueous solution. In more concentrated solution, however, a second equilibrium reaction becomes important with the fluoride ion forming the complex ion HF_2^-. The relevant equilibria are:

$$HF + H_2O \rightleftharpoons H_3O^+ + F^-$$

$$(HF)_2 + H_2O \rightleftharpoons HF_2^- + H_3O^+$$

or more generally

$$(HF)_n + H_2O \rightleftharpoons [H_{n-1}F_n]^- + H_3O^+$$

The second equilibrium is displaced to the right as the concentration of hydrogen fluoride is increased and it is found that at a concentration of approximately 5—15M, hydrogen fluoride is effectively a strong acid. In this way hydrogen fluoride differs from all the other hydrogen halides. Anhydrous hydrogen fluoride ionizes to a small extent and the following equilibria are established:

$$2HF \rightleftharpoons H_2F^+ + F^-$$

$$F^- + HF \rightleftharpoons HF_2^- \ (H_2F_3^-, H_3F_4^- \text{ etc.})$$

The liquid, like water, has a high relative permittivity and is weakly conducting. It is a good solvent for many inorganic and organic substances, to give conducting solutions. Substances which move the equilibria to the right when dissolved in hydrogen fluoride, by taking up the fluoride ions, are 'acids'. For example, boron trifluoride forms the tetrafluoroborate anion in a solution of hydrogen fluoride:

$$2HF + BF_3 \rightleftharpoons H_2F^+ + BF_4^-$$
$$\text{tetrafluoroborate ion}$$

However, many substances, notably alcohols, have a greater proton affinity than the hydrogen fluoride molecule, and so behave as bases, for example ethanol:

$$C_2H_5OH + HF \rightleftharpoons C_2H_5OH_2^+ + F^-$$

Even nitric acid will do this, i.e.:

$$HNO_3 + HF \rightleftharpoons H_2NO_3^+ + F^-$$

Thus nitric acid behaves as a base in hydrogen fluoride. Hence increases of conductivity when substances dissolve in hydrogen fluoride may be due to 'acidic' or 'basic' behaviour.

11.4.2   The preparation and reactions of hydrogen halides

Hydrogen fluoride, anhydrous hydrofluoric acid, HF
Hydrogen fluoride is the most important compound of fluorine. It is prepared in the laboratory, and on the large scale, by the reaction of calcium fluoride with concentrated sulphuric acid:

$$CaF_2 + H_2SO_4 \rightarrow CaSO_4 + 2HF\uparrow$$

The reaction is carried out in a lead retort; one suitable for the laboratory can be made from a piece of lead piping, bent like a retort and closed at the shorter end. This is charged with fluorspar and the acid and heated, and the hydrogen fluoride is distilled into a polythene vessel.

Anhydrous hydrogen fluoride (as distinct from an aqueous solution of hydrofluoric acid) does not attack silica or glass. It reacts with metals to give fluorides, for example with heated iron the anhydrous iron(II) fluoride is formed; the same product is obtained by displacement of chlorine from iron(II) chloride:

$$FeCl_2 + 2HF \rightarrow FeF_2 + 2HCl\uparrow$$

Hydrogen fluoride also effects replacement reactions in organic compounds. For example, carbon tetrachloride yields a mixture of chlorofluoromethanes CCl_3F, CCl_2F_2 and so on. Like all the other hydrogen halides, hydrogen fluoride adds on to alkenes, for example:

$$CH_2{=}CH_2 + HF \rightarrow CH_3CH_2F$$

Aqueous hydrogen fluoride is a weak acid (*see* p. 287) and dissolves silica and silicates to form hexafluorosilicic acid; hence glass is etched by the acid, which must be kept in polythene bottles.

In addition to the abnormal properties already discussed, aqueous hydrofluoric acid has the properties of a typical acid, attacking metals with the evolution of hydrogen and dissolving most metallic hydroxides and carbonates.

Uses of hydrogen fluoride. By far the largest use of hydrogen fluoride is in the manufacture of fluorocarbons which find a wide variety of uses including refrigerants, aerosol propellants and anaesthetics. Hydrogen fluoride is also used in the manufacture of synthetic cryolite, Na_3AlF_6, and the production of enriched uranium.

Hydrogen chloride

Hydrogen chloride is formed:
(1) By the direct union of hydrogen and chlorine. Very pure hydrogen chloride is made by direct union of pure hydrogen and chlorine in a quartz vessel.
(2) As the product of the hydrolysis of many substances in which chlorine is covalently bound, for example:

$$SOCl_2 + 2H_2O \rightarrow H_2SO_3 + 2HCl$$

$$PCl_3 + 3H_2O \rightarrow H_3PO_3 + 3HCl$$

It is prepared in the laboratory by warming sodium chloride with concentrated sulphuric acid:

$$NaCl + H_2SO_4 \rightarrow NaHSO_4 + HCl\uparrow$$

The gas is dried by passage through concentrated sulphuric acid and collected over mercury.

On the large scale, hydrogen chloride can be produced by the same reaction, which is usually carried a stage further by stronger heating, i.e.

$$NaCl + NaHSO_4 \rightarrow Na_2SO_4 + HCl\uparrow$$

Anhydrous hydrogen chloride is not particularly reactive, either as a gas at ordinary temperatures, or a liquid (b.p. 188 K) and does not react with metals such as iron or zinc, nor with dry oxides. A few reactive metals, such as sodium, will burn in the gas to give the chloride and hydrogen:

$$2Na + 2HCl \rightarrow 2NaCl + H_2\uparrow$$

However, if heated hydrogen chloride is passed over heated metals, the chloride is formed; in the case of a metal exhibiting variable oxidation state, the lower chloride is obtained:

$$Sn + 2HCl \rightarrow H_2\uparrow + SnCl_2$$
$$Fe + 2HCl \rightarrow H_2\uparrow + FeCl_2$$

Aqueous hydrochloric acid. In aqueous solution, hydrogen chloride forms hydrochloric acid. The concentrated acid contains about 40 per cent hydrogen chloride (about 12M). A graph of the boiling point of hydrogen chloride–water mixtures against composition shows a maximum at about 20 per cent HCl; hence if either the concentrated or dilute acids be distilled, then either hydrogen chloride or water respectively distil over, leaving behind 'constant boiling-point' acid.

Hydrochloric acid is a strong monobasic acid, dissolving metals to form salts and evolving hydrogen. The reaction may be slow if the chloride formed is insoluble (for example lead and silver are attacked very slowly). The rate of attack on a metal also depends on concentration; thus aluminium is attacked most rapidly by 9M hydrochloric acid, while with other metals such as zinc or iron, more dilute acid is best.

Electrolysis of hydrochloric acid yields hydrogen at the cathode and oxygen at the anode from the dilute acid, but chlorine at the anode (of carbon) from the concentrated acid. Electrolysis of the concentrated acid is used on the large scale to recover chlorine.

If tetramethylammonium chloride is dissolved in hydrochloric acid, the unstable salt $[(CH_3)_4N]^+[HCl_2]^-$, can be crystallized out; here chlorine is showing weak hydrogen bonding (cf. $F^-\ldots H\!-\!F$ which is stable, and $Cl^-\ldots H\!-\!Cl$ which is unstable).

Uses of hydrogen chloride. Hydrogen chloride is sometimes used in the preparation of an ester, for example ethyl benzoate, where it acts both as an acid catalyst and a dehydrating agent. Hydrochloric acid is used primarily to produce chlorides, for example ammonium chloride. It is extensively used in the manufacture of aniline dyes, and for cleaning iron before galvanizing and tin-plating.

Hydrogen bromide, HBr

Hydrogen bromide cannot be prepared readily by the action of sulphuric acid on a bromide, because the latter is too easily oxidized by the sulphuric acid to form bromine. It is therefore obtained by the hydrolysis of a covalent bromide; a convenient one is phosphorus tribromide. By dropping bromine on to a paste of red phosphorus and water, phosphorus tribromide is formed and immediately hydrolysed thus:

$$PBr_3 + 3H_2O \rightarrow H_3PO_3 + 3HBr\uparrow$$

Any free bromine can be removed by passing the evolved gas through a ∪ tube packed with glass beads covered with moist red phosphorus (*Figure 11.3*).

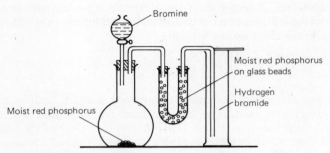

Figure 11.3 Preparation of hydrogen bromide

Hydrogen bromide may also be prepared by dropping bromine into benzene containing aluminium powder, which acts as a catalyst to the reaction:

$$C_6H_6 + Br_2 \xrightarrow{Al} C_6H_5Br + HBr\uparrow$$

Hydrogen bromide is a colourless gas similar in properties to hydrogen chloride. It is very soluble in water, giving *hydrobromic acid*. The latter can be prepared directly by slow hydrolysis of a covalent bromide: a convenient one is disulphur dibromide, S_2Br_2, made by dissolving sulphur in excess of liquid bromine. The mixture is then hydrolysed, and hydrobromic acid distilled off:

$$S_2Br_2 + 2Br_2 + 4H_2O \rightarrow 6HBr + H_2SO_4 + S\downarrow$$

The acid which comes over is a constant boiling mixture containing about 47 per cent hydrogen bromide (density = 1.46 g cm^{-3}).

Hydrobromic acid is rather easily oxidized when exposed to light and becomes brown owing to the bromine liberated. Otherwise, its properties are those of a strong acid, similar to hydrochloric acid.

Hydrogen iodide, HI

Hydrogen iodide is prepared in a similar way to hydrogen bromide, by the action of water on a mixture of iodine and violet (or red) phosphorus. The hydrogen iodide evolved may be collected by downward delivery or may be condensed (b.p. 238 K); it reacts with mercury and so cannot be collected over the latter.

An aqueous solution of hydrogen iodide, up to 50 per cent concentration, may be prepared by passing hydrogen sulphide (or sulphur dioxide) into a suspension of iodine in water:

$$H_2S + I_2 \rightarrow 2H^+ + 2I^- + S\downarrow$$

$$SO_3^{2-} + I_2 + H_2O \rightarrow 2H^+ + 2I^- + SO_4^{2-}$$

These reactions illustrate the oxidizing action of iodine. In the first reaction, sulphur may be filtered off, leaving only hydriodic acid.

Properties. Hydrogen iodide is a colourless gas. It is very soluble in water and fumes in moist air (cf. hydrogen chloride), to give *hydriodic acid*. Its solution forms a constant boiling mixture (cf. hydrochloric and hydrobromic acids). Because it attacks mercury so readily, hydrogen iodide is difficult to study as a gas, but the dissociation equilibrium has been investigated.

Hydriodic acid is a strong acid, reacting with bases to give iodides, containing the ion I^-. It is also a strong reducing agent (so also is hydrogen iodide, particularly at high temperatures, when dissociation into hydrogen and iodine is considerable). Thus, it reduces sulphuric acid to a mixture of sulphite, sulphur and hydrogen sulphide, the last reaction predominating:

$$H_2SO_4 + 8HI \rightarrow H_2S + 4I_2 + 4H_2O$$

Hence hydrogen iodide cannot be prepared by the reaction of sulphuric acid with an iodide. Hydriodic acid is slowly oxidized by air (more rapidly in light) liberating iodine:

$$4HI + O_2 \rightarrow 2H_2O + 2I_2$$

Other examples of its reducing action are:
(1) Reduction of dinitrogen oxide to ammonia (which gives the ammonium ion with the acid):

$$N_2O + 10HI \rightarrow 2NH_4^+ + 2I^- + H_2O + 4I_2$$

(2) Reduction of nitric to nitrous acid:

$$HNO_3 + 2HI \rightarrow HNO_2 + I_2 + H_2O$$

11.5 Oxides

None of the halogens reacts directly with oxygen but all form oxides by indirect methods.

11.5.1 Fluorine oxides

The oxides of fluorine are more correctly called oxygen fluorides because of the greater electronegativity of fluorine.

Oxygen difluoride, OF_2
This is obtained when a rapid stream of gaseous fluorine is passed through 2 per cent sodium hydroxide solution:

$$2F_2 + 2NaOH \rightarrow 2NaF + OF_2 + H_2O$$

It is a gas at room temperature with a boiling point of 128 K. It is a strong oxidizing agent, some reactions occurring with explosive violence. Water hydrolyses it slowly at room temperature, but the reaction evolving oxygen is rapid in the presence of a base, and explosive with steam:

$$OF_2 + H_2O \rightarrow O_2 + 2HF$$

Fluorine is known to form three other oxides, O_2F_2, O_3F_2 and O_4F_2 but all these decompose below 200 K.

11.5.2 Chlorine oxides

Chlorine forms several very reactive, unstable oxides. *Dichlorine monoxide* Cl_2O is a yellowish gas at room temperature, the liquid boiling at 275 K. It is prepared by treating freshly prepared yellow mercury(II) oxide with either chlorine gas, or with a solution of chlorine in tetrachloromethane (carbon tetrachloride):

$$2HgO + 2Cl_2 \rightarrow HgO.HgCl_2 + Cl_2O$$

On heating (and sometimes at ordinary temperatures) it explodes, yielding chlorine and oxygen — this decomposition also being catalysed by light. It dissolves in water to give an orange–yellow liquid containing some chloric(I) acid of which dichlorine monoxide is the formal anhydride. It is a strong oxidizing agent converting many metals into a mixture of their oxides and chlorides.

Liquid chlorine dioxide, ClO_2

This boils at 284 K to give an orange–yellow gas. A very reactive compound, it decomposes readily and violently into its constituents. It is a powerful oxidizing agent which has recently found favour as a commercial oxidizing agent and as a bleach for wood pulp and flour. In addition, it is used in water sterilization where, unlike chlorine, it does not produce an unpleasant taste. It is produced when potassium chlorate(V) is treated with concentrated sulphuric acid, the reaction being essentially a disproportionation of chloric(V) acid:

$$3KClO_3 + 3H_2SO_4 \rightarrow 3KHSO_4 + 3HClO_3$$

$$\underset{\text{chloric(V) acid}}{3HClO_3} \rightarrow 2ClO_2 + \underset{\text{chloric(VII) acid}}{HClO_4} + H_2O$$

The reaction usually proceeds with explosive violence and a better method of preparation is to heat, gently, moist crystals of ethanedioic acid (oxalic acid) and potassium chlorate(V):

$$2KClO_3 + 2H_2C_2O_4 \rightarrow K_2C_2O_4 + 2H_2O + 2CO_2 + 2ClO_2$$

Industrially an aqueous solution of chlorine dioxide can be prepared by passing nitrogen dioxide up a packed tower down which sodium chlorate(V) flows:

$$ClO_3^- + NO_2 \rightarrow NO_3^- + ClO_2$$

The aqueous solution is safe to handle, the dissolution being essentially physical. On standing in sunlight the solution slowly decomposes to a mixture of acids. In alkaline solution a mixture of chlorate(III), ClO_2^-, and chlorate(V), ClO_3^-, ions is rapidly produced. Chlorine dioxide is paramagnetic, the molecule containing an odd electron and having a structure very like that of NO_2 (p. 206).

Dichlorine hexoxide, Cl_2O_6

This is formed when chlorine dioxide is exposed to ultraviolet light or by the action of ozone on chlorine dioxide:

$$6ClO_2 + 2O_3 \rightarrow 3Cl_2O_6$$

It is a liquid at room temperature, melting point 276.5 K. The relative molecular mass, determined in carbon tetrachloride, indicates the dimeric formula, but magnetic measurements show the presence of small quantities of the paramagnetic monomer ClO_3 in the pure liquid. It is rather an unstable compound and decomposes slowly even at its melting point, and more rapidly on heating, forming finally oxygen and chlorine. It is a powerful oxidizing agent and reacts violently even with water with which it forms a mixture of chloric(V) and chloric(VII) acids.

Dichlorine heptoxide, Cl_2O_7

This is the most stable of the chlorine oxides. It is a yellow oil at room temperature, b.p. 353 K, which will explode on heating or when subjected to shock. It is the anhydride of chloric(VII) acid (perchloric acid) from which it is prepared by dehydration using phosphorus(V) oxide, the acid being slowly re-formed when water is added.

11.5.3   Bromine oxides

These are all unstable substances and little is known about them.

Dibromine monoxide, Br_2O

This is prepared, similarly to the corresponding dichlorine compound, by the action of a solution of bromine in carbon tetrachloride on yellow mercury(II) oxide:

$$2HgO + 2Br_2 \rightarrow Hg_2OBr_2 + Br_2O$$

It is a dark brown liquid, m.p. 256 K, which decomposes rapidly at room temperature.

Tribromine octoxide, Br_3O_8

This is a white solid obtained when ozone and bromine react together at 273 K at low pressure. It is unstable above 200 K in the absence of ozone. It is known to exist in two forms, both soluble in water.

Bromine dioxide, BrO_2

This is prepared by passing an electric discharge through a mixture of oxygen and bromine at low temperature and pressure. It is a yellow solid, stable only below 230 K, decomposing above this temperature to give oxygen and bromine.

11.5.4 Iodine oxides

There appears to be only one true oxide of iodine, *diiodine pentoxide*, I_2O_5. It is a white solid prepared by heating iodic(V) acid to 450 K:

$$2HIO_3 \rightarrow H_2O + I_2O_5$$

As the equation indicates, it is the anhydride of iodic acid(V), which is re-formed when water is added to the pentoxide. Mixed with concentrated sulphuric acid and silica, it is a quantitative oxidizing agent for carbon monoxide at room temperature:

$$5CO + I_2O_5 \rightarrow 5CO_2\uparrow + I_2$$

11.6 Oxoacids and their salts

For many years it was thought that fluorine did not form any oxoacids or oxoacid anions. Recent work, however, indicates the existence of fluoric(I) acid (hypofluorous acid), HFO, formed by the reaction of fluorine with water at 273 K. The acid forms colourless crystals, m.p. 156 K, is very unstable and has, as expected, very strong oxidizing properties.

The acids of chlorine(I), bromine(I) and iodine(I) are weak acids, the pK_a values being 7.4, 8.7 and 12.3 respectively. They are good oxidizing agents, especially in acid solutions. The acids decrease in stability from chloric(I) to iodic(I).

Only chlorine forms a +3 acid, $HClO_2$. This is also a weak acid and is unstable. The +5 acids, HXO_3, are formed by chlorine, bromine and iodine; they are stable compounds and behave as strong acids in water.

The existence of chloric(VII) (perchloric) and iodic(VII) (periodic) acids has long been known but bromic(VII) acid has only recently been prepared.

11.6.1 Halic(I) acids of chlorine, bromine and iodine

The amount of halic(I) acid* formed when the halogen reacts reversibly with water decreases from chlorine to iodine and the concentration of iodic(I) acid in a saturated solution of iodine is negligible. However the equilibrium

$$2H_2O + X_2 \rightleftharpoons HXO + H_3O^+ + X^-$$

can be displaced to the right by the removal of the halide ion, X^-, or the hydrogen ion, H_3O^+. Thus the halic(I) acids can be prepared by (a) passing the halogen into alkali [provided that disproportionation of the halate(I) can be minimized], or by (b) passing the halogen into a well-stirred suspension of yellow mercury(II) oxide, which removes the halide ion as insoluble

---

*A halic(I) acid is conventionally represented as HXO, but HOX represents the structure better.

mercury(II) halide:

$$Cl_2 + 2H_2O \rightleftharpoons HClO + H_3O^+ + Cl^-$$

$$HgO + 2H^+ + 2Cl^- \rightarrow H_2O + HgCl_2$$

All the halic(I) acids are unstable in aqueous solution with respect to disproportionation, the stability decreasing from chloric(I) to iodic(I):

$$3HXO \rightarrow 2HX + HXO_3$$

The acids are only known in aqueous solution; all are oxidizing agents; the standard redox potentials for the reaction

$$HXO + H^+ + 2e^- \rightarrow X^- + H_2O$$

are:

$$X = Cl \qquad E^{\ominus} = +1.49 \text{ V}$$
$$X = Br \qquad E^{\ominus} = +1.33 \text{ V}$$
$$X = I \qquad E^{\ominus} = +0.99 \text{ V}$$

The stability of the halate(I) ion decreases, as expected, from ClO^- to IO^- and only the chlorate(I) ion can be considered reasonably stable even in aqueous solution. Solid sodium bromate(I), NaBrO (with five or seven molecules of water of crystallization) can be obtained, but on standing or warming it disproportionates:

$$3BrO^- \rightarrow BrO_3^- + 2Br^-$$

The aqueous solution of sodium chlorate(I) is an important liquid bleach and disinfectant. It is produced commercially by the electrolysis of cold aqueous sodium chloride, the anode and cathode products being mixed. The sodium chloride remaining in the solution does not usually matter. There is evidence to suggest that iodic(I) acid has some basic character

$$IOH \rightleftharpoons I^+ + OH^-$$

and iodine monochloride, ICl, can be prepared by reacting iodic(I) acid with hydrochloric acid.

11.6.2 Halic(III) acids, HXO_2

Only chloric(III) acid, $HClO_2$, is definitely known to exist. It is formed as one of the products of the reaction of water with chlorine dioxide (see p. 293). Its salts, for example $NaClO_2$, are formed together with chlorates(V) by the action of chlorine dioxide on alkalis. Sodium chlorate(III) alone can be obtained by mixing aqueous solutions of sodium peroxide and chlorine dioxide:

$$2ClO_2 + Na_2O_2 \rightarrow 2NaClO_2 + O_2\uparrow$$

A solution of the free acid can be obtained by using hydrogen peroxide, instead of sodium peroxide.

Chloric(III) acid is a fairly weak acid, and is an oxidizing agent, for example it oxidizes aqueous iodide ion to iodine. Sodium chlorate(III) (prepared as above) is used commercially as a mild bleaching agent; it bleaches many natural and synthetic fibres without degrading them, and will also bleach, for example, oils, varnishes and beeswax.

Chlorates(III) *disproportionate* on heating, or on boiling the aqueous solution, thus:

$$3ClO_2^- \rightarrow 2ClO_3^- + Cl^-$$
$$\text{chlorate(V)} \quad \text{chloride}$$

11.6.3   Halic(V) acids

Chlorine, bromine and iodine form halic(V) acids but only iodic(V) acid, HIO_3, can be isolated. Solutions of the chloric(V) and bromic(V) acids can be prepared by the addition of dilute sulphuric acid to barium chlorate(V) and bromate(V) respectively, and then filtering (cf. the preparation of hydrogen peroxide). These two acids can also be prepared by decomposing the corresponding halic(I) acids, but in this case the halide ion is also present in the solution.

Attempts to concentrate chloric(V) and bromic(V) acids beyond certain limits lead to decomposition which may be violent.

Iodic(V) acid is prepared by oxidizing iodine with concentrated nitric acid:

$$3I_2 + 10HNO_3 \rightarrow 6HIO_3 + 10NO\uparrow + 2H_2O$$

The iodic acid(V) and some diiodine pentoxide separate out and the iodic(V) acid is purified by recrystallization from hot water.

All the halic(V) acids are strong acids and their salts are not appreciably hydrolysed in aqueous solution. They are also powerful oxidizing agents (*see* below).

Halate(V) salts

Generally the solubility of a given metal halate decreases from chlorate(V) to iodate(V) and many heavy metal iodates(V) are quantitatively insoluble. Like their parent acids, the halates(V) are strong oxidizing agents, especially in acid solution: their standard electrode potentials are given in *Table 11.4*.

Unexpectedly we find that the bromate(V) ion in acid solution [i.e. effectively bromic(V) acid] is a more powerful oxidizing agent than the chlorate(V) ion, ClO_3^-. The halates(V) are thermally unstable and can evolve oxygen as one of the decomposition products. Potassium chlorate(V), when heated, first melts, then resolidifies owing to the formation of potassium chlorate(VII) (perchlorate):

$$4KClO_3 \rightarrow 3KClO_4 + KCl$$

but a further, stronger heating will make the chlorate(VII) decompose evolving oxygen:

$$KClO_4 \rightarrow KCl + 2O_2$$

The decomposition of potassium chlorate(V) is catalysed by manganese(IV)

Table 11.4 Standard electrode potentials, $E^{\ominus}/V$, for oxidizing reactions of halates(V)

Solution	Reaction	X = Cl	Br	I
Acid	$XO_3^-(aq) + 6H_3O^+ + 6e^- \rightarrow X^-(aq) + 9H_2O$	+1.45	+1.67	+1.19
Alkaline	$XO_3^-(aq) + 3H_2O + 6e^- \rightarrow 6OH^-(aq) + X^-$	+0.62	+0.61	+0.26

oxide, MnO_2, and oxygen is evolved on heating the mixture below the melting point of the chlorate(V).

The ability of the solid chlorates(V) to provide oxygen led to their use in matches and fireworks. Bromates(V) and iodates(V) are used in quantitative volumetric analysis. Potassium hydrogen diiodate(V), $KH(IO_3)_2$, is used to standardize solutions of sodium thiosulphate(VI) since in the presence of excess of potassium iodide and acid, the reaction

$$IO_3^- + 5I^- + 6H^+ \rightarrow 3I_2 + 3H_2O$$

occurs quantitatively. The liberated iodide is then titrated using the thiosulphate solution of which the concentration is required:

$$I_2 + 2S_2O_3^{2-} \rightarrow 2I^- + S_4O_6^{2-}$$

11.6.4   Halic(VII) acids

The existence of chloric(VII) (perchloric), $HClO_4$, and several periodic(VII) acids has long been established. Bromic(VII) acid and the bromate(VII) ion have only recently been discovered.

These acids differ so greatly in their properties that they will be considered separately.

Chloric(VII) *acid and chlorates*(VII)

Chloric(VII) acid is prepared by carefully distilling potassium chlorate(VII) with concentrated sulphuric acid under reduced pressure:

$$KClO_4 + H_2SO_4 \rightarrow KHSO_4 + HClO_4$$

It is a liquid, b.p. 363 K, but if heated it decomposes and hence must be distilled under reduced pressure; decomposition may occur with explosive violence and this can occur even at room temperature if impurities are present. Combustible material, for example paper and wood, ignite spontaneously with explosive violence on contact with the acid, and it can produce painful blisters on the skin.

Chloric(VII) acid fumes in moist air and is very soluble in water, dissolving with the evolution of much heat. Several hydrates are known; the hydrate $HClO_4.H_2O$ is a solid at room temperature and has an ionic lattice $[H_3O^+][ClO_4^-]$.

The oxidizing properties of the aqueous solutions of chloric(VII) acid change dramatically with temperature and the concentration of the acid. Cold dilute solutions have *very weak oxidizing properties* and these solutions will react, for example, with metals, producing hydrogen without reduction of the chlorate(VII) ion occurring:

$$Zn + 2HClO_4 \rightarrow Zn(ClO_4)_2 + H_2\uparrow$$

Hot concentrated solutions of chloric(VII) acid and chlorates(VII), however, react vigorously and occasionally violently with reducing agents.

Chloric(VII) acid is one of the strongest acids known, and it behaves as such even when dissolved in solvents with poor proton affinity; thus it can be used as an acid in pure ethanoic acid as a solvent:

$$CH_3COOH + HClO_4 \rightleftharpoons CH_3COOH_2^+ + ClO_4^-$$

Chlorates(VII)

These can be prepared by electrolytic oxidation of chlorates(V) or by neutralization of the acid with metals. Many chlorates(VII) are very soluble in water and indeed barium and magnesium chlorates(VII) form hydrates of such low vapour pressure that they can be used as desiccants. The chlorate(VII) ion shows the least tendency of any negative ion to behave as a ligand, i.e. to form complexes with cations, and hence solutions of chlorates(VII) are used when it is desired to avoid complex formation in solution.

The chlorate(VII) ion, ClO_4^-, is isoelectronic with the sulphate(VI) ion, SO_4^{2-}, and has a similar tetrahedral symmetry.

11.6.5   Iodic(VII) acids

These are acids which can be regarded, in respect of their formulae (but not their properties) as hydrates of the hypothetical diiodine heptoxide, I_2O_7. The acid commonly called 'periodic acid', $I_2O_7.5H_2O$, is written H_5IO_6 (since the acid is pentabasic) and should strictly be called hexaoxoiodic(VII) acid. It is a weak acid and its salts are hydrolysed in solution. It can be prepared by electrolytic oxidation of iodic(V) acid at low temperatures:

$$IO_3^- + 2H_2O + OH^- \rightarrow H_5IO_6 + 2e^-$$

The 'periodic acids' and 'periodates' are powerful oxidizing agents and they will oxidize manganese to manganate(VII), a reaction used to determine small quantities of manganese in steel.

11.7   Halides

The rigid classification of halides into covalent and ionic can only be an oversimplification, and the properties of the halides of a given element can very greatly depend upon the halogen. Thus the classification is only one of convenience.

11.7.1 General methods of preparation

Many salt-like halides can be prepared by the action of the hydrohalic acid, HX, on the metal or its oxide, hydroxide or carbonate. The halides prepared by this method are often hydrated, particularly when a less electropositive metal is involved, for example zinc or iron.

Anhydrous halides, however, are obtained when the metal is heated with the dry hydrogen halide or the halogen. In the case of elements with more than one oxidation state, the hydrogen halide produces a lower halide and the halogen a higher halide, for example

$$Sn \ + \ 2HCl \ \rightarrow \ SnCl_2 \ + \ H_2\uparrow$$
$$Sn \ + \ 2Cl_2 \ \rightarrow \ SnCl_4$$

The higher iodides, however, tend to be unstable and decomposition occurs to the lower iodide ($PI_5 \ \rightarrow \ PI_3$). Anhydrous chlorides and bromides of some metals can also be prepared by the action of ethanoyl (acetyl) halide on the hydrated ethanoate (acetate) in benzene, for example cobalt(II) and nickel(II) chlorides:

$$Co(CH_3COO)_2 \ + \ 2CH_3COCl \ + \ 2H_2O \ \rightarrow \ CoCl_2\downarrow \ + \ 4CH_3COOH$$

Sulphur dichloride oxide (thionyl chloride) on the hydrated chloride can also be used to produce the anhydrous chloride in certain cases, for example copper(II) chloride and chromium(III) chloride:

$$CrCl_3.6H_2O \ + \ 6SOCl_2 \ \rightarrow \ 6SO_2\uparrow \ + \ 12HCl\uparrow \ + \ CrCl_3$$

Halides of non-metals are usually prepared by the direct combination of the elements. If the element exhibits more than one oxidation state, excess of the halogen favours the formation of the higher halide whilst excess of the element favours the formation of the lower halide (e.g. PCl_5 and PCl_3).

11.7.2 Ionic (salt-like) halides

These are halides formed by highly electropositive elements (for example those of Groups I and II, except for beryllium and lithium). They have ionic lattices, are non-volatile solids, and conduct when molten; they are usually soluble in polar solvents in which they produce conducting solutions, indicating the presence of ions.

The change from ionic to covalent bonding is gradual in a given group or period; for a given halogen, as the size of the metal ion decreases and more especially as its charge increases, the degree of covalency increases. Thus, for example, in the chlorides of the four elements, potassium, calcium, scandium and titanium, i.e. KCl, $CaCl_2$, $ScCl_3$ and $TiCl_4$, KCl is essentially ionic, $TiCl_4$ is essentially covalent.

When the several halides of a given element are considered, changes in bond character are also found. The fluoride is generally the most ionic with ionic character decreasing from fluoride to iodide, for example aluminium trifluoride, AlF_3, is ionic but the remaining aluminium halides are all essentially covalent.

When an element has more than one oxidation state the lower halides tend to be ionic whilst the higher ones are covalent — the anhydrous chlorides of lead are a good example, for whilst lead(II) chloride, $PbCl_2$, is a white non-volatile solid, soluble in water without hydrolysis, lead(IV) chloride, $PbCl_4$, is a liquid at room temperature (p. 179) and is immediately hydrolysed. This change of bonding with oxidation state follows from the rules given on p. 43.

The solid anhydrous halides of some of the transition metals are often intermediate in character between ionic and covalent; their structures are complicated by (a) the tendency of the central metal ion to co-ordinate the halide ions around it, to form an essentially covalent complex, (b) the tendency of halide ions to bridge, or link, two metal ions, again tending to covalency [cf. aluminium chloride, p. 140 and iron(III) chloride, p. 345].

Solubility

Many ionic halides dissolve in water to give hydrated ions. The solubility of a given halide depends on several factors, and generalizations are difficult. Ionic fluorides, however, often differ from other halides in solubility. For example, calcium fluoride is insoluble but the other halides of calcium are highly soluble; silver fluoride, AgF, is very soluble but the other silver halides are insoluble.

11.7.3 Covalent halides

These are formed by less electropositive elements. They are characterized by the existence of discrete molecules which exist even in the solid state. They have generally lower melting and boiling points than the ionic halides, are more volatile and dissolve in non-polar solvents.

The melting and boiling points of a series of similar covalent halides of a given element are found to increase from the fluoride to the iodide, i.e. as the relative molecular mass of the halide increases. Thus, the trihalides of phosphorus have melting points $PF_3 = 121.5\,K$, $PCl_3 = 161.2\,K$, $PBr_3 = 233\,K$, $PI_3 = 334\,K$.

Most covalent halides are hydrolysed by water (carbon tetrachloride being a notable exception, p. 175) to give acidic solutions, by either route (a) (example $FeCl_3$) or route (b) (example BCl_3):

(a) $FeCl_3 + 6H_2O \rightarrow [Fe(H_2O)_6]^{3+} + 3Cl^-$
     $[Fe(H_2O)_6]^{3+} + H_2O \rightleftharpoons [Fe(H_2O)_5(OH)]^{2+} + H_3O^+$ etc.

(b) $BCl_3 + 3H_2O \rightarrow H_3BO_3 + 3HCl$

The hydrolysis of phosphorus tribromide or triiodide is used in the preparation of hydrogen bromide and hydrogen iodide respectively:

$PBr_3 + 3H_2O \rightarrow H_3PO_3 + 3HBr\uparrow$
$PI_3 + 3H_2O \rightarrow H_3PO_3 + 3HI\uparrow$

11.7.4 Complex halides

Halogens can act as ligands and are commonly found in complex ions; the ability of fluorine to form stable complex ions with elements in high oxidation states has already been discussed (p. 277). However, the chlorides of silver, lead(II) and mercury(I) are worthy of note. These chlorides are insoluble in water and used as a test for the metal, but all dissolve in concentrated hydrochloric acid, whereupon the complex chlorides are produced, i.e. $[AgCl_2]^-$, $[PbCl_4]^{2-}$ and $[Hg^{II}Cl_3]^-$, in the latter case the mercury(I) chloride having also disproportionated.

11.8 Interhalogen compounds and polyhalides

There are four types of interhalogen compound (*Table 11.5*). Iodine monochloride, ICl, monobromide, IBr, and trichloride, ICl_3, are solids at room temperature, the remainder being volatile liquids or gases. They are

Table 11.5 Interhalogen compounds

Type	Class	Examples	Examples of names
XY	Monohalides	ClF, BrF, BrCl, ICl	chlorine monofluoride iodine monochloride
XY_3	Trihalides	ClF_3, BrF_3, ICl_3	bromine trifluoride iodine trichloride
XY_5	Pentafluorides	BrF_5, IF_5	bromine pentafluorides (other pentahalides not known)
XY_7	Heptafluoride	IF_7	iodine heptafluoride (only heptahalide known)

made by the direct combination of the halogens concerned. All are covalent with the larger halogen occupying a central position. With the exception of iodine pentafluoride, IF_5, they are extremely reactive, behaving (like halogens) as oxidizing agents and reacting with water. The two most important interhalogen compounds are the trifluorides of chlorine, ClF_3 (the only commercially available interhalogen compound) and bromine, BrF_3. These compounds, which react explosively with water, wood, rubber and other organic material — and even with concrete and asbestos — are used to fluorinate compounds, for example actinides to produce the hexafluorides (the most important being uranium hexafluoride, UF_6) and chlorinated hydrocarbons to produce chlorofluorocarbon lubricating oils. Bromine trifluoride has interesting properties as a polar solvent; it undergoes slight ionization thus:

$$2BrF_3 \rightleftharpoons BrF_2^+ + BrF_4^-$$

11.8.1 Polyhalides

The best known polyhalide is the triiodide ion, I_3^-, found when iodine dissolves in the aqueous solution of the iodide of a large unipositive cation (usually K^+):

$$I^- + I_2 \rightleftharpoons I_3^-$$

Iodine monochloride, formed when iodine reacts with the iodate(V) ion in the presence of an excess of concentrated hydrochloric acid,

$$IO_3^- + 2I_2 + 6H^+ + 5Cl^- \rightarrow 5ICl + 3H_2O$$

dissolves in the presence of excess of chloride:

$$ICl + Cl^- \rightleftharpoons ICl_2^-$$

Other polyhalides, all singly charged, are formed from one halide ion together with other halogen or interhalogen molecules adding on, for example $[ClIBr]^-$ and $[ICl_4]^-$. Many of these ions give salts with the alkali metal cations which, if the metal ion is large (for example the rubidium or caesium ion), can be crystallized from solution. The ion ICl_4^- is known in the solid acid, $HICl_4.4H_2O$, formed by adding iodine trichloride to hydrochloric acid. Many other polyhalide ions are less stable and tend to dissociate into the halide and interhalogen compound.

11.9 Use of halogens and their compounds

11.9.1 Fluorine

Fluorine in the free state is too reactive to be of a direct practical value, but it may be used to prepare other compounds of fluorine, which are then used as fluorinating agents, for example chlorine trifluoride, ClF_3, cobalt(III) fluoride, CoF_3, silver difluoride, AgF_2. Hydrofluoric acid is used to etch glass, to remove sand from precision castings, in the manufacture of synthetic cryolite, Na_3AlF_6, and as a preservative for yeast and anatomical specimens. Hydrogen fluoride is a catalyst in the alkylation of butane to give higher hydrocarbons, and in the presence of a catalyst is itself used to prepare fluorocarbons. A wide variety of fluorocarbons is known and used extensively as refrigerants, lubricants and as aerosol propellants. Tetrafluoroethene (tetrafluoroethylene), C_2F_4, is readily polymerized to give polytetrafluoroethene, PTFE, a plastic of high thermal stability and one not subject to chemical attack by most reagents which finds considerable use not only in the chemical industry but also in the manufacture of 'non-stick' pans and oven ware. Calcium fluoride, and other fluorides, are used as fluxes in making vitreous enamels.

11.9.2 Chlorine

World production of chlorine in 1976 was 29 million tons and the production has risen steadily each year since. Most of it is now used for chemical processes involving the introduction of chlorine into organic compounds, for example the chlorination of alkenes, manufacture of carbon tetrachloride, chlorination of paraffins to make grease solvents, and the manufacture of plastics and synthetic rubber. Hydrogen chloride is the by-product of many of these processes. Much goes into use for sterilizing water and sewage, and it is used directly or indirectly as a bleaching agent. The use of soluble chlorates(I) is replacing bleaching powder for such purposes as bleaching paper pulp and cotton.

Chlorine is also used in the manufacture of hydrochloric acid, the extraction of titanium, and the removing of tin from old tinplate ('de-tinning').

11.9.3   Bromine

Bromine is used in the manufacture of many important organic compounds including 1,2-dibromoethane (ethylene dibromide), added to petrol to prevent lead deposition which occurs by decomposition of the 'anti-knock' tetraethyllead; bromomethane (methyl bromide), a fumigating agent, and several compounds used to reduce flammability of polyester plastics and epoxide resins. Silver(I) bromide is used extensively in the photographic industry whilst calcium and potassium bromates(V) are used in the malting industry to suppress root formation after germination of barley. Bromine is sometimes used in place of chlorine for sterilizing water.

11.9.4   Iodine

Iodine as such finds few uses but a solution in alcohol and water, also containing potassium iodide ('tincture of iodine') was commonly used as an antiseptic for cuts and wounds, but had rather an irritant action. Iodoform (triiodomethane), CHI_3, is also an antiseptic, but newer compounds of iodine are now in use. Silver iodide, like silver bromide, is extensively used in the photographic industry.

11.10   Tests for halides

11.10.1   Tests for fluoride

Most fluorine-containing compounds can be reduced to the fluoride ion, F^-, which can be detected by the tests given below.

(1) The action of concentrated sulphuric acid liberates hydrogen fluoride, which attacks glass, forming silicon tetrafluoride; the latter is hydrolysed to 'silicic acid' by water, which therefore becomes turbid.

(2) Addition of calcium nitrate solution to a fluoride gives a white precipitate of calcium fluoride, CaF_2. If the latter is precipitated slowly it can be filtered off and weighed to estimate the fluoride. Fluoride can also be determined by the addition of sodium chloride and lead nitrate which precipitate lead chlorofluoride, $PbClF$. This is filtered off and weighed.

11.10.2   Tests for chloride

Most chlorine-containing compounds can be converted to give chloride ions, for example covalent chlorides by hydrolysis, chlorates by reduction. The chloride ion is then tested for thus:

(1) Addition of silver nitrate to a solution of a chloride in dilute nitric acid gives a white precipitate of silver chloride, AgCl, soluble in ammonia solution. This test may be used for gravimetric or volumetric estimation of chloride; the silver chloride can be filtered off, dried and weighed, or the chloride titrated with standard silver nitrate using potassium chromate(VI) or fluorescein as indicator.

(2) If a chloride is heated with manganese(IV) oxide and concentrated sulphuric acid, chlorine is evolved.

(3) If the chloride is heated with sodium or potassium dichromate(VI) and concentrated sulphuric acid, a red gas, chromium(VI) dichloride dioxide, CrO_2Cl_2, is evolved; if this is passed into water, a yellow solution of a chromate(VI) is formed.

11.10.3   Tests for bromide

(1) Addition of silver nitrate to a solution of a bromide in dilute nitric acid produces a cream-coloured precipitate of silver bromide, soluble in ammonia (but not so readily as silver chloride). The reaction may be used quantitatively, as for a chloride.

(2) Addition of concentrated sulphuric acid to a solid bromide produces hydrobromic acid, but also some bromine (brown vapour).

(3) Addition of chlorine water to a bromide solution liberates bromine, which colours the solution brown.

11.10.4   Tests for iodide

(1) Addition of silver nitrate to a solution of an iodide in dilute nitric acid, yields a yellow precipitate of silver iodide practically insoluble in ammonia.

(2) Addition of an oxidizing agent to a solution of an iodide (for example concentrated sulphuric acid, hydrogen peroxide, chlorine water, potassium dichromate) yields iodine; the iodine can be recognized by extracting the solutions with carbon tetrachloride which gives a purple solution of iodine, or by the blue-black colour elemental iodine gives with a solution of starch.

(3) Addition of mercury(II) chloride solution to a solution of an iodide gives a scarlet precipitate of mercury(II) iodide, soluble in excess of iodide:

$$2I^- + HgCl_2 \rightarrow HgI_2\downarrow + 2Cl^-$$

$$HgI_2 + 2I^- \rightarrow [HgI_4]^{2-}$$

Indication of the presence of a given halide ion can be obtained by the series of tests given in *Table 11.6*. Confirmatory tests can then be performed.

Table 11.6 Preliminary tests for halide ions

Test	F^-	Cl^-	Br^-	I^-
Warm concentrated H_2SO_4 on the dry solid	HF evolved	HCl evolved	HBr, SO_2 and Br_2 evolved	SO_2, H_2S, and I_2 evolved
Silver nitrate solution	No ppt.	White ppt., soluble in dil. ammonia solution	Cream ppt., soluble in conc. ammonia solution	Yellow ppt., almost insoluble in conc. ammonia solution
Chlorine water (acidified NaClO solution)	No action	No action	Br_2 liberated	I_2 liberated
Calcium nitrate solution	White ppt.	No ppt.	No ppt.	No ppt.

Summary

For a summary *see Table 11.7.*

Questions

1 Give a comparative account of the oxo-acids of the halogens from the viewpoint of:
(a) their acid properties or the thermal stability of their alkali salts,
(b) their properties as oxidants.

L,S

2 Iodic acid may be made by oxidizing iodine with excess of fuming nitric acid according to the equation

$$I_2 + 10HNO_3 \rightarrow 2HIO_3 + 10NO_2 + 4H_2O$$

The iodic acid may then be dehydrated by heat, giving iodine pentoxide:

$$2HIO_3 \rightarrow I_2O_5 + H_2O$$

The practical details are as follows:
About 0.5 g of iodine is placed in a small flask fitted with a long reflux air condenser and 15 cm^3 of fuming nitric acid (b.p. 380 K) are added. The mixture is then heated on a water-bath at 385—390 K in a fume cupboard until the reaction seems to be complete. This takes about an hour. The solution is then transferred to an evaporating basin and evaporated to

Table 11.7 Summary of Group VII, the halogens

Element	Fluorine	Chlorine	Bromine	Iodine
	F_2 gas, green-yellow	Cl_2 gas, yellow	Br_2 gas/liquid, red	I_2 solid, violet
Oxidation states	-1 (1)	$-1, +1, +3, +4, +5, +7$	$-1, +1, +4, +5, +7$	$-1, +5, +7$
Reactions: hydrogen		$H_2 + X_2 \rightarrow 2HX$, vigour of reaction decreases $\longrightarrow$		
other elements	reacts with most	reacts with many (not C, N, O)	reacts with most	less reactive
water	(g) $\rightarrow$ HF, O_2; (l) $\rightarrow$ H_2O_2, OF_2; dilute $\rightarrow$ OF_2; conc. $\rightarrow$ O_2	low temp.: hydrate then $\rightarrow$ HClO + HCl	low temp.: hydrate then $\rightarrow$ HBrO + HBr	slightly soluble; very little reaction
alkalis		leads to X^- + XO^- and XO_3^-		
Compounds: hydrides	HF, hydrogen-bonded liquid (aq) weak acid	HCl, gas (aq) strong acid	HBr, gas (aq) strong acid	HI, gas, dissociates (aq) strong acid
oxides	OF_2 very reactive; O_2F_2 very reactive	Cl_2O, ClO_2, Cl_2O_6 unstable; Cl_2O_7 more stable	Br_2O, Br_3O_8, BrO_2	I_2O_5
oxoacids	HFO very unstable	HXO, decreasing stability and oxidizing power $\longrightarrow$		
		HXO$_3$, oxidizing power Cl I		
		$HClO_4$ very strong acid	$HBrO_4$	H_5IO_6
interhalogens		ClF, ClF_3	BrF, BrCl, BrF_3, BrF_5	ICl, ICl_3, IF_5, IF_7

dryness on a steam-bath. The iodic acid is then recrystallized from 50 per cent nitric acid. The iodic acid is then heated at a temperature maintained between 500 K and 550 K in order to dehydrate it to iodine pentoxide.

(a) Indicate which elements change in oxidation number during this set of reactions and the changes involved.

(b) Why is it necessary to perform the oxidation of iodine in a fume cupboard?

(c) State one observation which would tell you the oxidation of iodine is complete.

(d) Iodine vaporizes readily. Explain how loss of iodine from the reaction mixture is prevented in this experiment.

(e) Describe briefly how you would recrystallize iodic acid from 50 per cent nitric acid.

(f) How would you heat iodic acid in such a way as to maintain its temperature between 500 K and 550 K?

N,A

3   By considering the trends in the vertical groups of the Periodic Table, deduce possible answers to the following questions concerning the element astatine (At), atomic number 85.

(a) State, giving an equation, how astatine could be prepared from an aqueous solution of potassium astatide K^+At^-.

(b) State what you expect to observe when concentrated sulphuric acid is added to solid potassium astatide.

(c) Name an insoluble astatide, and write its formula.

(d) State, giving a reason, whether ethyl astatide would be more or less reactive than ethyl chloride, when heated with a nucleophilic reagent.

(e) The isotope $^{210}_{85}At$ is formed by the emission of one β- particle from an unstable nucleus. Give the mass number and the number of neutrons in this parent element.

(f) State two reasons why you are unlikely to perform (or see performed) experiments involving astatine.

JMB,A

4   The following table shows the atomic numbers of the elements in Group VII of the Period Table and the melting points of their hydrides.

	Fluorine	Chlorine	Bromine	Iodine
Atomic number	9	17	35	53
Melting point of hydride/K	210	178	205	236

(a) (i) What is the general chemical formula of the hydrides?
    (ii) What is the type of chemical bonding encountered in the pure hydrides?

(b) Refer to the data in the table and explain briefly
    (i) the increase in melting point of the hydrides along the series chlorine, bromine and iodine,
    (ii) the relatively high melting point of the hydride of fluorine.

(c) Give balanced ionic equations describing the reaction(s) between concentrated sulphuric acid and
  (i) solid sodium chloride,
  (ii) solid sodium iodide.

L,A

5   Comment on the following:
  (a) The electron affinities of fluorine and chlorine are -333 and -364 kJ mol^{-1} respectively; but their standard electrode potentials are $+2.87$ and $+1.36$ V respectively.
  (b) Iodine forms some electropositive compounds.
  (c) In dilute aqueous solution hydrogen fluoride is a weak acid but the acid strength increases with the concentration of hydrogen fluoride.
  (d) Elements exhibit their highest oxidation state when combined with fluorine.
  (e) NaF is slightly alkaline in aqueous solution.

6   Element X is in Group I of the periodic table and has an electronegativity value of 0.8. Element Y is in Group VII and its electronegativity is 2.8. The electronegativity of hydrogen is 2.1.
  (a) Give the formula of the compound formed between X and hydrogen.
  (b) State the type of bonding in the compound in (a).
  (c) Give the formula of the compound formed between Y and hydrogen.
  (d) Describe the bonding in the compound in (c).
  (e) Explain why the compound in (a) melts with decomposition at about 770 K whilst that in (c) is a gas at room temperature, condensing to a liquid at approximately 200 K.

JMB,A

7   Iodine dissolves in hot concentrated solutions of sodium hydroxide according to the equation

$$3I_2(s) + 6NaOH(aq) \rightarrow NaIO_3(aq) + 5NaI(aq) + 3H_2O(l)$$

In one experiment 3.81 g of iodine was dissolved in 4M sodium hydroxide solution. (Relative atomic masses: H $= 1$, O $= 16$, Na $= 23$, I $= 127$)
  (a) (i) How many moles of iodine were used?
      (ii) What volume of 4M sodium hydroxide solution would be just sufficient to react with the iodine?
  (b) What reagent(s) would you add to solid sodium iodide to produce pure hydrogen iodide gas?
  (c) Iodine also reacts with aqueous sodium thiosulphate solution producing sodium iodide solution.
      (i) Write a balanced equation, with state symbols, for the reaction.
      (ii) Suggest a procedure by which solid sodium iodide might be obtained from the reaction mixture.

N,A

Chapter 12
The noble gases
Helium, neon, argon, krypton, xenon, radon

These elements were unknown when Mendeléef constructed his periodic table, and are often said to constitute 'Group O'. However, a more logical classification would be in 'Group VIII'. They all exist as free atoms.

12.1 Physical properties

These are given in *Table 12.1*. The following are to be noted:
(1) The increase in atomic radius (in this group, the actual radius of the *free atom*).
(2) The increase in melting point and boiling point, and the very narrow liquid range.
(3) The large ionization energies, as expected for atoms with complete quantum levels.
(4) Helium and neon have small exothermic electron affinities (p. 29).

The increase in melting point and boiling point arise because of increased attraction between the *free atoms*; these forces of attraction are van der Waals forces (p. 41) and they increase with increase of size. These forces are at their weakest between helium atoms, and helium approaches most closely to the 'ideal gas'; liquid helium has some notable characteristics, for example it expands on cooling and has very high thermal conductivity.

12.2 Occurrence and isolation

The most important source of helium is the natural gas from certain petroleum wells in the United States and Canada. This gas may contain as much as 8 per cent of helium. Because helium has a lower boiling point (*Table 12.1*) than any other gas, it is readily obtained by cooling natural gas to a temperature at which all the other gases are liquid (77 K); almost pure helium can then be pumped off. The yearly production in this way may be many millions of m^3 of gas, but something like 10^{11} m^3 per year is still wasted.

The other noble gases (except radon) are obtained from liquid air, which can readily be separated into liquid nitrogen (b.p. 77 K) and oxygen (b.p. 90 K) by fractionation. Helium and neon are found in the nitrogen fraction, and argon, krypton and xenon with the oxygen. Argon, containing only a little oxygen, is obtained by further fractionation, and the remaining oxygen

Table 12.1 Selected physical properties of the elements

Element	Atomic number	Outer electrons	Atomic radius* nm	m.p./K	b.p./K	First ionization energy kJ mol^{-1}
He	2	$1s^2$	0.099	4†	4	2372
Ne	10	$2s^2 2p^6$	0.160	25	27	2080
Ar	18	$3s^2 3p^6$	0.192	84	87	1520
Kr	36	$4s^2 4p^6$	0.197	116	120	1351
Xe	54	$5s^2 5p^6$	0.217	161	165	1169
Rn	86	$6s^2 6p^6$	—	202	211	1037

*van der Waals radius.
†Pressure 100 atm.

is removed by burning with hydrogen or by passage over hot copper. Krypton and xenon are obtained by fractionation over activated charcoal, and neon and helium are separated in a similar manner. Small amounts of radon are contained in the gas pumped off from acidified radium chloride solution; oxygen, carbon dioxide and water are removed from it by ordinary chemical methods. The radon is frozen and any other gases can then be drawn off, leaving pure radon.

12.3   Chemical properties

The simple fact that the noble gases exist as separate atoms — a unique property at ordinary temperatures — is sufficient indication of their chemical inactivity. Calculations of the heats of formation of hypothetical noble gas ionic compounds have been made, using methods similar to those described in Chapter 3 for 'NaCl$_3$' or MgCl'; they indicated that, if the noble gases are to form cations X^+, then the anion must have a large electron affinity to 'compensate' for the large ionization energy of X (*Table 12.1*). The discovery by Bartlett that the *compound* platinum(VI) fluoride, PtF$_6$, had a sufficiently large electron affinity to unite directly with molecular oxygen O$_2$ (first ionization energy 1176 kJ mol^{-1}) to form the essentially ionic compound O$_2$PtF$_6$ (i.e. O$_2^+$[PtF$_6$]$^-$), suggested that xenon (first ionization energy 1169 kJ mol^{-1}) might form a similar compound XePtF$_6$, and this compound was made by direct reaction of xenon with platinum(VI) fluoride.

Following Bartlett's discovery of xenon hexafluoroplatinate(VI), xenon and fluorine were found to combine to give several volatile, essentially covalent fluorides, and at least one fluoride of krypton has been obtained. From the xenon fluorides, compounds containing xenon–oxygen bonds have been made; much of the known chemistry of xenon is set out in *Figure 12.1*.

It can be seen that xenon has valencies or oxidation states of 2, 4, 6 and 8; compounds with xenon in higher oxidation states are powerful oxidizing agents, for example xenate(VIII) will oxidize a manganese(II) salt to

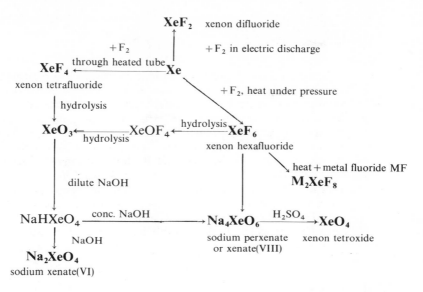

Figure 12.1 The chemistry of xenon

manganese(VII) salt. All the fluorides are readily hydrolysed to give, finally, xenon gas and hydrofluoric acid; hence hydrolysis is a means of analysis. The xenon fluorides are solids; xenon trioxide is a white, explosive solid, while xenon tetroxide is a gas.

The structures of the three xenon fluorides are shown in *Figure 12.2*, the exact position of the single lone pair in xenon hexafluoride being uncertain. These structures may be compared with those of the polyhalide ions; XeF_2 is linear like $[ICl_2]^-$, XeF_4 is planar like $[ICl_4]^-$. Now an *ion* $[I(halogen)_x]^-$ is

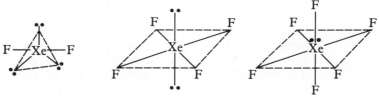

Figure 12.2 Structures of xenon fluorides

isoelectronic with (has the same total number of electrons as) a *molecule* $Xe(halogen)_x$, and hence similarity between the two kinds of structure is to be expected; this means that xenon is behaving in some ways like iodine plus one electron. Hence we are justified in putting the noble gas group next to the Group VII halogens, rather than before Group I.

In xenon difluoride, the electronic structure shows three lone pairs around the xenon, and two covalent bonds to the two fluorine atoms; hence it is believed that here xenon is using *one p* (double-pear) orbital to form *two* bonds:

Freezing water in presence of noble gases such as krypton and argon leads to the formation of *noble gas hydrates*, which dissociate when the temperature is raised. Here the noble gas atoms are 'caged' in holes in the ice-like lattice; we have seen (p. 282) that chlorine molecules can be trapped in relatively large holes in this kind of lattice, and the smaller noble gas atoms are accommodated both in these and also in some smaller holes to give a limiting composition $X.(5.76H_2O)$. If a hot solution of benzene-1,4-diol (*para*-quinol), $C_6H_4(OH)_2$, is cooled in an atmosphere of argon or krypton (under pressure) three molecules of the quinol unite on crystallization for form a cage-like structure inside which one noble gas atom is imprisoned. This has been called a 'clathrate' compound (Latin, *clathri* = lattice), but there are no chemical forces between the noble gas atom and the atoms of the cage, so such a substance is not really a compound of the noble gas.

12.4 Uses

Helium has been used in quantity as a substitute for hydrogen in filling airships. A mixture of 80 per cent helium and 20 per cent oxygen is used instead of air in diving apparatus because helium, unlike nitrogen, is not appreciably soluble in blood even under pressure. (The liberation of dissolved nitrogen from the blood, when the pressure is released, gives rise to 'caisson disease' or 'the bends'.) A similar helium–oxygen mixture has been used to assist breathing in cases of asthma and other respiratory diseases.

Helium has two important scientific uses. First, liquid helium is used to realize very low temperatures, in order to study peculiar phenomena which occur near the absolute zero — *cryogenics*. Some metals attain enormously high electrical conductivity when cooled down to near absolute zero, and hence powerful electromagnets can be made using very small coils cooled in liquid helium. Secondly, it is used in gas thermometers for low temperature measurement. Further, any of the rare gases may be used to give an inert atmosphere for handling very reactive metals; for example an atmosphere of argon is used in the preparation of titanium and in metallurgical processes, involving this metal, because it is attacked at red heat by both oxygen and nitrogen.

Electric discharge tubes are filled with neon (which causes the familiar red glow) and ordinary electric filament lamps with argon. The higher the temperature of the filament in such a lamp, the greater is its efficiency of illumination, but the greater also is its loss of metal by evaporation; metal vapour condenses on the glass bulb, blackening it, and the filament soon evaporates. To permit the use of a high temperature filament without evaporation, a gas is used to fill the lamp; and the greater the molecular mass of this gas, the less tendency there is for metal atoms to diffuse through it. Hence argon (40) is better than nitrogen (28) for this purpose, and of course, krypton and xenon are better still, though more expensive to use.

Radon, sealed in small capsules called 'seeds', has been used as a radioactive substance in medicine, but is being superseded by more convenient artificially-produced radioisotopes.

Questions

1   'The elements of Group 0 of the Periodic Classification are rare and inert.' Criticize this statement, giving evidence in support of your criticisms.

Liverpool B.Sc., Part I

2   Survey and account for the group characteristics and trends in the elements of Group 0 (He–Rn). Outline the preparation and sterochemistry of xenon tetrafluoride.

JMB,A

3   Discuss the following statements:
(a) A number of oxides and fluorides are known for xenon but similar compounds do not appear to be formed by neon.
(b) Argon forms clathrate compounds but helium does not.
(c) Xenon dissolves in water to form a hydrate $Xe.6H_2O$.

Chapter 13
The transition elements
Scandium to zinc

13.1 Physical properties of the elements

In the periodic table, the elements from scandium to zinc in Period 4 lie
between calcium in Group II and gallium in Group III. These elements are
termed *transition* elements (deriving from the use of this word by Mendeléef)
or *d*-block elements, because in them the inner 3*d* energy level is filling up.
Similar blocks of elements occur in Periods 5 and 6 (p. 14). *Table 13.1* suggests
that the transition elements of Period 4 should end at nickel, because in the
next two elements, copper and zinc, the 3*d* energy levels are full. Copper
shows many of the characteristic properties of transition elements, and zinc
is, as it were, half-way between a transition and a main group element. It is
therefore convenient to include copper and zinc in the first transition series
(*Table 13.2*).

It is immediately obvious that the transition metals are more dense,
harder, and have higher melting points and boiling points than the main
group metals (for example, the metals of Group II, Chapter 6). We note,
however, that there is not a smooth increase in the magnitude of these
properties as the atomic number increases; the metals seem to divide into two
sets, Sc—Mn and Mn—Zn, with 'peaks' at Ti—V and Co—Ni, and this is well
illustrated by a graph of boiling point against atomic number (*Figure 13.1*).

This division of the first transition series into two 'sets' is clearly related to
the filling of the *d* orbitals — at the dividing element, manganese, the 3*d* level

Table 13.1 Electronic configurations of the elements

Element	Symbol	Atomic number	Electronic configuration
Scandium	Sc	21	$[\text{Ar}]3d^14s^2$
Titanium	Ti	22	$[\text{Ar}]3d^24s^2$
Vanadium	V	23	$[\text{Ar}]3d^34s^2$
Chromium	Cr	24	$[\text{Ar}]3d^54s^1$
Manganese	Mn	25	$[\text{Ar}]3d^54s^2$
Iron	Fe	26	$[\text{Ar}]3d^64s^2$
Cobalt	Co	27	$[\text{Ar}]3d^74s^2$
Nickel	Ni	28	$[\text{Ar}]3d^84s^2$
Copper	Cu	29	$[\text{Ar}]3d^{10}4s^1$
Zinc	Zn	30	$[\text{Ar}]3d^{10}4s^2$

Table 13.2 Physical properties of the first transition series elements

Element	Sc	Ti	V	Cr	Mn	Fe	Co	Ni	Cu	Zn
Density/g cm^{-3}	3.2	4.5	6.0	7.1	7.4	7.9	8.7	8.9	8.9	7.1
Hardness/kg mm^{-2}*	—	200	—	100	300	70	48	70–80	30–40	30
m.p./K	1673	1950	2190	2176	1517	1812	1768	1728	1356	693
b.p./K	2750	3550	3650	2915	2314	3160	3150	3110	2855	1181

*These values on the Brinell scale are very dependent on the purity and heat-treatment of the metal.

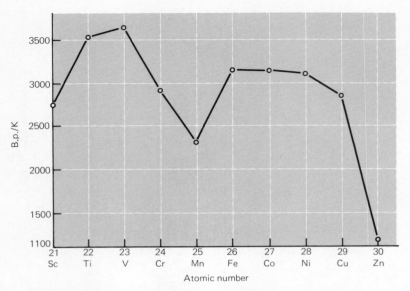

Figure 13.1 Graph of boiling point against atomic number for the first transition series

is half-filled (one electron in each d orbital), thereafter the singly-occupied d orbitals become double-filled until filling is complete at copper and zinc. The fact that the configurations $3d^5$ (half-full) and $3d^{10}$ (full) are obtained at chromium and copper respectively, in each case (see *Table 13.1*) (at the cost of removing an electron from the $4s$ level) suggests that these configurations $3d^5$ and $3d^{10}$ are particularly 'stable'; we shall see confirmation of this idea when the chemical properties are examined later. In the discussion of the metallic bond in Chapter 2 we have already seen that the notable physical properties of the transition metals (greater density, hardness, etc.) are attributed to the greater number of valency electrons per atom available for bonding in the metal, and this number clearly depends on the number of d electrons.

When we look at other physical properties of these transition elements (*Table 13.3*), the regularities which we have previously observed in the groups are not so clear across the series. The atomic radius (in the metal) falls from scandium to vanadium, rises again in chromium and manganese, falls at iron and thereafter rises slowly until zinc is reached. The radius of the M^{2+} ion falls irregularly to copper and rises again at zinc; the first ionization energy rises irregularly, then sharply at zinc.

13.2 Chemical properties

13.2.1 Oxidation states

The transition elements are often said to exhibit 'variable valency'. Because they so readily form complex compounds, it is better to use the term 'variety

Table 13.3 Further physical properties of the first transition series elements

	Sc	Ti	V	Cr	Mn	Fe	Co	Ni	Cu	Zn
Atomic radius/nm	0.161	0.145	0.132	0.137	0.137	0.124	0.125	0.125	0.128	0.133
Radius of M^{2+}/nm	—	0.090	0.088	0.088	0.080	0.076	0.074	0.072	0.069	0.074
First ionization energy/kJ mol^{-1}	631	656	650	653	717	762	758	737	745	906

of oxidation states'. The states usually found for the elements Sc—Zn are shown in *Table 13.4*, where the states which are most stable with respect to decomposition or oxidation/reduction are in bold type.

We may note (a) the common occurrence of oxidation state $+2$ where the $4s^2$ electrons have been formally lost, (b) the increase in the number of oxidation states from scandium to manganese; in the latter element, the

Table 13.4 Oxidation states of transition elements of the first series

Sc	Ti	V	Cr	Mn	Fe	Co	Ni	Cu	Zn
			0	0	0	0	0	0	
								+1	
	+2	+2	+2	**+2**	+2	+2	**+2**	**+2**	**+2**
+3	+3	+3	**+3**	+3	+3	+3			
	+4	+4		+4					
		+5							
			+6	+6					
				+7					

oxidation state $+7$ corresponds to the formal loss of the $3s^2$ and $3d^5$ electrons, (c) the sharp decrease in the number of oxidation states after manganese, suggesting that removal of the paired $3d$ electrons is less easy; (d) the oxidation state 0, occurring for many of the later elements in the series*.

Some of the oxidation states given above, especially the higher oxidation states (7,6) and oxidation state 0, are found only when the metal atom or ion has attached to it certain groups or *ligands*. Indeed the chemistry of the transition elements is so dominated by their tendency to form coordination complexes that this aspect of their behaviour must be considered in some detail.

13.3   Coordination complexes

Complexes have already received some discussion; it will be recalled that they are defined in terms of (a) the central metal atom or ion and its oxidation state, (b) the number of surrounding ligands which may be ions, atoms or polar molecules, (c) the overall charge on the complex, determined by the oxidation state of the central atom and the charges (if any) on the ligands. Some examples are shown in *Table 13.5*.

Note that complexes can have negative, positive or zero overall charge. The examples MnO_4^-, CrO_4^{2-} are usually considered to be oxoacid anions (p. 38); but there is no essential difference between these and other complexes. For example, the anion MnO_4^- can be regarded formally as a manganese ion in oxidation state $+7$ surrounded by four oxide ion (O^{2-}) ligands (in fact of course there is covalent bonding between the oxide ligands and the Mn^{VII} ion,

*Some transition metal *atoms* combined with uncharged molecules as ligands (notably carbon monoxide, CO) have a formal oxidation state of 0, for example $Ni + 4CO \rightleftharpoons Ni^0(CO)_4$.

Table 13.5 Some coordination complexes

Oxidation state of central atom or ion	Example	Common name	Preferred name	Full name
7	MnO_4^-	permanganate	manganate(VII)	tetraoxomanganate(VII)
6	CrO_4^{2-}	chromate	chromate(VI)	tetraoxochromate(VI)
4	$TiCl_4$	titanium tetrachloride	tetrachlorotitanium(IV)	
3	$[Fe(CN)_6]^{3-}$	ferricyanide	hexacyanoferrate(III)	
2	$[Ni(NH_3)_6]^{2-}$		hexaamminonickel(II)	
0	$Fe(CO)_5$	iron pentacarbonyl	pentacarbonyliron(0)	

leading to partial transfer of the oxide negative charges to the manganese). In general, high oxidation states (for example those of manganese $+7$ and chromium $+6$) are only found in oxides (for example Mn_2O_7, CrO_3), oxoacid anions (MnO_4^-, CrO_4^{2-}, $Cr_2O_7^{2-}$) and sometimes fluorides (there is no MnF_7 known, but CrF_6 is known). Hence the number of complexes in high oxidation states is very limited. At lower oxidation states, a variety of ligands can form complexes — some common ligands are shown in *Table 13.6*. However, stable complexes where the oxidation state of the central

Table 13.6 Examples of ligands

Ligand	H_2O	NH_3	CN^-	Cl^-
Example of occurrence	$[Fe(H_2O)_6]^{2+}$	$[Co(NH_3)_6]^{3+}$	$[Ni(CN)_4]^{2-}$	$[CuCl_4]^{2-}$

metal atom is 0 are only formed with a very few ligands, notably carbon monoxide, for example $Ni(CO)_4$ and $Fe(CO)_5$, and phosphorus trifluoride, PF_3, for example $Ni(PF_3)_4$.

Some important properties of these coordination complexes will now be considered.

13.3.1 Shape

The rules governing the shapes of molecules and complex ions have already been discussed (pp. 32, 39). The common shapes of complexes are *octahedral*, for coordination number 6, and *tetrahedral*, for coordination number 4; all the 6- and 4-coordinate complexes so far considered have these shapes. Other coordination numbers [for example, 2 in $Ag(CN)_2^-$ (*linear*) and 5 in $Fe(CO)_5$] (*trigonal bipyramidal*) are less common, and lie outside the scope of this book. Sometimes other shapes are possible; thus, for example, platinum(II) forms *planar* 4-coordinate complexes (for example $[PtCl_4]^{2-}$), and 6-coordinate copper(II) usually forms *distorted octahedral* complexes in which two of the ligands are further away from the central copper ion than the other four. Moreover, the coordination number and shape of a complex may vary for a given transition ion when complexed with different ligands; thus, cobalt(II) forms 6-coordinate octahedral complexes with water or ammonia as ligands, ($[Co(H_2O)_6]^{2+}$, $[Co(NH_3)_6]^{2+}$) but a tetrahedral 4-coordinate complex with chloride as ligand ($[CoCl_4]^{2-}$).

13.3.2 Colour

Transition metal compounds are very often coloured; frequently (but not always) the colour is due to the presence of coordination complexes. When a cation containing d electrons is surrounded by other ions or polar molecules, either in solution or in a solid, a splitting of the energy levels of the five d orbitals (all originally having the same energy) occurs (p. 52); when light falls on such a system, electrons can move between these split levels. The energy absorbed in this process corresponds to absorption of the light at certain wavelengths, usually in the visible part of the spectrum, hence colour is observed. For a given cation the kind of absorption produced — its intensity and position in the spectrum — depends very much upon the coordination number and surrounding ligands. We can illustrate this by reference to the Cu^{2+} ion. In solid *anhydrous* copper(II) sulphate, the Cu^{2+} ion is surrounded by ions SO_4^{2-}; in this environment, the d orbital splitting is such that absorption of light by the Cu^{2+} cation is not in the visible part of the spectrum, and the substance appears white. If the solid is now dissolved in water, the Cu^{2+} ion becomes surrounded by water molecules, and complex species such as $Cu(H_2O)_6^{2+}$ are formed — these absorb light in the visible part of the spectrum and appear pale blue. If this solution of copper(II) sulphate is allowed to crystallize, water molecules remain coordinated round the Cu^{2+} ion in the solid copper(II) sulphate pentahydrate ($CuSO_4.5H_2O$) and the solid is pale blue. When an excess of ammonia is added to the original solution, some of the water ligands around the copper(II) ion are replaced by ammonia:

$$[Cu(H_2O)_6]^{2+} + 4NH_3 \rightarrow [Cu(NH_3)_4(H_2O)_2]^{2+} + 4H_2O$$
pale blue   deep blue

A different d orbital splitting results and the absorption now results in a deep colour*.

If excess of chloride ion is added to a blue solution containing $[Cu(H_2O)_6]^{2+}$, then

$$[Cu(H_2O)_6]^{2+} + 4Cl^- \rightarrow [CuCl_4]^{2-} + 6H_2O$$
distorted   distorted
octahedral,   tetrahedral,
pale blue   yellow

and here the new splitting results in a yellow-green colour.

The d orbital splitting depends on the oxidation state of a given ion; hence two complex ions with the same shape, ligands and coordination number can differ in colour, for example

$$[Co(NH_3)_6]^{2+} \xrightarrow{\text{oxidize}} [Co(NH_3)_6]^{3+}$$
+2   +3
octahedral,   octahedral,
pink   yellow

13.3.3   Magnetic properties

The splitting of the d orbital energy levels when ligands are bonded to a central transition atom or ion has already been mentioned (p. 52). Consider the two ions $[Co(NH_3)_6]^{3+}$ and $[Co(NH_3)_6]^{2+}$ we have just discussed. The splitting of the d orbital energy levels for these two ions is shown in *Figure 13.2*.

*The change in colour when one ligand is replaced by another can be used to determine the coordination number; thus if the colour change is measured in a spectrophotometer as the new ligand is added, the intensity of new colour reaches a maximum when the metal/ligand ratio is that in the new complex.

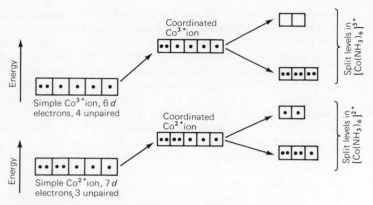

Figure 13.2 Splitting of d orbitals in cobalt complexes

The ions Co^{2+} and Co^{3+} have seven and six d electrons respectively. In orbitals of the same (or nearly the same) energy, the electrons remain unpaired as far as possible by distributing themselves over all the orbitals. In the case of $[Co(NH_3)_6]^{2+}$, the energy split in the d orbitals due to octahedral attachment of the six ammonia ligands is small, and the electrons remain as in Co^{2+} ion, i.e. three unpaired. For $[Co(NH_3)_6]^{3+}$ the split is much larger, and the electrons pair up in the lower energy orbitals as shown. Now unpaired electrons in a substance give rise to *paramagnetism* — the substance is weakly attracted to a magnet, and the larger the number of unpaired electrons, the larger is the magnetic moment (which can be determined by measuring the attraction). Hence it is found that solids or solutions containing the $[Co(NH_3)_6]^{2+}$ ion are paramagnetic, but those containing the $[Co(NH_3)_6]^{3+}$ ion are not; they are in fact very weakly repelled by a magnetic field and are termed *diamagnetic*. Complexes with unpaired electrons are often called 'spin-free' (because the electron spins are not 'paired-off') and those with paired electrons 'spin-paired'. Measurement of the magnetic moment of a complex can often tell us how many unpaired electrons are present, and this is useful information when bonding in the complex is considered.

13.3.4   Chemical properties

We have already seen that in the aqua-complex which is usually formed when a simple transition metal salt dissolves in water, the water ligands can be partly or completely *displaced* by addition of other ligands such as ammonia or chloride ion. The factors which govern the displacement of one ligand by another are rather complicated; thus, for example, ammonia will often replace water as a ligand, to form ammonia–metal complexes, but this does not happen readily with all transition metal ions (notably not with Fe^{2+}, Fe^{3+} and Mn^{2+}). However, most complexes of metal ions in oxidation states 2 or 3 are prepared by displacement of the water by other ligands, for example NH_3, CN^-, halide$^-$. Complexes with metal oxidation states 0 are not easily prepared in solution; the metal carbonyls can, however, be prepared by direct reaction e.g.

$$Ni + 4CO \rightarrow Ni(CO)_4$$

finely
divided
metal

For complexes with high metal oxidation states, special methods are used, since these complexes can only exist with certain ligands (*see* p. 320).

13.3.5 Some properties of complex metal ions in aqueous solution

In an aqua-complex, loss of protons from the coordinated water molecules can occur, as with hydrated non-transition metal ions (p. 40). To prevent proton loss by aqua-complexes, therefore, acid must usually be added. It is for these conditions that redox potentials in Chapter 4 are usually quoted. Thus, in acid solutions

$$[Fe(H_2O)_6]^{3+} + e^- \rightarrow [Fe(H_2O)_6]^{2+} \qquad E^{\ominus} = +0.77\,V$$

In the absence of acid, the half-reaction will approximate to:

$$[Fe(H_2O)_5(OH)]^{2+} + e^- \rightarrow [Fe(H_2O)_5(OH)]^+$$

for which $E^{\ominus}$ is indeterminate, but certainly less than $E^{\ominus}$ in acid solution. In presence of alkali, the half-reaction becomes, effectively,

$$[Fe(H_2O)_3(OH)_3] + H_2O + e^- \rightarrow [Fe(H_2O)_4(OH)_2] + OH^- \qquad E^{\ominus} = -0.56\,V$$

Hence the less acidic a solution containing Fe(II) is, the more easily is it oxidized and solutions of iron(II) salts must be acidified to prevent oxidation by air. A more impressive demonstration of the effect of change of ligand on oxidation–reduction behaviour is provided by the scheme shown in *Figure 13.3*.

Here, the pink aqua-cation (**A**) [produced when a cobalt(II) salt dissolves in water] cannot be oxidized to the +3 state (**B**) in aqueous solution, since **B**

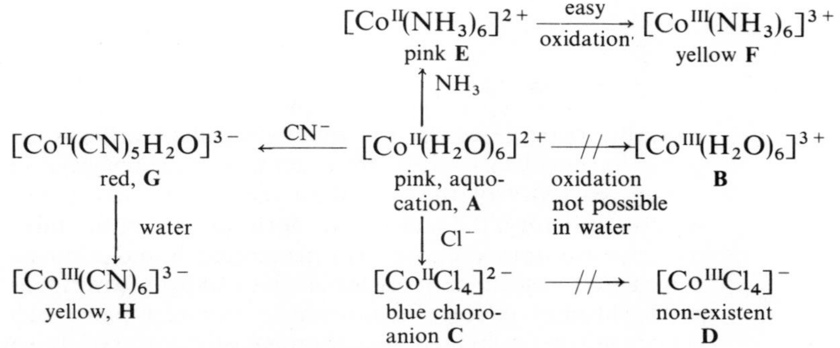

$$[Co^{II}(NH_3)_6]^{2+} \xrightarrow[\text{oxidation}]{\text{easy}} [Co^{III}(NH_3)_6]^{3+}$$
pink **E**   yellow **F**

$\uparrow NH_3$

$$[Co^{II}(CN)_5H_2O]^{3-} \xleftarrow{CN^-} [Co^{II}(H_2O)_6]^{2+} \xrightarrow{-\!/\!/\!\rightarrow} [Co^{III}(H_2O)_6]^{3+}$$
red, **G**   pink, aquo-   oxidation   **B**
                          cation, **A**   not possible
                                             in water

$\downarrow$ water $\downarrow Cl^-$

$$[Co^{III}(CN)_6]^{3-} \qquad [Co^{II}Cl_4]^{2-} \xrightarrow{-\!/\!/\!\rightarrow} [Co^{III}Cl_4]^-$$
yellow, **H**   blue chloro-   non-existent
                          anion **C**   **D**

Figure 13.3 Redox behaviour in cobalt complexes

would itself oxidize water to give oxygen. Replacement of the water ligands by chloride alters the shape, colour and redox potential, but again oxidation of **C** to **D** is not possible. However, replacement of water ligands by ammonia to give **E** allows easy oxidation to the stable $+3$ complex **F**. Replacement of water by cyanide would be expected to give **G**; in fact this is immediately oxidized by the solvent water (with evolution of hydrogen) to the $+3$ complex **H**.

13.4   Other chemical properties of the metals

13.4.1   Alloys

Reference has already been made to the high melting point, boiling point and strength of transition metals, and this has been attributed to high valency electron–atom ratios. Transition metals quite readily form *alloys* with each other, and with non-transition metals; in some of these alloys, definite *intermetallic* compounds appear (for example $CuZn$, $CoZn_3$, $Cu_{31}Sn_8$, Ag_5Al_3) and in these the formulae correspond to certain definite electron–atom ratios.

13.4.2   Interstitial compounds

The transition metal structures consist of close-packed (p. 21) arrays of relatively large atoms. Between these atoms, in the 'holes', small atoms, notably those of hydrogen, nitrogen and carbon, can be inserted, without very much distortion of the original metal structure, to give *interstitial* compounds (for example the hydrides, p. 103).

Because the metal structure is 'locked' by these atoms, the resulting compound is often much harder than the original metal, and some of the compounds are therefore of industrial importance (*see* under iron). Since there is a definite ratio of holes to atoms, filling of all the holes yields compounds with definite small atom–metal atom ratios; in practice, all the holes are not always filled, and compounds of less definite composition (*non-stoichiometric compounds*) are formed.

13.4.3   Other properties

*Ad*sorption of gases on to transition metal surfaces is important, and transition metals or alloys are often used as heterogeneous catalysts.

The reactivity of the transition metals towards other elements varies widely. In theory, the tendency to form other compounds both in the solid state (for example reactions to form cations) should diminish along the series; in practice, resistance to reaction with oxygen (owing to formation of a surface layer of oxide) causes chromium (for example) to behave abnormally; hence regularities in reactivity are not easily observed. It is now appropriate to consider the individual transition metals.

13.5 Scandium

Scandium is not an uncommon element, but is difficult to extract. The only oxidation state in its compounds is $+3$, where it has formally lost the $3d^1 4s^2$ electrons, and it shows virtually no transition characteristics. In fact, its chemistry is very similar to that of aluminium (for example hydrous oxide Sc_2O_3, amphoteric; forms a complex $[ScF_6]^{3-}$; chloride $ScCl_3$ hydrolysed by water).

13.6 Titanium

13.6.1 The element

Titanium is not a rare element; it is the most abundant transition metal after iron, and is widely distributed in the Earth's surface, mainly as the dioxide TiO_2 and *ilmenite* $FeTiO_3$. It has become of commercial importance since World War II mainly because of its high strength–weight ratio (use in aircraft, especially supersonic), its resistance to corrosion (use in chemical plant), and its retention of these properties up to about 800 K.

The extraction of titanium is still relatively costly; first the dioxide TiO_2 is converted into the tetrachloride $TiCl_4$ by heating with carbon in a stream of chlorine; the tetrachloride is a volatile liquid which can be rendered pure by fractional distillation. The next stage is costly; the reduction of the tetrachloride to the metal, with magnesium, must be carried out in a molybdenum-coated iron crucible in an atmospheric of argon at about 1100 K:

$$TiCl_4 + 2Mg \rightarrow Ti + 2MgCl_2 \qquad \Delta H = -540 \text{ kJ mol}^{-1}$$

The precautions stated are to avoid uptake of oxygen, nitrogen and other impurities which render the metal brittle; the excess of magnesium and magnesium chloride can be removed by volatilization above 1300 K.

13.6.2 Properties

Titanium is a silver-grey metal, density 4.5 g cm^{-3}, m.p. about 1950 K. When pure it is soft: presence of small amounts of impurity make it hard and brittle, and heating with the non-metals boron, carbon, nitrogen and oxygen gives solids which approach the compositions TiB_2, TiC, TiN and TiO_2; some of these are interstitial compounds, which tend to be non-stoichiometric and harder than the pure metal (p. 324). With hydrogen, heating gives a non-stoichiometric hydride, which loses hydrogen at higher temperatures. The metal resists attack by chlorine except at elevated temperatures.

13.6.3 Compounds of titanium

Oxidation state +4
In this oxidation state the titanium atom has formally lost its $3d^2$ and $4s^2$ electrons; as expected, therefore, it forms compounds which do not have the characteristics of transition metal compounds, and which indeed show

strong resemblances to the corresponding compounds of the lower elements (Si, Ge, Sn, Pb) of Group IV — the group into which Mendeléef put titanium in his original form of the periodic table.

Chlorides. The important halide is the tetrachloride, $TiCl_4$, made from the dioxide as already stated (p. 325). It is a colourless volatile liquid, b.p. 409 K, readily hydrolysed by water (*see* below); the Ti—Cl bonds are covalent, and the molecule is monomeric and tetrahedral (cf. the halides of Group IV). It dissolves in concentrated hydrochloric acid to give the hexachlorotitanate(IV) anion, $(TiCl_6)^{2-}$; salts of this anion can be precipitated from the solution by addition of an alkali metal chloride; for example KCl gives K_2TiCl_6 (compare again the behaviour of the Group IV halides). The $[TiCl_6]^{2-}$ ion has an octahedral configuration and is the simplest representative of a large number of titanium(IV) *complexes*, of general formula $[TiX_6]^{n-}$, where X represents a number of possible ligands and $n=0$, 1 or 2. This ability of TiX_4 compounds to increase their coordination has an important practical use. If trimethyl aluminium, $(CH_3)_3Al$, is added to a solution of titanium tetrachloride and an alkene such as ethene passed into the mixture, the alkene is readily polymerized. This is the basis of the Ziegler–Natta process for making polyalkenes, for example 'polypropylene', and the mechanism is believed to involve the coordination of the alkene to molecules of the type CH_3TiCl_3.

Titanium tetrachloride is hydrolysed by water, to give a mixture of anions, for example $[Ti(OH)Cl_5]^-$ and $[TiCl_6]^{2-}$, together with some hydrated titanium dioxide ($TiO_2.4H_2O$ is one possible hydrate, being equivalent to $[Ti(OH)_4(H_2O)_2]$). This suggests that titanium dioxide is amphoteric (*see* below).

Titanium dioxide. This occurs naturally as a white solid in various crystalline forms, in all of which six oxygen atoms surround each titanium atom. Titanium dioxide is important as a white pigment, because it is non-toxic, chemically inert and highly opaque, and can be finely ground; for paint purposes it is often prepared by dissolving the natural form in sulphuric acid, hydrolysing to the hydrated dioxide and heating the latter to make the anhydrous form.

Anhydrous titanium dioxide is only soluble with difficulty in hot concentrated sulphuric acid; dilution allows the crystallization of a sulphate of formula $TiOSO_4.H_2O$, but it is doubtful if the 'titanyl' cation TiO^{2+} actually exists, either in solution or the solid. Certainly $[Ti(H_2O)_n]^{4+}$ does *not* exist, and solutions of 'titanyl' salts may best be considered to contain ions $[Ti(OH)_2(H_2O_4)]^{2+}$. Titanium dioxide is not soluble in aqueous alkali, but with fused alkali gives a *titanate*, for example

$$2KOH + TiO_2 \rightarrow K_2TiO_3 + H_2O$$

Hence titanium dioxide is clearly amphoteric.

Oxidation state +3

In this oxidation state the outer electronic configuration is $3d^1$, so the compounds are necessarily paramagnetic (p. 322) and are coloured.

Titanium(III) *chloride*, $TiCl_3$. This is made by reduction of the tetrachloride with, for example, hydrogen. In the anhydrous form it has a covalent polymeric structure and is coloured violet or brown (there are two crystalline forms). In water, it forms a violet/green solution, and from a slightly acid solution a hydrated solid $TiCl_3.6H_2O$ can be obtained. Hence, clearly, $[Ti(H_2O)_6]^{3+}$ can exist [as might be expected since (Ti^{3+}) would have a lower charge and larger radius than (Ti^{4+})]. The aqueous solution has reducing properties:

$$TiO^{2+}(aq) + 2H_3O^+ + e^- \rightarrow Ti^{3+}(aq) + 3H_2O \qquad E^{\ominus} = +0.1 \text{ V}$$

It must be kept under an atmosphere of nitrogen or carbon dioxide; it reduces, for example, Fe(III) to Fe(II) and nitro-organic compounds RNO_2 to amines RNH_2 (it may be used quantitatively to estimate nitro-compounds). In neutral solution, hydrolysis occurs to give species such as $[Ti(OH)(H_2O)_5]^{2+}$, and with alkali an insoluble substance formulated as 'Ti_2O_3 aq' is produced; this is rapidly oxidized in air.

Complexes of titanium(III) can be made from the trichloride — these are either approximately octahedral, 6-coordinate (for example $TiCl_3.3L$ (L = ligand) and $[TiCl_2(H_2O)_4]^+$, formed when $TiCl_3$ dissolves in aqueous hydrochloric acid), or 5-coordinate with a trigonal bipyramid structure.

Other oxidation states

Titanium forms dihalides TiX_2, for example titanium(II) chloride, formed by heating titanium metal and the tetrachloride to about 1200 K. $TiCl_2$ is a black solid, which disproportionates on standing to $TiCl_4 + Ti$. Since it reduces water to hydrogen, there is no aqueous chemistry for titanium(II). A solid oxide TiO is known.

13.6.4   Tests for titanium

Aqueous solutions containing titanium(IV) give an orange-yellow colour on addition of hydrogen peroxide; the colour is due to the formation of peroxo-titanium complexes, but the exact nature of these is not known.

13.7   Vanadium

13.7.1   The element

Vanadium is by no means as common as titanium, but it occurs in over sixty widely distributed vanadium ores. It is named after Vanadis (a name of the Scandinavian goddess Freia), because it forms compounds having many rich colours. Vanadium is a silver-grey metal; it is not very useful itself, and most of the metal produced is in the form of an alloy *ferrovanadium*, containing between 40 and 90 per cent vanadium. This is added to steel to produce a very tough 'high-speed' steel. Ferrovanadium is obtained by reduction of the oxide V_2O_5 with 'ferrosilicon' (Fe + Si). The pure metal is very difficult to prepare because it combines even more readily with hydrogen, carbon, nitrogen and oxygen than does titanium; as with the latter, the compounds produced are often interstitial and non-stoichiometric, but with oxygen the pentoxide V_2O_5 is ultimately obtained. Vanadium dissolves readily in oxidizing acids.

With the outer electronic configuration $3d^3 4s^2$ vanadium can attain an oxidation state of $+5$, but it shows all oxidation states between $+5$ and $+2$ in aqueous solution (cf. titanium).

13.7.2   Compounds of vanadium

Oxidation state +5

Although vanadium has formally lost all its outer electrons in this state, the resemblance to the Group V elements is not so marked as that of titanium(IV) to Group IV.

Halides. The vanadium(V) state is very strongly oxidizing; hence the only stable halide is the fluoride VF_5, a white, easily hydrolysed solid which readily melts and vaporizes, to give a monomeric vapour with a pentagonal bipyramid structure (cf. PF_5, p. 35). It reacts directly with potassium fluoride at room temperature to give the hexafluorovanadate(V), KVF_6 (containing the octahedral complex ion VF_6^-). Oxide halides VOX_3 (X = F, Cl, Br) are known (cf. phosphorus).

Vanadium pentoxide, vanadium(V) *oxide,* V_2O_5. This is the most important compound in this oxidation state. It is a coloured solid (colour due to charge transfer, p. 52), the colour varying somewhat (red $\rightarrow$ brown) with the state of subdivision; it is formed when vanadium (or some of its compounds) is completely oxidized, and also by heating ammonium vanadate(V):

$$2NH_4VO_3 \rightarrow V_2O_5 + 2NH_3 + H_2O$$

It is extensively used industrially as a catalyst, notably in the oxidation of sulphur dioxide to the trioxide in sulphuric acid manufacture. It is an essentially acidic oxide, dissolving in alkalis to give vanadates; however, addition of acid converts the anionic vanadate species into cationic species, by processes which are very complex, but which overall amount to the following:

$$VO_4^{3-} \rightleftharpoons (VO_3^-)_n \rightleftharpoons \text{polyvanadates} \rightleftharpoons VO_2^+(aq)$$

as the pH varies as shown in *Table 13.7.*

Oxidation state +4

This is the important state of vanadium in aqueous solution; it is neither strongly oxidizing nor strongly reducing and acidic solutions are stable to atmospheric oxidation:

$$[V(OH)_4]^+ + 2H_3O^+ + e^- \; \underset{MnO_4^-}{\overset{HSO_3^-}{\rightleftharpoons}} \; VO^{2+}(aq) \quad + 5H_2O$$

V(V)   oxovanadium(IV)
colourless   or vanadyl, blue

As the scheme indicates, the blue 'vanadyl' oxovanadium cation can be

Table 13.7 Vanadium(V) species

Approx. pH range	14-12	10-7	6-2	below 2
Species present	VO_4^{3-}	$(VO_3^-)_n$	polyvanadates	$VO_2^+(aq)$
Name	orthovanadate tetraoxovanadate(V)	polymetavanadate polytrioxovanadate(V)		dioxovanadium(V)
Colour	colourless	colourless	yellow	red
Structure	tetrahedral	tetrahedral coordination around vanadium	—	—

(quantitatively) oxidized to vanadium(V) and the latter is reduced by hydrogensulphite. The VO^{2+}(aq) cation is probably best represented as $[VO(H_2O)_5]^{2+}$, with the oxygen occupying one coordination position in the octahedral complex. However the 'VO' entity is found in many other complexes, both cationic and anionic; an example of the latter is $[VOCl_4]^-$ where the vanadium(V) is 5-coordinate, thus

$$
\left[
\begin{array}{c}
O \\
\| \\
Cl\text{---}V\text{---}Cl \\
Cl \quad\quad Cl
\end{array}
\right]^-
$$

The V(IV) species are all d^1 complexes, hence their colour. Besides the 'VO' compounds, some *halides* VX_4 are known, for example VCl_4, a liquid with a tetrahedral, covalent molecule and properties similar to those of $TiCl_4$, but coloured (red-brown).

Other oxidation states

In the $+3$ *oxidation state*, vanadium forms an oxide V_2O_3, and the blue $[V(H_2O)_6]^{3+}$ cation in acid solution; the latter is obtained by reduction of V(IV) or V(V):

$$VO^{2+}(aq) + 2H_3O^+ + e^- \rightarrow V^{3+}(aq) + 3H_2O \qquad E^\ominus = +0.36\ V$$

The hexaaqua-cation occurs in the blue-violet alums, for example

$$NH_4V(SO_4)_2.12H_2O$$

The $+2$ *oxidation state* is achieved by drastic reduction (zinc and acid) of the $+5$, $+4$ or $+3$ states: thus addition of zinc and acid to a solution of a yellow vanadate(V) gives, successively, blue $[VO(H_2O)_5]^{2+}$, green $[VCl_2(H_2O)_4]^+$ and violet $[V(H_2O)_6]^{2+}$. The latter is of course easily oxidized, for example, by air. The oxide VO is usually non-stoichiometric, but anhydrous halides VX_2 are known.

The 0 *oxidation state* is known in vanadium hexacarbonyl, $V(CO)_6$, a blue-green, sublimable solid. In the molecule $V(CO)_6$, if each CO molecule is assumed to donate two electrons to the vanadium atom, the latter is still one electron short of the next noble gas configuration (krypton); the compound is therefore paramagnetic, and is easily reduced to form $[V(CO_6)]^-$, giving it the one electron required (and also giving the vanadium a formal oxidation state of -1).

13.7.3 Tests for vanadium

The colour sequence already described, for the reduction of vanadium(V) to vanadium(II) by zinc and acid, gives a very characteristic test for vanadium. Addition of a few drops of hydrogen peroxide to a vanadate(V) gives a red colour (formation of a peroxo-complex) (cf. titanium, which gives an orange-yellow colour).

13.8 Chromium

13.8.1 The element

Chromium occurs quite extensively, mainly as the ore *chromite* or *chrome ironstone*, a mixed oxide of iron(II) and chromium(III). Presence of chromium in the mineral beryl produces the green colour of emeralds and the red colour of ruby is due to the substitution of Cr(III) for Al(III) in the mineral aluminium(III) oxide; hence the name 'chromium' derived from the Greek for colour. Direct reduction of chromate by heating with carbon and calcium oxide gives an alloy of iron and chromium, *ferrochrome*, which can be added to steel, to make stainless steel (12—15 per cent chromium). The pure metal can be prepared by reduction of the $+3$ oxide, Cr_2O_3, using powdered aluminium, or by electrolytic reduction of the $+6$ oxide CrO_3. The metal is extensively used in *chromium plating* because it is relatively inert to chemical attack. However, the extent of inertness is dependent on its purity. It is inert to the oxidizing oxoacids (phosphoric, nitric, aqua-regia, concentrated sulphuric); these render it passive, probably by formation of a surface layer of oxide. It remains bright in air, despite formation of a surface layer of oxide. When pure (no oxide layer) it is readily soluble in dilute hydrochloric acid [to give a chromium(II) cation, *see* p. 336] and displaces copper, tin and metal from solutions of their salts.

The outer electron configuration, $3d^5 4s^1$, indicates the stability of the half-filled d level, $3d^5 4s^1$ being more stable than the expected $3d^4 4s^2$ for the free atom. Like vanadium and titanium, chromium can lose all its outer electrons, giving chromium(VI); however, the latter is strongly oxidizing and is therefore only found in combination with oxygen and fluorine. Of the lower oxidation states, the $+3$ is the most stable and common.

13.8.2 Compounds of chromium

Oxidation state $+6$

In this state, chromium compounds are usually coloured yellow or red [but owing to charge transfer (p. 52) and not to the presence of $3d$ electrons on the chromium ion]. The only halide known is the unstable chromium(VI) fluoride CrF_6, a yellow solid. However, oxide halides are known, for example CrO_2Cl_2 ('chromyl chloride'), formed as a red vapour when concentrated sulphuric acid is added to a chromate(VI) (or dichromate) mixed with a chloride:

$$Cr_2O_7^{2-} + 4Cl^- + 6H_2SO_4 \rightarrow 2CrO_2Cl_2 + 6HSO_4^- + 3H_2O$$

(This reaction can be used to distinguish a chloride from a bromide, since CrO_2Br_2 is unstable under these conditions.)

The most important compounds containing Cr(VI) are the oxide CrO_3 and the oxoanions CrO_4^{2-}, chromate(VI) and $Cr_2O_7^{2-}$, dichromate(VI).

Chromium(VI) *oxide* (*chromium trioxide*). Chromium trioxide is obtained as bright red crystals when concentrated sulphuric acid is added cautiously to a concentrated aqueous solution of a chromate or dichromate(VI). It can be filtered off through sintered glass or asbestos, but is a very strong oxidizing agent and so oxidizes paper and other organic matter (hence the use of a solution of the oxide — 'chromic acid' — as a cleansing agent for glassware).

Chromium(VI) oxide is very soluble in water; initially, 'chromic acid', H_2CrO_4, may be formed, but this has not been isolated. If it dissociates thus:

$$H_2CrO_4 \rightleftharpoons H^+ + HCrO_4^-$$

then the $HCrO_4^-$ ions probably form dichromate ions:

$$2HCrO_4^- \rightleftharpoons Cr_2O_7^{2-} + H_2O$$

Chromium(VI) oxide is acidic, and the corresponding salts are the *chromates* and *dichromates*, containing the ions CrO_4^{2-} and $Cr_2O_7^{2-}$, i.e. $[CrO_4 + CrO_3]^{2-}$. The oxidation state of chromium is $+6$ in each ion (cf. sulphur in SO_4^{2-} and $S_2O_7^{2-}$).

The chromates(VI). The chromates of the alkali metals and of magnesium and calcium are soluble in water; the other chromates are insoluble. The chromate ion is yellow, but some insoluble chromates are red (for example silver chromate, Ag_2CrO_4). Chromates are often isomorphous with sulphates, which suggests that the chromate ion, CrO_4^{2-}, has a tetrahedral structure similar to that of the sulphate ion, SO_4^{2-}. Chromates can be prepared by oxidizing chromium(III) salts; the oxidation can be carried out by fusion with sodium peroxide, or by adding sodium peroxide to a solution of the chromium(III) salt. The use of sodium peroxide ensures an alkaline solution; otherwise, under acid conditions, the chromate ion is converted into the orange-coloured *dichromate* ion:

$$2CrO_4^{2-} + 2H^+ \underset{\text{alkali}}{\overset{\text{acid}}{\rightleftharpoons}} Cr_2O_7^{2-} + H_2O$$

The dichromate ion has the following geometrical structure (single lines not necessarily implying single bonds):

i.e. two tetrahedral CrO_4 groups joined by a common oxygen atom.

If a metal ion of an insoluble chromate is added to a solution containing the dichromate ion, the chromate is precipitated; for example with a soluble lead(II) salt:

$$2Pb^{2+} + Cr_2O_7^{2-} + H_2O \rightarrow 2PbCrO_4\downarrow + 2H^+$$
$$\text{yellow precipitate}$$
$$\text{of lead chromate}$$

Sodium dichromate is prepared on the large scale by heating powdered chromite with sodium carbonate, with free access of air; the sodium chromate first formed is treated with acid:

$$4FeCr_2O_4 + 8Na_2CO_3 + 7O_2 \rightarrow 8Na_2CrO_4 + 2Fe_2O_3 + 8CO_2\uparrow$$
$$2Na_2CrO_4 + H_2SO_4 \rightarrow Na_2SO_4 + Na_2Cr_2O_7 + H_2O$$

Sodium sulphate crystallizes out in hydrated form (common ion effect) and is filtered off; on concentration, sodium dichromate is obtained. For analytical purposes, the potassium salt, $K_2Cr_2O_7$, is preferred; potassium chloride is added and the less soluble potassium dichromate obtained.

The dichromate ion is a useful oxidizing agent in acid solution, and is used in volumetric analysis:

$$Cr_2O_7^{2-}(aq) + 14H_3O^+ + 6e^- \rightarrow 2Cr^{3+}(aq) + 21H_2O \qquad E^\ominus = +1.33 \text{ V}$$

A standard solution of potassium dichromate can be made up by accurately weighing the pure salt. [A standard solution of potassium manganate(VII) *cannot* be made up by direct weighing, since the salt always gives a little manganese(IV) oxide in water.] Sulphuric acid is added to the solution to be titrated, but hydrochloric acid can be present, since the chloride ion is not easily oxidized by dichromate [cf. manganate(VII)]. The end-point is not easy to detect with dichromate, since the orange colour of the latter has merely been replaced by the green colour of the hydrated Cr^{3+} ion. It is therefore useful to use an oxidation–reduction indicator, such as diphenylamine, which turns from colourless to blue at the end point.

The dichromate ion oxidizes iron(II) to iron(III), sulphite to sulphate ion*, iodide ion to iodine and arsenic(III) to arsenic(V) (arsenate). Reduction of dichromate by sulphite can be used to prepare chrome alum, since, if sulphur dioxide is passed into potassium dichromate acidified with sulphuric acid, potassium and chromium(III) ions are formed in the correct ratio to form the alum, which appears on crystallization:

$$K_2Cr_2O_7 + H_2SO_4 + 3SO_2 \rightarrow \underbrace{K_2SO_4 + Cr_2(SO_4)_3} + H_2O$$

$$2[KCr(SO_4)_2.12H_2O]$$

Chrome alum is also obtained if the acidified dichromate is boiled with ethanol, the ethanal formed distilling off.

Reduction of dichromate by strong reducing agents yields the chromium(II) ion, Cr^{2+} (*see* p. 336).

The addition of concentrated sulphuric acid to a solid dichromate mixed with a chloride produces a red vapour, chromium(VI) dioxide dichloride, CrO_2Cl_2 (cf. sulphur dioxide dichloride, SO_2Cl_2). Chromium(VI) dioxide dichloride reacts with water immediately:

$$2CrO_2Cl_2 + 3H_2O \rightarrow Cr_2O_7^{2-} + 6H^+ + 4Cl^-$$

If it is passed into a concentrated solution of a chloride, however, a *chlorochromate*(VI) is formed:

$$CrO_2Cl_2 + Cl^- + H_2O \rightarrow [CrO_3Cl]^- + 2HCl$$

*Thus, filter paper which has been dipped into a solution of potassium dichromate turns green in the presence of sulphur dioxide. This reaction provides the usual test for sulphur dioxide.

Addition of hydrogen peroxide to a solution of a dichromate yields the blue colour of 'peroxochromic acid'. This is a test for soluble chromates and dichromates.

Chromates and dichromates are used in industry as oxidizing agents, for example in the coal tar industry, in the leather industry (chrome tanning), and in the dye industry as mordants. Some chromates are used as pigments, for example those of zinc and lead. Chromates and dichromates are poisonous.

Oxidation state +3

This is the most common and stable state of chromium in aqueous solution. The Cr^{3+} ion, with $3d^3$ electrons, forms mainly octahedral complexes of the general form $[CrX_6]$, which are usually coloured, and are *kinetically inert*, i.e. the rate of substitution of X by another ligand is very slow; consequently a large number of such complexes have been isolated [see below, under chromium(III) chloride].

Chromium(III) *chloride*, $CrCl_3$. Chromium(III) chloride is prepared in the anhydrous form:

(1)   By the reaction of chlorine with a heated mixture of chromium(III) oxide and carbon:

$$Cr_2O_3 + 3Cl_2 + 3C \rightarrow 3CO\uparrow + 2CrCl_3$$

(2)   By the reaction of sulphur dichloride oxide with the hydrated chloride:

$$CrCl_3.6H_2O + 6SOCl_2 \rightarrow CrCl_3 + 6SO_2\uparrow + 12HCl\uparrow$$

Anhydrous chromium(III) chloride is a peach-coloured solid, which is insoluble in water unless a trace of reducing agent is present. Solution then occurs readily to give a green solution from which the green *hydrated chloride*, $CrCl_3.6H_2O$, can be crystallized out. If this substance is treated with silver nitrate, only one third of the chlorine is precipitated; hence the formula is $[Cr^{III}(H_2O)_4Cl_2]^+Cl^-.2H_2O$, with two chloride ions as ligands in the complex ion. Two other forms of formula $CrCl_3.6H_2O$ are known; one is (pale green) $[Cr(H_2O)_5Cl^{2+}[Cl^-]_2.H_2O$ from which silver nitrate precipitates two thirds of the chlorine; and the other is $[Cr(H_2O)_6]Cl_3$ (grey-blue) from which all the chlorine is precipitated by silver nitrate. These three compounds are *isomers*, and the cations can be represented as in *Figure 13.4*.

The compounds also illustrate the very great tendency of tripositive chromium to form complexes, which are usually of the octahedral form $[CrX_6]$, for example $[Cr(NH_3)_6]^{3+}$, $[Cr(NH_3)_5NO_2]^{2+}$ and $[Cr(CN)_6]^{3-}$.

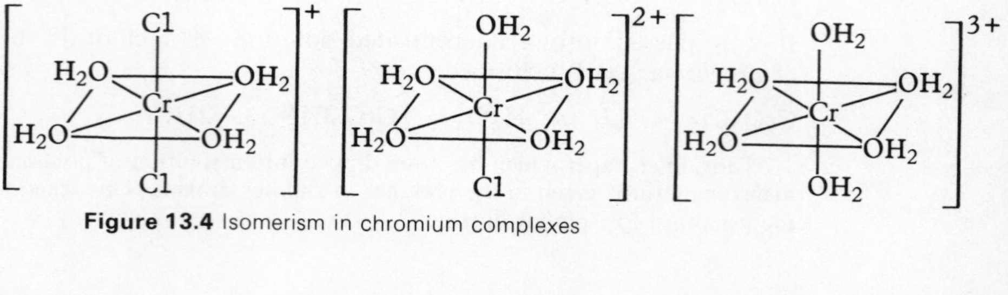

Figure 13.4 Isomerism in chromium complexes

Chromium(III) *oxide*, Cr_2O_3. Chromium(III) oxide is prepared:
(1) By heating chromium(III) hydroxide (*see* below).
(2) By heating ammonium dichromate:

$$(NH_4)_2Cr^{VI}_2O_7 \rightarrow N_2\uparrow + 4H_2O + Cr^{III}_2O_3$$

It is a green powder, insoluble in water and in acids (cf. aluminium oxide, Al_2O_3). It is not reduced by hydrogen.

It catalyses the decomposition of potassium chlorate(V). Mixed with zinc oxide, it is used as a catalyst in the manufacture of methanol. It is used as a pigment, being very resistant to weathering.

Chromium(III) *hydroxide*, $Cr(OH)_3$ (*hydrated*). Chromium(III) hydroxide is obtained as a light green gelatinous precipitate when an alkali or ammonia is added to a chromium(III) salt:

$$Cr^{3+} + 3OH^- \xrightarrow{\ H_2O\ } Cr(OH)_3\downarrow \ (or \ Cr_2O_3.xH_2O)$$

This reaction is better represented, as shown in *Figure 13.5*, as a removal of hydrogen ions from the hydrated Cr^{3+} ion [equation (1)]; the hydroxide

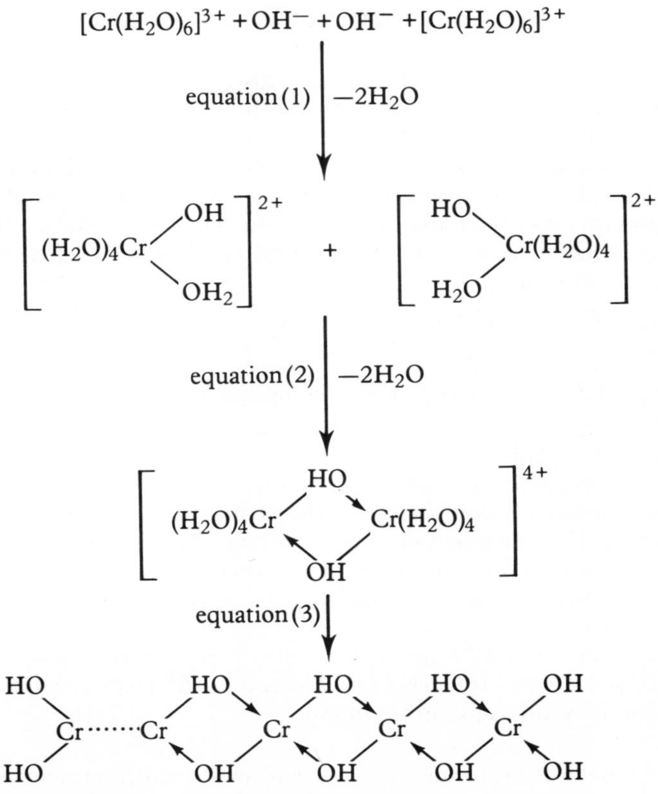

Figure 13.5 Aggregation of chromium(III) hydroxide

groups left are believed to act as bridges, so building up aggregates of ions [equation (2)] these forming first colloidal particles and then larger aggregates [equation (3)]*.

Chromium(III) hydroxide, like aluminium hydroxide, possesses *ad*sorptive power, and the use of chromium compounds as mordants is due to this property.

Chromium(III) hydroxide dissolves in acids to form hydrated chromium(III) salts; in concentrated alkali, hydroxo-complexes $[Cr(OH)_6]^{3-}$ are formed.

Chromium(III) sulphate, $Cr_2(SO_4)_3.18H_2O$. Hydrated chromium(III) sulphate exhibits different colours and different forms from which varying amounts of sulphate ion can be precipitated by barium chloride, owing to the formation of sulphato-complexes. Chromium(III) sulphate can form alums.

Hydrated chromium(II) nitrate, $Cr(NO_3)_3.9H_2O$. Hydrated chromium(III) nitrate is a dark green, very deliquescent solid, very soluble in water. The anhydrous nitrate is covalent.

Oxidation state +2
This state is strongly reducing, often coloured, and paramagnetic.

Chromium(II) chloride, $CrCl_2$. This is prepared by passing dry hydrogen chloride over chromium, or hydrogen over anhydrous chromium(III) chloride. It is a white solid. If *pure* chromium is dissolved in dilute hydrochloric acid in the absence of air, a blue solution of the hydrated chloride, containing the hexaaqua-ion $[Cr(H_2O)_6]^{2+}$, is obtained. The same solution is also obtained by reduction of the +6 oxidation state (through the +3) using a solution of a dichromate(VI) and reducing with zinc and hydrochloric acid:

$$Cr_2O_7^{2-} \rightarrow Cr^{3+}(aq) \rightarrow Cr^{2+}(aq)$$
orange   green   blue

[cf. the colour change when vanadium(V) is similarly reduced, p. 330].

Other oxidation states
Chromium forms a white, solid *hexacarbonyl*, $Cr(CO)_6$, with the chromium in formal oxidation state 0; the structure is octahedral, and if each CO molecule donates two electrons, the chromium attains the noble gas structure. Many complexes are known where one or more of the carbon monoxide ligands are replaced by other groups of ions, for example $[Cr(CO)_5I]^-$.

In dibenzenechromium, the chromium atom is 'sandwiched' between two benzene rings (*Figure 13.6*). Here also the rings are uncharged, and the complex contains chromium(0).

---

*Ions with hydroxide bridges are probably formed from other hydrated metal ions, e.g. $(Al(H_2O)_6)^{3+}$ and $(Fe(H_2O)_6)^{3+}$.

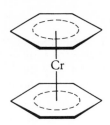

Figure 13.6 Structure of dibenzenechromium

13.8.3   Tests for chromium

Fusion of any chromium compound with a mixture of potassium nitrate and carbonate gives a yellow chromate(VI)*.

Tests for chromates and dichromates(VI)
(1)   Addition of lead(II) nitrate in ethanoic acid solution gives a yellow precipitate of lead chromate, $PbCrO_4$.
(2)   A reducing agent (for example sulphur dioxide) reduces the yellow chromate or orange dichromate to the green chromium(III) state.
(3)   Hydrogen peroxide with a chromate or a dichromate gives a blue colour.

Tests for chromium(III) *salts* (*i.e. for hydrated* Cr^{3+} *ion*)
(1)   Addition of alkali gives a green gelatinous precipitate of chromium(III) hydroxide, soluble in a large excess of strong alkali.
(2)   Addition of sodium peroxide to a solution gives a yellow colour of the chromate.

13.9   Manganese

13.9.1   The element

Manganese is the third most abundant transition metal, and is widely distributed in the Earth's crust. The most important ore is *pyrolusite*, manganese(IV) oxide. Reduction of this ore by heating with aluminium gives an explosive reaction and the oxide Mn_3O_4 must be used to obtain the metal. The latter is purified by distillation *in vacuo* just above its melting point (1517 K); the pure metal can also be obtained by electrolysis of aqueous manganese(II) sulphate.

The metal looks like iron; it exists in four allotropic modifications, stable over various temperature ranges. Although not easily attacked by air, it is slowly attacked by water and dissolves readily in dilute acids to give manganese(II) salts. The stable form of the metal at ordinary temperatures is hard and brittle — hence manganese is only of value in alloys, for example in steels (ferroalloys) and with aluminium, copper and nickel.

*Fused potassium nitrate is a powerful oxidizing agent (cf. the oxidation of manganese compounds, p. 338).

13.9.2   Compounds of manganese

Although it exhibits a wide range of oxidation states, from $+7$ (corresponding to formal loss of all the outer electrons, $3d^5 4s^2$) to 0, it differs from the preceding transition metals in having a very stable $+2$ oxidation state, corresponding to loss of only the $4s^2$ electrons, and indicative of the stability of the half-filled $3d$ energy levels.

Oxidation state $+7$
Apart from two unstable oxide halides, MnO_3F and MnO_3Cl, this state is exclusively represented by the oxide Mn_2O_7 and the anion MnO_4^-.

Manganese(VII) *oxide, dimanganese heptoxide,* Mn_2O_7. This oxide is obtained by adding potassium manganate(VII) to concentrated sulphuric acid, when it appears as a dark coloured oil which readily decomposes (explosively on heating) to manganese(IV) oxide and oxygen:

$$2KMnO_4 + 2H_2SO_4 \rightarrow Mn_2O_7 + 2KHSO_4 + H_2O$$
$$2Mn_2O_7 \rightarrow 4MnO_2 + 3O_2$$

It is a powerful and violent oxidizing agent. It dissolves in water, and *manganic*(VII) *acid* (permanganic acid) $HMnO_4$ and its dihydrate $HMnO_4.2H_2O$ can be isolated as purple solids by low temperature evaporation of the frozen solution. Manganic(VII) acid is also a violent oxidizing agent, especially with any organic material; it decomposes quickly at 276 K.

The manganates(VII). The purple manganate(VII) or permanganate anion, MnO_4^- is tetrahedral; it owes its intense colour to charge transfer (manganese with an oxidation number $+7$ has no $3d$ electrons). The potassium salt $KMnO_4$ is the usual form, but many other cations form soluble manganate(VII) salts (all purple); those with large unipositive cations (for example Cs^+) are less soluble. Potassium manganate(VII) can be prepared by (a) electrolytic oxidation of manganese metal (oxidation from 0 to $+7$) using a manganese anode in potassium carbonate solution, (b) oxidation of manganate(II) (oxidation $+2$ to $+7$), using a manganese(II) salt and the peroxodisulphate ion $S_2O_8^{2-}$, which oxidizes thus:

$$S_2O_8^{2-} + 2e^- \rightarrow 2SO_4^{2-} \qquad E^\ominus = 2.0 \text{ V}$$

and (c) oxidation of manganese(IV), by fusion of MnO_2 with potassium hydroxide, the usual method. This fusion, in air or in the presence of a solid oxidizing agent (KNO_3), produces manganates(VI):

$$2Mn^{IV}O_2 + 4KOH + O_2 \rightarrow 2K_2Mn^{VI}O_4 + 2H_2O$$

The green manganate(VI) is extracted with water, then oxidized to manganate(VII). This is usually carried out electrolytically, at an anode, but in the laboratory chlorine may be used:

$$MnO_4^{2-} \rightarrow MnO_4^- + e^-$$
$$2MnO_4^{2-} + Cl_2 \rightarrow 2MnO_4^- + 2Cl^-$$

(Note that here 'chlorine' is oxidizing the manganate(VI) to manganate(VII); under more acid conditions, the latter oxidizes chloride to chlorine, p. 339).

Potassium manganate(VII) decomposes on heating:

$$2KMn^{VII}O_4 \rightarrow K_2Mn^{VI}O_4 + Mn^{IV}O_2 + O_2$$

The manganate(VII) ion slowly oxidizes water, the essential reaction being

$$4MnO_4^- + 4H^+ \rightarrow 4MnO_2 + 2H_2O + 3O_2$$

This reaction proceeds very slowly in absence of light, and aqueous solutions of potassium manganate(VII) are effectively stable for long periods if kept in dark bottles.

The manganate(VII) ion is one of the more useful oxidizing agents; in acid solution we have

$$MnO_4^-(aq) + 8H_3O^+ + 5e^- \rightarrow Mn^{2+}(aq) + 12H_2O \qquad E^{\ominus} = +1.52 \text{ V}$$

Hence manganate(VII) is used in acid solution to oxidize, for example,

$$Fe(II) \rightarrow Fe(III) \qquad\qquad NO_2^- \rightarrow NO_3^- \qquad\qquad H_2O_2 \rightarrow O_2$$
$$C_2O_4^{2-} \rightarrow 2CO_2$$

quantitatively; the equivalence point is recognized by persistence of the purple colour. (Sulphuric acid is used to acidify, since hydrochloric acid is oxidized to chlorine and nitric acid is an oxidizing agent.) Manganate(VII) is also used extensively in organic chemistry, for example to oxidize alcohols to aldehydes; here it may be used in acid or (more commonly) in alkaline solution, when manganese(IV) oxide is the product:

$$MnO_4^-(aq) + 2H_2O + 3e^- \rightarrow MnO_2(s) + 4OH^-(aq) \qquad E^{\ominus} = +0.59 \text{ V}$$

In concentrated alkali, manganese(VI) is more stable than manganese(VII) and the following reaction occurs:

$$4MnO_4^- + 4OH^- \rightarrow 4MnO_4^{2-} + 2H_2O + O_2$$

(cf. the reverse reaction with chlorine, above).

Oxidation state +6
This is only found in the green manganate(VI) ion, already described. It is only stable in alkaline conditions; in neutral or acid solution it disproportionates:

$$3Mn^{VI}O_4^{2-} + 2H_2O \rightarrow Mn^{IV}O_2 + 2Mn^{VII}O_4^- + 4OH^-$$

Oxidation state +5
This state exists as a manganate(V), the *blue* MnO_4^{3-}; the salt $Na_3MnO_4.10H_2O$ is isomorphous with Na_3VO_4 (p. 329).

Oxidation state +4
Manganese(IV) *oxide*, MnO_2. Manganese(IV) oxide is the only familiar example of this oxidation state. It occurs naturally as *pyrolusite*, but can be prepared in an anhydrous form by strong heating of manganese(II) nitrate:

$$Mn^{II}(NO_3)_2 \rightarrow MnO_2 + 2NO_2\uparrow$$

It can also be precipitated in a hydrated form by the oxidation of a manganese(II) salt, by, for example, a peroxodisulphate:

$$Mn^{2+} + S_2O_8^{2-} + 2H_2O \rightarrow 2SO_4^{2-} + MnO_2\downarrow + 4H^+$$

Manganese(IV) oxide is a dark-brown solid, insoluble in water and dilute acids. Its catalytic decomposition of potassium chlorate(V) and hydrogen peroxide has already been mentioned. It dissolves slowly in alkalis to form *manganates*(IV), but the constitution of these is uncertain. It dissolves in ice-cold concentrated hydrochloric acid forming the complex octahedral hexachloromanganate(IV) ion:

$$MnO_2 + 6HCl \rightarrow [Mn^{IV}Cl_6]^{2-} + 2H^+ + 2H_2O$$

This ion is derived from manganese(IV) chloride, $MnCl_4$, but the latter has not been isolated. The $MnCl_6^{2-}$ ion is unstable, breaking down to give chlorine thus:

$$[MnCl_6]^{2-} \rightarrow Mn^{2+} + 4Cl^- + Cl_2\uparrow$$

Hence, under ordinary conditions, manganese(IV) oxide oxidizes concentrated hydrochloric acid to chlorine, but the above shows that the oxidation process is essentially:

$$Mn^{IV} + 2e^- \rightarrow Mn^{II}$$

An oxidation which can be used to estimate the amount of manganese(IV) oxide in a sample of pyrolusite is that of ethanedioic acid:

$$MnO_2 + (COOH)_2 + H_2SO_4 \rightarrow MnSO_4 + 2CO_2\uparrow + 2H_2O$$

Excess of standard acid is added, and the excess (after disappearance of the solid oxide) is estimated by titration with standard potassium manganate(VII).

Alternatively, a known mass of the pyrolusite may be heated with concentrated hydrochloric acid and the chlorine evolved passed into potassium iodide solution. The iodine liberated is titrated with sodium thiosulphate:

$$MnO_2 \equiv Cl_2 \equiv I_2 \equiv 2S_2O_3^{2-}$$

Manganese(IV) oxide is used as a depolarizer in Leclanché cells (the cells used in ordinary batteries), as a glaze for pottery and as a decolorizer for glass. The decolorizing action occurs because the manganese(IV) oxide oxidizes green iron(II) silicates to the less evident iron(III) compounds; hence the one-time name of 'glass-maker's soap' and also 'pyrolusite' (Greek *pur* and *lusis*, dissolution by fire).

Although the complex ion $[MnCl_6]^{2-}$ is unstable, salts such as $K_2[MnF_6]$ [containing the octahedral hexafluoromanganate(IV) ion] are much more stable and can be crystallized from solution.

Oxidation state +3
This state is unstable with respect to disproportionation in aqueous solution:

$$2Mn^{3+}(aq) + 2H_2O \rightarrow Mn^{2+}(aq) + MnO_2 + 4H^+$$

However the Mn^{3+}(aq) ion can be stabilized by using acid solutions or by complex formation; it can be prepared by electrolytic oxidation of manganese(II) solutions. The alum $CsMn(SO_4)_2.12H_2O$ contains the hydrated Mn^{3+} ion, which (as expected for a tripositive cation), is strongly acidic.

The complexes of manganese(III) include $[Mn(CN)_6]^{3-}$ [formed when manganese(II) salts are oxidized in presence of cyanide ions], and $[MnF_5(H_2O)]^{2-}$, formed when a manganese(II) salt is oxidized by a manganate(VII) in presence of hydrofluoric acid:

$$4Mn^{2+} + 8H^+ + MnO_4^- \rightarrow 5Mn^{3+} + 4H_2O$$

$$Mn^{3+} + H_2O + 5F^- \rightarrow [MnF_5(H_2O)]^{2-}$$

Oxidation of manganese(II) hydroxide by air gives the brown hydrated oxide $Mn_2O_3.aq$, and this on drying gives $MnO(OH)$ which occurs in nature as *manganite*. (The oxide Mn_2O_3 also occurs naturally as *braunite*.) Heating of the oxide Mn_2O_3 gives the mixed oxide Mn_3O_4 [manganese(II) dimanganese(III) oxide].

In general, manganese(III) compounds are coloured, and the complexes are octahedral in shape; with four d electrons, the colour is attributable in part to d–d transitions.

Oxidation state +2

This is the most common and stable state of manganese; the five d electrons half fill the five d-orbitals, and hence any transition of d electrons in a complex of manganese(II) must involve the pairing of electrons, a process which requires energy. Hence electron transitions between the split d-orbitals are weak for manganese(II), and the colour is correspondingly pale (usually pink). The stability of the d^5 configuration with respect to either loss or gain of electrons also means that manganese(II) salts are not easily reduced or oxidized. Indeed, in oxidation state $+2$, manganese shows fewer 'transition-like' characteristics than any other transition metal ion; thus the aqua-ion $[Mn(H_2O)_6]^{2+}$ is barely acidic, allowing formation of a 'normal' *carbonate* $MnCO_3$ which is insoluble in water and occurs naturally as 'manganese spar'. The aqua-ion forms typical hydrated salts, for example $MnSO_4.7H_2O$, $MnCl_2.xH_2O$ and double salts, for example $(NH_4)_2Mn(SO_4)_2.6H_2O$; dehydration of the simple hydrated salts, by heating, produces the anhydrous salt without decomposition. Addition of alkali precipitates the white basic manganese(II) hydroxide $Mn(OH)_2$; if left in the alkaline medium it is oxidized readily by air to brown $Mn_2O_3.aq$*.

The *oxide* MnO is obtained by heating the carbonate $MnCO_3$. Oxidation of manganese(II) in aqueous *acid* solution requires a strong oxidizing agent, for example

$$MnO_4^-(aq) + 8H_3O^+ + 5e^- \rightarrow Mn^{2+}(aq) + 12H_2O \qquad E^\ominus = 1.52 \text{ V}$$
$$MnO_2(s) + 4H_3O^+ + 2e^- \rightarrow Mn^{2+}(aq) + 6H_2O \qquad E^\ominus = 1.35 \text{ V}$$

*In water pollution studies, the oxygen content can be measured by making the water alkaline and shaking a measured volume with an oxygen-free solution containing Mn^{2+}(aq). The solution is acidified with sulphuric acid, potassium iodide added and the liberated iodine titrated with sodium thiosulphate.

Thus, for example, peroxodisulphate(VI) will oxidize Mn(II) to Mn(VII):

$$2Mn^{2+} + 5S_2O_8^{2-} + 8H_2O \rightarrow 2MnO_4^- + 16H^+ + 10SO_4^{2-}$$

However, the Mn(II) ion forms a variety of complexes in solution, some of which may be more easily oxidized; these complexes can be either tetrahedral, for example $[MnCl_4]^{2-}$, or octahedral, for example $[Mn(CN)_6]^{4-}$. Addition of ammonia to an aqueous solution of a manganese(II) salt precipitates $Mn(OH)_2$; reaction of ammonia with anhydrous manganese(II) salts can yield the ion $[Mn(NH_3)_6]^{2+}$.

Low oxidation states
Manganese forms a decacarbonyl $Mn_2(CO)_{10}$ in which each manganese atom has the required share in 18 electrons to achieve the noble gas configuration. Reduction of this covalent compound with sodium amalgam gives the salt $Na[Mn(CO)_5]$, sodium pentacarbonylmanganate(-1); in the ion $Mn(CO)_5^-$ the noble gas structure is again attained.

13.9.3   Tests for manganese

Fusion of a manganese compound with sodium carbonate and potassium nitrate (on porcelain) gives a green manganate(VI) (p. 338).

Test for MnO_4^- ion
The purple colour of this ion alone is a sufficient test for its presence: addition of sulphuric acid and hydrogen peroxide discharges the colour.

Test for Mn^{2+} ions
If a manganese(II) salt is boiled with a strong oxidizing agent such as a peroxodisulphate or lead(IV) oxide and concentrated nitric acid, the purple colour of the mangante(VII) ion is seen.

13.10   Iron

13.10.1   The element

After aluminium, iron is the most abundant metal; and the fourth most abundant of all the elements; it occurs chiefly as oxides [for example *haematite* (Fe_2O_3), *magnetite* (lodestone) (Fe_3O_4)] and as *iron pyrites* ($FeS)_2$. Free iron is found in meteorites, and it is probable that primitive man used this source of iron for tools and weapons. The extraction of iron began several thousand years ago, and it is still the most important metal in everyday life because of its abundance and cheapness, and its ability to be cast, drawn and forged for a variety of uses.

The process of extraction requires first *smelting* (to obtain the crude metal) and then *refining*. In smelting, iron ore (usually an oxide) is mixed with coke and limestone and heated, and hot air (often enriched with oxygen) is blown in from beneath (in a blast furnace). At the lower, hotter part of the furnace, carbon monoxide is produced and this is the essential reducing agent. The reduction reactions occurring may be represented for simplicity as:

(1) $3CO + Fe_2O_3 \rightleftharpoons 2Fe + 3CO_2$
(2) $Fe_2O_3 + CO \rightarrow 2FeO + CO_2$
(3) $FeO + C \rightarrow Fe + CO$

Reaction (1) is exothermic and reversible, and begins at about 700 K; by Le Chatelier's Principle, more iron is produced higher up the furnace (cooler) than below (hotter). In the hotter region (around 900 K), reaction (2) occurs irreversibly and the iron(II) oxide formed is reduced by the coke [reaction (3)] further down. The limestone forms calcium oxide which fuses with earthy material in the ore to give a slag of calcium silicate; this floats on the molten iron (which falls to the bottom of the furnace) and can be run off at intervals. The iron is run off and solidifed as 'pigs' — boat-shaped pieces about 40 cm long.

Pig-iron or cast iron contains impurities, chiefly carbon (up to 5 per cent), free or combined as iron carbides. These impurities, some of which form interstitial compounds (p. 324) with the iron, make it hard and brittle, and it melts fairly sharply at temperatures between 1400 and 1500 K; pure iron becomes soft before it melts (at 1812 K). Hence cast iron cannot be forged or welded.

When iron is refined, the process is essentially one of melting the iron in presence of materials which will react with the impurities — for example air (or oxygen) to remove chiefly carbon, and calcium oxide (added as carbonate) to remove phosphorus. There are a variety of refining processes, each depending on the composition of the initial iron and the sort of iron or steel destined as the end product. *Steels* have a carbon content of 0.1—1.5 per cent, and addition of other transition metals imparts certain properties (for example a little manganese, elasticity and high tensile strength; more manganese, great hardness; chromium, resistance to chemical attack, as in stainless steel; nickel, a reduced expansivity; tungsten and vanadium, hardness retained at high temperatures).

Pure iron is prepared by reduction of iron(II) oxide with hydrogen, or by electrolysis of an iron(II)-containing aqueous solution. It is a fairly soft metal, existing in different form according to temperature:

α-iron	$\xrightleftharpoons{1041\ K}$	β-iron	$\xrightleftharpoons{1179\ K}$	γ-iron	$\xrightleftharpoons{1674\ K}$	δ-iron
('ferrite')	(Curie	non-		face-		body-
ferro-	point)	magnetic		centred		centred
magnetic				cubic		cubic
body-centred	→	no change				
cubic lattice		of struc-				
		ture				

(It should be noted that the magnetic properties of iron are dependent on purity of the iron and the nature of any impurities.)

Iron combines with most non-metals on heating, and forms the oxides Fe_2O_3 and (mainly) Fe_3O_4 when heated in air above 430 K. Steam above 800 K produces the oxide Fe_3O_4 and hydrogen. Iron dissolves in most dilute acids, giving iron(II) solutions, i.e.

$$Fe + 2H^+(aq) \rightarrow Fe^{2+}(aq) + H_2$$

This follows from the $E^{\ominus}$ value for the half-reaction

$$Fe^{2+}(aq) + 2e^- \rightarrow Fe(s) \qquad E^{\ominus} = -0.44 \text{ V}$$

(The impurities in ordinary iron assist dissolution in acid, and are responsible for the characteristic smell of the hydrogen from this source.) In dilute nitric acid, ammonium nitrate is formed:

$$4Fe + 10H^+ + NO_3^- \rightarrow 4Fe^{2+} + NH_4^+ + 3H_2O$$

Concentrated nitric acid renders the metal 'passive', i.e. chemically unreactive, owing to formation of a thin oxide surface film (which can be removed by scratching or heating in hydrogen).

Iron is a good reducing agent (see the $E^{\ominus}$ value just given); it reduces some cations to the metal (for example copper) in aqueous solution, giving iron(II).

Iron adsorbs hydrogen readily and is a hydrogenation catalyst. In Mendeléef's form of the periodic table, iron (together with cobalt and nickel) was placed in Group VIII and the three elements together were called 'a transitional triad'. Hence there was no resemblance to any of the elements in the main Groups I—VII; these triad elements have properties which are similar, and which show some resemblances to the earlier transition metal properties. However, unlike manganese and the preceding transition elements, iron does not show the maximum possible oxidation state $+8$ corresponding to the removal of all its eight outer electrons ($3d^6 4s^2$): the actual maximum oxidation state is $+6$, but oxidation states above $+3$ are not very important, and $+3$ and $+2$ are the predominant and important states for iron. (Cobalt and nickel similarly do not show high oxidation states.)

Oxidation states above +3

As might be expected, these higher oxidation states are found almost exclusively in anionic form, and are produced only under strongly oxidizing conditions.

Alkali metal ferrates(VI), for example K_2FeO_4, are obtained by oxidation of a suspension of hydrous iron(III) oxide [assumed to be $Fe(OH)_3$ in the equation below] by chlorate(I) in concentrated alkali:

$$2Fe(OH)_3 + 3ClO^- + 4OH^- \rightarrow 2FeO_4^{2-} + 3Cl^- + 5H_2O$$

The deep red FeO_4^{2-} is stable only in alkali; in acid, iron(III) is produced:

$$2FeO_4^{2-} + 10H^+ \rightarrow 2Fe^{3+}(aq) + 5H_2O + \tfrac{3}{2}O_2$$

Ferrate(VI) has powerful oxidizing properties; for example ammonia is oxidized to nitrogen. Potassium ferrate(VI) is isomorphous with potassium chromate(VI), and both anions are tetrahedral.

Decomposition of potassium ferrate(VI) at 1000 K gives a ferrate(V), K_3FeO_4, and several types of ferrate(IV), for example FeO_3^{2-}, FeO_4^{4-} are known; these ferrates(IV) have no solution chemistry and are probably best regarded as mixed oxides, since the FeO_4^{4-} ion has no identifiable structure.

Oxidation state +3

In this state, iron has five d electrons, but does not show any strong resemblance to manganese(II), except that most iron(III) compounds show high paramagnetism, i.e. the electrons remain unpaired.

Iron(III) *chloride*. This is a black, essentially covalent solid, in which each iron atom is surrounded octahedrally by six chlorine atoms. It is prepared by direct combination of iron with chlorine or by dehydration of the hydrated chloride, by one of the methods given on p. 299.

When the anhydrous solid is heated, it vaporizes to form first Fe_2Cl_6 molecules, then the monomer $FeCl_3$ and finally $FeCl_2$ and chlorine. It fumes in air (with hydrolysis) and dissolves readily in water to give a yellow (dilute) or brown (concentrated) solution, which is strongly acidic. Crystallization gives the yellow hydrate $FeCl_3.6H_2O$ which has the structure $[FeCl_2(H_2O)_4]Cl.2H_2O$, i.e. contains the octahedral complex ion $[FeCl_2(H_2O)_4]^+$; ions of this general type are responsible for the colours of the aqueous solution of iron(III) chloride. In the presence of excess of chloride ion, both tetrahedral $[FeCl_4]^-$ and octahedral $[FeCl_6]^{3-}$ can be formed.

Iron(III) chloride forms numerous addition compounds, especially with organic molecules which contain donor atoms, for example ethers, alcohols, aldehydes, ketones and amines. Anhydrous iron(III) chloride is soluble in, for example, ether, and can be extracted into this solvent from water; the extraction is more effective in presence of chloride ion. Of other iron(III) halides, iron(III) bromide and iron(III) iodide decompose rather readily into the $+2$ halide and halogen.

Iron(III) *oxides and hydroxide*. If an aqueous solution of an iron(III) salt is treated with alkali, a red-brown precipitate of 'iron(III) hydroxide' is obtained; this is probably best represented as $FeO(OH)$. On strong heating it gives the red oxide Fe_2O_3. *Iron*(III) *oxide*, Fe_2O_3, occurs naturally as haematite, and can also be prepared by strong heating of iron(II) sulphate:

$$2FeSO_4 \rightarrow Fe_2O_3 + SO_2 + SO_3$$

It shows some amphoteric behaviour, since it dissolves in alkali (concentrated aqueous or fused) to give a ferrate(III); the equation may be written as

$$Fe_2O_3 + 2OH^- \rightleftharpoons 2FeO_2^- + H_2O$$

Iron(II) oxide exists in two forms, the red α-form (paramagnetic) and the γ-form (ferromagnetic) obtained by careful heating of 'FeO(OH)'. The α-form is used as a red pigment, as a metal polish ('jeweller's rouge') and as a catalyst.

The mixed oxide Fe_3O_4 (*tri-iron tetroxide*) is a black solid, which occurs naturally as magnetite; it is formed when iron(III) oxide is strongly heated, and its structure is effectively made up of oxide (O^{2-}) and iron(II) and iron(III) ions.

Iron(III) very readily forms complexes, which are commonly 6-coordinate and octahedral. The pale violet hexaaqua-ion $[Fe(H_2O)_6]^{3+}$ is only found as such in a few solid hydrated salts (or in their acidified solutions), for example $Fe_2(SO_4)_3.9H_2O$, $Fe(ClO_4)_3.10H_2O$. In many other salts, the anion may form a complex with the iron(III) and produce a consequent colour change, for example iron(III) chloride hydrate or solution, p. 345. Stable anionic complexes are formed with a number of ions, for example with ethanedioate (oxalate), $C_2O_4^{2-}$, and cyanide. The redox potential of the iron(II)–iron(III) system is altered by complex formation with each of these ligands; indeed, the hexacyanoferrate(III) ion, $[Fe(CN)_6]^{3-}$, is most readily obtained by oxidation of the corresponding iron(II) complex, because

$$[Fe(H_2O)_6]^{3+} + e^- \xrightarrow{\text{acid}} [Fe(H_2O)_6]^{2+} \qquad E^\ominus = +0.77 \text{ V}$$

$$[Fe(CN)_6]^{3-} + e^- \xrightarrow{\text{acid}} [Fe(CN)_6]^{4-} \qquad E^\ominus = +0.36 \text{ V}$$

The thiocyanate ion SCN^- forms an intensely red-coloured complex (most simply represented as $[Fe(SCN)(H_2O)_5]^{2+}$) which is a test for iron(III). However, unlike cobalt(III), iron(III) does not form stable hexaammines in aqueous solution, although salts containing the ion $[Fe(NH_3)_6]^{3+}$ can be obtained by dissolving anhydrous iron(III) salts in liquid ammonia.

Oxidation state +2
In this oxidation state, iron is quite readily oxidized by mild oxidizing agents, and hence in many of the reactions it is a mild reducing agent. For acid conditions

$$Fe^{3+}(aq) + e^- \rightarrow Fe^{2+}(aq) \qquad E^\ominus = +0.77 \text{ V}$$

and hence air (oxygen) will be expected to oxidize the +2 to the +3 state. In practice, this process is usually slow, but more powerful oxidizing agents [e.g. manganate(VII) ion, dichromate(VI) ion, hydrogen peroxide] act more rapidly and quantitatively. However this applies strictly only to the green hexaaqua-ion $[Fe(H_2O)_6]^{2+}$; a change to higher pH, i.e. to more alkaline conditions, changes the +2 species finally to insoluble 'Fe(OH)$_2$' (or hydrated oxide): for this

$$Fe(OH)_3 + e^- \rightarrow Fe(OH)_2 + OH^-(aq) \qquad E^\ominus = -0.56 \text{ V}$$

and hence the reducing power is greatly increased, and 'Fe(OH)$_2$' (white when pure) is rapidly oxidized by air. Again, replacement of the water ligands of $[Fe(H_2O)_6]^{2+}$ by other ligands will alter the value of $E^\ominus$ (*see* p. 347).

The halides. The anhydrous halides FeX_2 are pale-coloured solids ($FeCl_2$ is yellow) with very high melting points. The chloride can be obtained by heating the metal in a stream of dry hydrogen chloride; it shows some solubility in organic liquids and may be a partly covalent solid. However, all the halides are deliquescent, and very readily form *hydrates*. Thus iron(II) chloride forms $FeCl_2.4H_2O$ and $FeCl_2.6H_2O$ (both green); in the latter, there are neutral complexes $[FeCl_2(H_2O)_4]$.

The oxides. Iron(II) oxide FeO is prepared by heating iron(II) ethanedioate (oxalate) *in vacuo*:

$$FeC_2O_4 \rightarrow FeO + CO + CO_2$$

It is a black powder, often pyrophoric, and is non-stoichiometric, the formula

$Fe_{0.95}O$ more correctly representing its average composition.

The 'hydroxide, $Fe(OH)_2$' has been referred to above.

Other important compounds. Other iron(II) salts include, notably, the green *sulphate heptahydrate* $FeSO_4.7H_2O$ which on heating yields first the white anhydrous salt $FeSO_4$ and then decomposes:

$$2FeSO_4 \rightarrow Fe_2O_3 + SO_2 + SO_3$$

Double salts of general formula $M_2^1SO_4.FeSO_4.6H_2O$ (M = alkali metal or ammonium) can be obtained by crystallization of solutions containing the appropriate proportions of the two simple salts; an acid solution of the salt with M = NH_4 (Mohr's salt, 'ferrous ammonium sulphate') is much less quickly oxidized by air than is the simple iron(II) sulphate solution, and hence is used in volumetric analysis. *Iron*(II) *sulphide*, FeS can be prepared by heating the elements together, or by precipitation from an iron(II) solution by sulphide ion; it is a black solid which is non-stoichiometric, like the oxide. The yellow sulphide FeS_2 (made up essentially of Fe^{2+} and S_2^{2-} ions) occurs naturally as *pyrites*.

Complexes. As with the $+3$ state, iron(II) forms a variety of complexes which are usually 6-coordinate and octahedral. Replacement of the water ligands in green $[Fe(H_2O)_6]^{2+}$ (itself an octahedral complex) by ammonia molecules is incomplete in aqueous ammonia, but reaction of the anhydrous chloride with gaseous or liquid ammonia gives the complex $[Fe(NH_3)_6]Cl_2$. The water ligands are more easily replaced by cyanide ions to give the hexacyanoferrate(II) ion, $[Fe(CN)_6]^{4-}$. Many salts of this ion are known, for example the soluble yellow hydrate $K_4[Fe(CN)_6].3H_2O$, and the insoluble brown copper(II) salt $Cu_2[Fe(CN)_6]$ once much used as a semipermeable membrane in osmotic pressure determinations. The reaction between aqueous Fe^{3+} ions and $[Fe(CN)_6]^{4-}$ yields an intense blue precipitate, *Prussian blue*, which is iron(III) hexacyanoferrate(II), $Fe_4[Fe(CN)_6]_3$; the same material, called *Turnbull's blue*, is obtained by addition of Fe^{2+}(aq) ions to $[Fe(CN)_6]^{3-}$ ions. The intense colour of this compound is due to charge-transfer (p. 52). The formation of $[Fe(CN)_6]^{4-}$ ions causes the iron(II) to change its properties (for example it is not precipitated as the hydroxide with alkali or as the sulphide with S^{2-} ions); it is more readily oxidized to the $+3$ state, since

$$[Fe(CN)_6]^{3-}(aq) + e^- \rightarrow [Fe(CN)_6]^{4-}(aq) \qquad E^\ominus = +0.36 \text{ V}$$

When concentrated sulphuric acid is added to a nitrate in the presence of aqueous iron(II) sulphate, the nitrogen monoxide liberated forms a brown complex $[Fe(H_2O)_5NO]^{2+}$ which appears as a 'brown ring' at the acid–aqueous interface (test for a nitrate, p. 215).

Perhaps the most important complex of iron(II) is *heme* (or *haeme*). Haemoglobin, the iron-containing constituent of the blood consists essentially of a protein, globin, attached through a nitrogen atom at one coordination position of an octahedral complex of iron(II). Of the other five coordination positions, four (in a plane) are occupied by nitrogen atoms, each of which is part of an organic ring system — the whole system is a

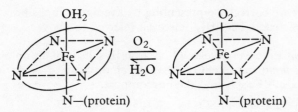

Figure 13.7 Schematic representation of haem; the porphin rings are not shown

porphin. The sixth position (*Figure 13.7*) is occupied either by an oxygen molecule *or* a water molecule, and here reversible oxygen uptake can occur, as shown, thereby enabling oxygen to be transported from one part of the body to another. Coordination of a ligand CN^- or CO instead of water prevents this process, and the toxicity of cyanide or carbon monoxide is, in part, due to this fact.

Low oxidation states
Iron forms the carbonyls $Fe(CO)_5$, $Fe_2(CO)_9$ and $Fe_3(CO)_{12}$. In iron pentacarbonyl, the iron(0) is 5-coordinated, as shown in *Figure 13.8* to give a trigonal bipyramid; the substance is volatile and covalent. Donation of an electron pair by each CO ligand gives the iron the configuration of the next noble gas and the ion $[Fe(CO)_4]^{2-}$ and some halides $Fe(CO)_4X_2(X = Cl, Br, I)$ are known, the carbonyl halides being octahedral.

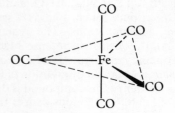

Figure 13.8 Structure of iron(0) pentacarbonyl

13.10.2   The rusting of iron

This is the most important reaction of iron from an economic point of view; essentially, rusting is the formation of hydrated iron(III) oxide in the presence of oxygen and water. The process is essentially electrolytic. Defects in the iron lattice caused by strain or the presence of impurities produce areas with differing electrode potentials, i.e. the metal is no longer under standard conditions, and a cell is produced. In the presence of an electrolyte the cells become active and a current flows through the iron. The cell is shown diagrammatically in *Figure 13.9*.

In the anodic areas iron goes into solution:

$$Fe \rightarrow Fe^{2+}(aq) + 2e^-$$

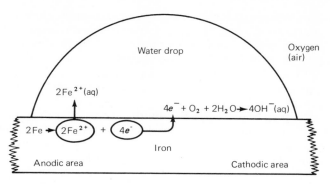

Figure 13.9 Rusting of iron in contact with a drop of water

whilst oxygen is reduced in cathodic areas:

$$O_2 + 2H_2O + 4e^- \rightarrow 4OH^-(aq)$$

Clearly then, if either water or oxygen is absent, corrosion cannot occur. The presence of an electrolyte, which imparts conductivity to the solution, increases the rate of corrosion.

The existence of anode and cathode areas can be seen by the following experiment. A few drops of phenolphthalein are added to a solution of potassium hexacyanoferrate(III) and hydrochloric acid added, drop by drop, until the solution is colourless. [The phenolphthalein turns pink owing to hydrolysis of the potassium hexacyanoferrate(III).] Drops of this solution, about 1 cm in diameter, are now placed on a sheet of freshly abraded steel, pink cathode areas and blue anode areas appear.

Corrosion problems are particularly important when two metals are in contact. The more reactive metal becomes the cathode of the cell and goes into solution when the cell is activated by an electrolyte. A typical cell is shown in *Figure 13.10*. When the metal in contact with iron is more reactive than iron itself, the iron is protected from corrosion. This is important when

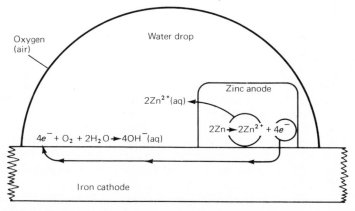

Figure 13.10 Corrosion of iron in contact with zinc and a drop of water

mechanical strength depends on iron, for example in a motor car. However, if iron is in contact with a less reactive metal the iron corrodes. This problem is encountered when a 'tin can' is scratched. If it is necessary to join iron to a less reactive metal, to prevent corrosion of the iron, a sacrificial anode must be added. Thus, for example, large pieces of magnesium are bolted to ships to prevent corrosion of the iron propeller shaft which is bolted to a brass propeller.

Rusting can be prevented by painting or coating with a continuous layer of another metal which does not itself corrode rapidly, for example zinc or tin. More recently, steel has been coated with plastics by electrophoretic decomposition from an emulsion of the plastic.

13.10.3 Tests for iron

Some reactions of iron(II) and iron(III) ions in aqueous solution are given in *Table 13.8*.

Table 13.8 Reactions of iron(II) and iron(III) ions

Reagent	Iron(II)	Iron(III)
Ammonia or sodium hydroxide (hydroxyl ions)	Green precipitate turns brown on exposure to air	Red-brown precipitate
Potassium hexacyano-ferrate(II), $K_4Fe(CN)_6$	White precipitate, rapidly turning blue	Prussian blue precipitate
Potassium hexacyano-ferrate(III), $K_3Fe(CN)_6$	Dark blue precipitate (Turnbull's blue)	Reddish-brown coloration (no precipitate)
Potassium thiocyanate, KCNS	No coloration*	Blood red coloration

*This test is extremely sensitive and usually sufficient ferric ions are present in an iron(II) salt to give some coloration. The blood red colour appears to be due to a complex.

13.11 Cobalt

13.11.1 The element

Cobalt compounds have been in use for centuries, notably as pigments ('cobalt blue') in glass and porcelain (a double silicate of cobalt and potassium); the metal itself has been produced on an industrial scale only during the twentieth century. Cobalt is relatively uncommon but widely distributed; it occurs biologically in vitamin B_{12}, a complex of cobalt(III) in which the cobalt is bonded octahedrally (compare haem, p. 348). In its ores, it is usually in combination with sulphur or arsenic, and other metals, notably copper and silver, are often present. Extraction is carried out by a process essentially similar to that used for iron, but is complicated because of the need to remove arsenic and other metals.

Cobalt is a bluish silvery metal, exhibits ferromagnetism, and can exist in more than one crystal form; it is used in alloys for special purposes.

Chemically it is somewhat similar to iron; when heated in air it gives the oxides Co_3O_4 and CoO, but it is less readily attacked by dilute acids. With halogens, the cobalt(II) halides are formed, except that with fluorine cobalt(III) fluoride, CoF_3, is obtained.

Like iron and the next transition element, nickel, cobalt is not generally found in any oxidation state above $+3$, and this and $+2$ are the usual states. The *simple* compounds of cobalt(III) are strongly oxidizing:

$$[Co(H_2O)_6]^{3+} + e^- \rightarrow [Co(H_2O)_6]^{2+} \qquad E^{\ominus} = +1.81\ V$$

and hence the simple cobalt(III) cation cannot exist in aqueous solution (which it would oxidize to oxygen). However, the chemistry of cobalt is notable for the ease with which complexes are formed, and for the big effect which complex formation has on the relative stabilities of the $+2$ and $+3$ states. Historically, this was observed as early as 1798; Tassaert observed that an ammoniacal solution of a cobalt(II) salt changed colour on exposure to air, and some years later it was shown that, if cobalt(II) chloride was oxidized in presence of ammonia, the yellow product had the formula $CoCl_3.6NH_3$, a formula which posed a valency problem to the chemists of that time. Alfred Werner, in the period 1890—1913 (he was awarded the Nobel Prize for chemistry in 1913), was primarily concerned with elucidating the nature of 'CoCl$_3$.6NH$_3$' and similar compounds; his investigations (carried out in the absence of the structural methods available to us today) showed conclusively that the compound was a complex $[Co(NH_3)_6]Cl_3$, hexaamminecobalt(III) chloride, which has the octahedral structure shown in *Figure 13.11*, and Werner pioneered the study of coordination compounds. We shall consider a few of the reactions investigated by Werner later in this chapter.

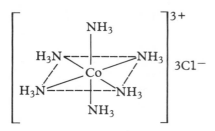

Figure 13.11 Octahedral structure of hexaamminecobalt(III) chloride

13.11.2   Compounds of cobalt

Oxidation state $+3$

As already noted, the simple salts in this oxidation state are powerful oxidizing agents and oxidize water. Since, also, Co(III) would oxidize any halide except fluoride to halogen, the only simple halide salt is CoF_3, *cobalt(III) fluoride*, obtained by reaction of fluorine with cobalt(II) fluoride; it is a useful fluorinating agent.

Cobalt(III) oxide is obtained as a brown precipitate Co_2O_3.aq when cobalt(II) hydroxide is oxidized in alkaline conditions [or when a cobalt(III) compound is decomposed by aqueous alkali]. On heating it gives the black mixed oxide Co_3O_4.

Hydrated cobalt(III) *sulphate*, $Co_2(SO_4)_3.18H_2O$ is obtained when cobalt(II) sulphate is oxidized electrolytically in moderately concentrated sulphuric acid solution; it is stable when dry but liberates oxygen from water. Some alums, for example $KCo(SO_4)_2.12H_2O$ can be obtained by crystallization from sulphuric acid solutions. In these and the sulphate, the cation $[Co(H_2O)_6]^{3+}$ may exist; it is both acidic and strongly oxidizing.

Cobalt(III) *nitrate*, $Co(NO_3)_3$ has been prepared by the reaction of dinitrogen pentoxide with cobalt(III) fluoride.

Complexes. Cobalt(III) contains six $3d$ electrons; in the presence of six appropriate ligands, arranged octahedrally, a large splitting of the d orbitals occurs, and all these electrons are paired in a more stable energy level (p. 322). Such an arrangement is stable with respect to oxidation or reduction. 'Appropriate' ligands are those containing a nitrogen donor atom, for example ammonia NH_3, cyanide CN^- and nitro NO_2^-, and cobalt has a strong affinity for all these. Thus if cobalt(II) chloride is oxidized by air in presence of ammonia, with ammonium chloride added to provide the required anion, the orange *hexaamminecobalt*(III) *chloride* is precipitated:

$$4[Co(H_2O)_6]Cl_2 + 4NH_4Cl + 20NH_3 + O_2 \rightarrow 4[Co(NH_3)_6]Cl_3 + 26H_2O$$

For this reaction, charcoal is a catalyst; if this is omitted and hydrogen peroxide is used as the oxidant, a red *aquapentaamminecobalt*(III) *chloride*, $[Co(NH_3)_5H_2O]Cl_3$, is formed and treatment of this with concentrated hydrochloric acid gives the red *chloropentaamminecobalt*(III) *chloride*, $[Co(NH_3)_5Cl]Cl_2$. In the last two compounds, one ammonia ligand is replaced by one water molecule or one chloride ion; it is a peculiarity of cobalt that these replacements are so easy and the pure products so readily isolated. In the examples quoted, the complex cobalt(III) state is easily obtained by oxidation of cobalt(II) in presence of ammonia, since

$$[Co(NH_3)_6]^{3+}(aq) + e^- \rightarrow [Co(NH_3)_6]^{2-}(aq) \qquad E^{\ominus} = +0.1 \text{ V}$$

Cobalt(II) is also easily oxidized in the presence of the nitrite ion NO_2^- as ligand. Thus, if excess of sodium nitrite is added to a cobalt(II) salt in presence of ethanoic acid (a strong acid would decompose the nitrite, p. 215), the following reaction occurs:

$$Co^{2+}(aq) + 7NO_2^- + 2H^+ \rightarrow NO + H_2O + [Co(NO_2)_6]^{3-}$$

Here, effectively, the Co^{2+}(aq) is being oxidized by the nitrite ion and the latter (in excess) is simultaneously acting as a ligand to form the hexanitrocobaltate(III) anion. In presence of cyanide ion CN^-, cobalt(II) salts actually reduce water to hydrogen since

$$[Co(CN)_6]^{3-}(aq) + e^- \rightarrow [Co(CN)_5(H_2O)]^{3-}(aq) + CN^- \qquad E^{\ominus} = -0.8 \text{ V}$$

Oxidation state +2

Salts. In some respects these salts resemble those of iron; the aqua-cation $[Co(H_2O)_6]^{2+}$ (pink) occurs in solution and in some solid salts, for example $CoSO_4.7H_2O$ (cf. $FeSO_4.7H_2O$). However, this aqua-cation is less strongly reducing than $[Fe(H_2O)_6]^{2+}$, and the water ligands are more readily replaced by other ligands than for iron(II) (*see* below). $[Co(H_2O)_6]^{2+}$ is only slightly acid and a normal, hydrated carbonate $CoCO_3.6H_2O$ can be precipitated by addition of carbonate ion to a simple cobalt(II) salt, provided that an atmosphere of carbon dioxide is maintained over the solution.

Cobalt(II) *halides* can be obtained by direct combination of the elements, or by dehydration of their hydrates. Anhydrous cobalt(II) chloride is blue, and the solid contains octahedrally coordinated cobalt; the hydrated salt $CoCl_2.6H_2O$ is pink, with each cobalt surrounded by four water molecules and two chloride ions in a distorted octahedron.

Cobalt(II) *hydroxide* is obtained as a precipitate when hydroxide ion is added to a solution containing cobalt(II) ions. The precipitate is often blue, but becomes pink on standing; it dissolves in excess of alkali to give the blue $[Co(OH)_4]^{2-}$ ion, and in slightly alkaline solution is easily oxidized by air to a brown solid of composition $Co^{III}O(OH)$.

Cobalt(II) *sulphide* is precipitated as a black solid by addition of sulphide ion to a solution of a cobalt(II) salt, in alkaline solution.

Complexes. These are of two general kinds: octahedral, pink complexes and tetrahedral, blue complexes. If cobalt(II) chloride is dissolved in aqueous solution, the predominant species is the hexaaqua-ion $[Co(H_2O)_6]^{2+}$ (pink). If this solution is heated, it becomes blue, and the same effect is observed if chloride ion is added in excess. This colour change is associated with the change

$$[Co(H_2O)_6]^{2+} \underset{\underset{H_2O}{\longleftarrow}}{\overset{Cl^-}{\underset{\text{or heat}}{\longrightarrow}}} [CoCl_4]^{2-}$$

pink, octahedral   blue, tetrahedral

but ions intermediate between these two species can also exist in the solution. None of these species can be oxidized to cobalt(III) in aqueous solution; but if ammonia is added to the pink solution containing the hexaaqua-ion, the water ligands are displaced by ammonia and the hexaammine ion $[Co(NH_3)_6]^{2+}$ is formed; this is easily oxidized to the $+3$ state. A large number of other cobalt(II) complexes, cationic, neutral and anionic, are known.

Lower oxidation states

Cobalt has an odd number of electrons, and does not form a *simple* carbonyl in oxidation state 0. However, carbonyls of formulae $Co_2(CO)_8$, $Co_4(CO)_{12}$ and $Co_6(CO)_{16}$ are known; reduction of these by an alkali metal dissolved in liquid ammonia (p. 197) gives the ion $[Co(CO)_4]^-$. Both $Co_2(CO)_8$ and $[Co(CO)_4]^-$ are important as catalysts for organic syntheses. In the so-called 'oxo' reaction, where an alkene reacts with carbon monoxide and hydrogen, under pressure, to give an aldehyde, dicobalt octacarbonyl is used as catalyst:

$$\text{C=C} \quad + \quad \text{CO} \quad + \quad \text{H}_2 \quad \xrightarrow[\substack{400\,\text{K} \\ 100\,\text{atm}}]{\text{Co}_2(\text{CO})_8} \quad \text{C-C}$$

alkene   aldehyde

13.11.3 Tests for cobalt

For a cobalt(II) salt, the precipitation of the blue→pink cobalt(II) hydroxide by alkali, or precipitation of black cobalt(II) sulphide by hydrogen sulphide provide useful tests; the hydroxide is soluble in excess of alkali and is oxidized by air to the brown 'CoO(OH)'.

Addition of excess of potassium nitrite acidified with ethanoic acid gives a precipitate of the potassium hexanitrocobaltate(III), $K_3[Co(NO_2)_6]$ (p. 352).

Decomposition of most cobalt(III) complexes by boiling with alkali gives a brown precipitate of the hydrated oxide Co_2O_3.aq (p. 351). This will quantitatively oxidize iodide to iodine.

13.12 Nickel

13.12.1 The element

Nickel occurs more abundantly than cobalt but only a few deposits are economically useful for extraction. The metal is obtained by heating with sulphur compounds to give the sulphide, which is roasted to form the oxide; the latter may be reduced directly by heating with coke or dissolved to give a solution containing nickel(II) from which the nickel can be deposited electrolytically. The metal obtained by reduction can be purified by the Mond process, in which it is heated to 320 K with carbon monoxide to give the pure, volatile tetracarbonyl $Ni(CO)_4$; the latter when heated to 500 K gives the pure metal and carbon monoxide is recovered:

$$Ni + 4CO \rightleftharpoons Ni(CO)_4$$

Nickel is a moderately lustrous, silvery metal, and is extensively used in alloys (for example coinage, stainless steel) and for plating where a durable resistant surface is required. It is also used as an industrial catalyst, for example in the hydrogenation of unsaturated organic compounds. It is slowly attacked by dilute aqueous acids but not by alkalis; it combines readily with many non-metals on heating.

In the chemistry of nickel, we observe the continuing tendency for the higher oxidation states to decrease in stability along the first transition series; unlike cobalt and iron, the +3 state is rare and relatively unimportant for nickel and the +2 state is the only important one.

13.12.1   Compounds of nickel

Oxidation state +2

Nickel forms yellow anhydrous halides NiX_2 (X = F, Cl, Br) and a black iodide NiI_2: all these halides are made by direct combination of the elements, and the chloride by reaction of sulphur dichloride oxide with the hydrated salt. All dissolve in water to give green solutions from which the hydrates can be crystallized; the solutions contain the ion $[Ni(H_2O)_6]^{2+}$, and the chloride crystallizes as $NiCl_2.6H_2O$, nickel(II) chloride hexahydrate.

Addition of an alkali metal hydroxide solution to an aqueous solution of a nickel(II) salt precipitates a finely-divided green powder, *nickel(II) hydroxide* $Ni(OH)_2$; on heating this gives the black *oxide*, NiO, which is also obtained by heating nickel(II) carbonate or the hydrated nitrate. Black nickel(II) sulphide, NiS, is obtained by passing hydrogen sulphide into a solution of a nickel(II) salt.

Nickel forms a green hydrated sulphate $NiSO_4.7H_2O$ and the double sulphate $(NH_4)_2SO_4.NiSO_4.6H_2O$ (cf. iron, p. 347).

Complexes. Nickel(II) forms a great variety of complexes, in which there may be either six ligands (octahedral or distorted octahedral), five ligands (square pyramidal or trigonal biprism) or four (tetrahedral or square planar), and which may be cationic, neutral or anionic. The simple hydrated cation $[Ni(H_2O)_6]^{2+}$ is octahedral; addition of concentrated aqueous ammonia in excess to an aqueous solution of a nickel(II) salt gives the purple octahedral complex $[Ni(NH_3)_6]^{2+}$ by replacement of the water ligands; this forms sparingly soluble salts with some anions, for example Br^-. The scarlet-coloured complex formed when butanedione dioxime (formerly called dimethylglyoxime) is added to a nickel(II) solution is a neutral *planar* complex:

$$CH_3-C=NOH \atop CH_3-C=NOH \;\; + \; Ni^{2+} \;\rightarrow$$

scarlet
(....are hydrogen bonds)

If nickel(II) cyanide, $Ni(CN)_2$, is dissolved in excess of potassium cyanide, the orange-red complex salt $K_2Ni(CN)_4.H_2O$ can be crystallized out; this contains the stable square-planar $[Ni(CN)_4]^{2-}$ anion [cf. $(NiCl_4)^{2-}$ (tetrahedral)].

Low oxidation states

Nickel tetracarbonyl $Ni(CO)_4$ was the first metal carbonyl to be discovered, by Mond in 1890; it is obtained by passage of carbon monoxide over nickel metal heated to 320 K. It is a volatile, toxic liquid (b.p. 315 K), and has a tetrahedral structure. It has considerable stability, but inflames in air; it is believed that in the structure there is some double bonding between the nickel and carbon atoms, as shown in *Figure 13.12*.

If the $+2$ complex $K_2[Ni(CN)_4]$ (*see* p. 355) is dissolved in liquid ammonia, addition of potassium produces the yellow $K_4[Ni(CN)_4]$; the

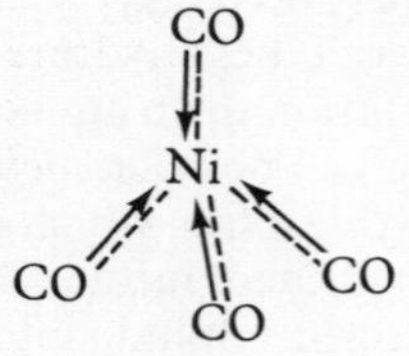

Figure 13.12 Tetracarbonylnickel(0)

$[Ni(CN)_4]^{4-}$ ion has nickel in oxidation state 0, is isoelectronic with $Ni(CO)_4$, and is believed to be tetrahedral.

13.12.3   Tests for nickel

The reactions of aqueous solutions of nickel(II) salts with hydroxide ions, with excess of ammonia, with sulphide ion and with butanedione dioxime (*see* above) all provide useful tests for nickel(II) ions.

13.13   Copper

13.13.1   The element

Copper has been used, especially in alloys with tin (bronze), since about 3000 B.C., and the Romans used it extensively. Small amounts of the free metal are found naturally, but its compounds (mostly sulphides) are abundant; the most important ore is *chalcopyrite* or *copper pyrites* CuFeS. Other natural forms include the basic carbonates $CuCO_3.Cu(OH)_2$ (*malachite*) and $2CuCO_3.Cu(OH)_2$ (*azurite*). The process of extraction consists essentially of (a) separation of the ore from rock, by flotation (selective wetting), (b) conversion of the sulphide ore into the crude metal, by blowing air through the molten ore, (c) purification of the crude metal, usually by electrolysis; the crude copper is the anode in an electrolyte of acidified aqueous copper(II) sulphate, and the pure metal deposits on 'starting' sheets of copper as cathode. The metal is extensively used for electrical purposes, for water tanks and pipes, and for roofing. Alloys include the *bronzes* containing tin, and sometimes phosphorus (for hardness–phosphor-bronze); *brass*, containing zinc and *cupro-nickel* (for coinage). Compounds of copper are used as fungicides, and as catalysts. Copper has importance in living systems; some lower animals (for example snails and crabs) utilize a copper-protein complex called *hemocyanin*, as an oxygen carrier, analogous to haemoglobin in mammals.

Copper differs in its chemistry from the earlier members of the first transition series. The outer electronic configuration $3d^{10}4s^1$ contains a completely-filled set of d-orbitals and, as expected, copper forms compounds where it has the oxidation state $+1$, losing the outer $(4s)$ electron and retaining all the $3d$ electrons. However, like the transition metals preceding it, it also shows the oxidation state $+2$; oxidation states other than $+1$ and $+2$ are unimportant.

The metal melts at 1356 K and oxidizes at red heat in air to give the black $+2$ oxide CuO; at higher temperatures the red-yellow $+1$ oxide Cu_2O is obtained. In dry air, little corrosion occurs, but in the ordinary atmosphere a green film slowly forms, and this protects the metal from further corrosion (hence its use in roofing). The composition of the green film varies; normally it is a basic carbonate of copper, but near the sea basic chloride is also a component and in industrial areas a basic sulphate is found. Copper is readily attacked by halogens and by sulphur on heating. Since

$$Cu^{2+}(aq) + 2e^- \rightarrow Cu(s) \qquad E^\ominus = +0.34 \text{ V}$$

copper is not attacked by water or by dilute non-oxidizing acids to give hydrogen. It is attacked by nitric acid, to give a solution of copper(II) nitrate $Cu(NO_3)_2$ and oxides of nitrogen, the nature of the latter depending on the concentration of acid (dilute gives nitrogen monoxide, concentrated the dioxide). In concentrated sulphuric acid, some copper(II) sulphate is formed in solution, and sulphur dioxide is evolved, but other products [for example sulphur, copper(II) sulphate] may also be formed, and the reaction is unsuitable for preparative purposes.

Copper is precipitated on the surface of some metals which reduce it from an aqueous solution of its $+2$ salts, for example

$$Fe + Cu^{2+}(aq) \rightarrow Cu + Fe^{2+}(aq)$$

13.13.2 Compounds of copper

Oxidation state $+2$
In this oxidation state with nine $3d$ electrons, copper compounds are usually coloured and paramagnetic.

Copper(II) halides, CuX_2. The anhydrous fluoride CuF_2 is white, the chloride yellow and the bromide almost black; in the crystal of the chloride, each copper atom is surrounded by four chlorine atoms at the corners of a square and two chlorine atoms above and below, giving a distorted octahedral structure:

The anhydrous chloride is prepared by standard methods. It is readily soluble in water to give a blue-green solution from which the blue hydrated salt $CuCl_2.2H_2O$ can be crystallized; here, two water molecules replace two of the planar chlorine ligands in the structure given above. Addition of dilute hydrochloric acid to copper(II) hydroxide or carbonate also gives a blue-green solution of the chloride $CuCl_2$; but addition of concentrated hydrochloric acid (or any source of chloride ion) produces a yellow solution owing to formation of chloro-copper(II) complexes (*see* below).

In the presence of *excess* of iodide ions, copper(II) salts produce the white insoluble copper(I) iodide and free iodine, because copper(II) oxidizes iodide under these conditions. The redox potential for the half-reaction

$$Cu^{2+}(aq) + e^- \rightarrow Cu^+(aq) \qquad E^\ominus = +0.15 \text{ V}$$

must be modified because the concentration of the reduced species, $Cu^+(aq)$, is greatly diminished in the presence of excess of I^-:

$$Cu^+(aq) + I^-(aq) \rightleftharpoons CuI(s)$$

The half-reaction is better written as

$$Cu^{2+}(aq) + I^-(aq) + e^- \rightarrow CuI(s) \qquad E^\ominus = +0.86 \text{ V}$$

and hence iodide is readily oxidized:

$$I_2(aq) + 2e^- \rightarrow 2I^-(aq) \qquad E^\ominus = +0.54 \text{ V}$$

Bromide ion is not oxidized in this way.

Copper(II) *oxides. Copper*(II) *oxide*, CuO, is a black powder, insoluble in water; it is prepared by heating the hydroxide, or the hydrated nitrate, or the basic carbonate of copper(II). It dissolves in acids to give solutions of copper(II) salts. It is readily reduced to the metal by heating with hydrogen and is used to determine carbon and hydrogen in organic compounds [the carbon as carbon monoxide reduces the copper(II) oxide to copper].

Hydrated copper(II) *hydroxide*, $Cu(OH)_2$, is precipitated as a pale blue solid when alkali is added to an aqueous solution of a copper(II) salt:

$$\left.\begin{array}{c} [Cu(H_2O)_6]^{2+} \\ +H_2O \end{array}\right\} \xrightleftharpoons[\text{acid}]{\text{alkali}} \left\{\begin{array}{c} [Cu(OH)(H_2O)_5]^+ \\ +H_3O^+ \end{array}\right. \left.\begin{array}{c} \\ \end{array}\right\} \xrightleftharpoons[\text{acid}]{\text{alkali}} \left\{\begin{array}{c} [Cu(OH)_2(H_2O)_4] \downarrow \\ +H_3O^+ \end{array}\right.$$

It is readily dehydrated on warming, to give the black oxide CuO. It dissolves in excess of concentrated alkali to form blue hydroxocuprate(II) ions, of variable composition; it is therefore slightly amphoteric. If aqueous ammonia is used to precipitate the hydroxide, the latter dissolves in excess of ammonia to give the deep blue ammine complexes, for example $[Cu(NH_3)_4(H_2O)_2]^{2+}$.

Copper(II) *carbonate*. The 'normal' carbonate $CuCO_3$ is not known; two naturally occurring basic carbonates have already been mentioned. If a solution of, for example, sodium carbonate is added to a solution of a copper(II) salt, a green basic carbonate is precipitated; the reactions are:

$$[Cu(H_2O)_6]^{2+} + H_2O \rightleftharpoons [Cu(OH)(H_2O)_5]^+ + H_3O^+$$

$$2[Cu(OH)(H_2O)_5]^+ + CO_3^{2-} \rightarrow [Cu(OH)(H_2O)_5]_2CO_3 \text{ i.e. } CuCO_3.Cu(OH)_2aq$$

$$2H_3O^+ + CO_3^{2-} \rightarrow CO_2 + 3H_2O$$

On heating, the basic carbonate readily yields the black copper(II) oxide.

Copper(II) *sulphate.* This substance is familiar as the blue crystalline pentahydrate $CuSO_4.5H_2O$. In this crystal, each Cu^{2+} ion is surrounded by four water molecules at the corners of a square, while the fifth water molecule is held by hydrogen bonds (*see Figure 13.13*).

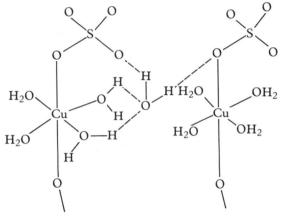

Figure 13.13 Structure of crystalline $CuSO_4.5H_2O$

When the pentahydrate is heated four molecules of water are lost fairly readily, at about 380 K and the fifth at about 600 K; the anhydrous salt then obtained is white; the Cu^{2+} ion is now surrounded by sulphate ions, but the *d* level splitting energy does not now correspond to the visible part of the spectrum, and the compound is not coloured. Copper(II) sulphate is soluble in water; the solution has a slightly acid reaction owing to formation of $[Cu(H_2O)_5OH]^+$ species. Addition of concentrated ammonia solution produces the deep blue solution already mentioned; if ethanol is then added, dark blue crystals of the ammine $CuSO_4.4NH_3.H_2O$ can be obtained; in these, the four ammonia molecules are approximately square-planar around the copper, and the water molecule is above this *plane*, forming a square pyramid. If ammonia *gas* is passed over *anhydrous* copper(II) sulphate, a violet-coloured pentaammine $CuSO_4.5NH_3$ is formed.

Copper(II) sulphate pentahydrate is made on a large scale by blowing air through a mixture of scrap copper and dilute sulphuric acid, the air acting as an oxidizing agent. It is used (in solution) as a fungicide, a wood preservative, in electroplating and in reprography.

Copper(II) *nitrate.* If copper is treated with a solution of dinitrogen tetroxide in ethyl ethanoate (acetate), a blue solution is obtained, which on evaporation gives a blue solid $Cu(NO_3)_2.N_2O_4$; this gives the blue anhydrous nitrate $Cu(NO_3)_2$ on heating. This compound is covalent; it is volatile and can readily by sublimed, to give a blue vapour containing molecules with the *geometrical* structure

Addition of water gives the hydrated nitrate $Cu(NO_3)_2.3H_2O$, the product obtained when copper (or the $+2$ oxide or carbonate) is dissolved in nitric acid. Attempts to dehydrate the hydrated nitrate, for example by gently heating *in vacuo*, yield a basic nitrate, *not* the anhydrous salt.

Copper(II) *sulphide*, CuS, is obtained as a black precipitate when hydrogen sulphide is passed into a solution of a copper(II) salt.

Complexes of copper(II)

When a copper(II) salt dissolves in water, the complex aqua-ion $[Cu(H_2O)_6]^{2+}$ is formed; this has a distorted octahedral (tetragonal) structure, with four 'near' water molecules in a square plane around the copper and two 'far' water molecules, one above and one below this plane. Addition of excess of ammonia replaces only the four planar water molecules, to give the deep blue complex $[Cu(NH_3)_4(H_2O)_2]^{2+}$ (often written as $[Cu(NH_3)_4]^{2+}$ for simplicity). To obtain $[Cu(NH_3)_6]^{2+}$, water must be absent, and an anhydrous copper(II) salt must be treated with liquid ammonia.

Addition of halide ions to aqueous copper(II) solutions can give a variety of halo-complexes; for example $[CuCl_4]^{2-}$ (yellow, square-planar, but in crystals with larger cations becomes a flattened tetrahedron); $[CuCl_3]^-$ (red, units linked together in crystals to give tetrahedral or distorted octahedral coordination around each copper).

Addition of aqueous cyanide ion to a copper(II) solution gives a brown precipitate of copper(II) cyanide, soluble in excess of cyanide to give the tetracyanocuprate(II) complex $[Cu(CN)_4]^{2-}$. However, copper(II) cyanide rapidly decomposes at room temperature, to give copper(I) cyanide and cyanogen $(CN)_2$ [cf. the similar decomposition of copper(II) iodide, p. 362]; excess of cyanide then gives the tetracyanocuprate(I) $[Cu(CN)_4]^{3-}$.

Oxidation state +1

In contrast to the $+2$ state, copper(I) compounds are less frequently coloured and are diamagnetic, as expected since the $3d$ level is full. However, the copper(I) ion, unlike copper(II), is unstable in aqueous solution where it disproportionates into copper(II) and copper(0) (i.e. copper metal).

Consider the half-reactions in aqueous solution:

$Cu^+(aq) + e^- \rightarrow Cu(s)$ $\qquad E^{\ominus} = +0.52$ V
$Cu^{2+}(aq) + e^- \rightarrow Cu^+(aq)$ $\qquad E^{\ominus} = +0.15$ V

We see that the $Cu^+(aq)$ ion (in the first equation) can oxidize the $Cu^+(aq)$ ion (in the second equation), and hence

$Cu^+(aq) + Cu^+(aq) \rightarrow Cu + Cu^{2+}(aq)$

i.e.

$2Cu^+(aq) \rightarrow Cu + Cu^{2+}(aq)$, i.e. *disproportionation*

In the presence of appropriate ligands, the $E^\ominus$ values may be affected sufficiently to make Cu(I) stable; but since the likely aqua-complex which Cu(I) would form is $[Cu(H_2O)_2]^+$, with only two water ligands, the (hypothetical) hydration energy of Cu^+ is therefore much less than that of the higher charged, more strongly aquated $[Cu(H_2O)_6]^{2+}$

Copper(I) *oxide*, Cu_2O. This occurs naturally as the red *cuprite*. It is obtained as an orange-yellow precipitate by the reduction of a copper(II) salt in alkaline solution by a mild reducing agent, for example glucose, hydroxylamine or sodium sulphite:

$2Cu^{2+} + SO_3^{2-} + 4OH^- \rightarrow Cu_2O\downarrow + SO_4^{2-} + 2H_2O$

It dissolves in oxoacids with disproportionation, for example

$Cu_2O + H_2SO_4 \rightarrow CuSO_4 + Cu\downarrow + H_2O$

Copper(I) *chloride*, CuCl. This is a white solid, insoluble in water. It is prepared as follows:
(1)   By warming either copper(I) oxide or a mixture of copper(II) chloride and copper with concentrated hydrochloric acid, until a deep brown solution is formed:

$Cu_2O + 2HCl \rightarrow 2CuCl + H_2O$

$CuCl_2 + Cu \xrightarrow{\text{HCl}} 2CuCl$

In both cases the copper(I) chloride dissolves in the acid to form the complex $[Cu^ICl_4]^{3-}$. When the brown solution is poured into water, white copper(I) chloride separates, but if air is present in the water, it rapidly turns blue owing to the formation of the copper(II) ion.
(2)   By the reduction of copper(II) chloride or a mixed solution of copper(II) sulphate and common salt by sulphur dioxide:

$2Cu^{2+} + 2Cl^- + 2H_2O + SO_2 \rightarrow SO_4^{2-} + 4H^+ + 2CuCl\downarrow$

In both cases, the precipitate must be filtered off and dried quickly, by washing first with alcohol and then with ether [to prevent formation of the copper(II) compound].

Measurements on copper(I) chloride show the vapour to be the dimer of formula Cu_2Cl_2, but determinations of relative molecular mass in certain solvents such as pyridine show it to be present in solution as single molecules, probably because coordination compounds such as py$\rightarrow$CuCl (py = pyridine) are formed.
The solid readily dissolves chemically in concentrated hydrochloric acid,

forming a complex, and in ammonia as the colourless, linear, complex cation $[H_3N \rightarrow Cu \leftarrow NH_3]^+$ (cf. AgCl) if air is absent [in the presence of air, this is oxidized to a blue ammine-copper(II) complex]. This solution of ammoniacal copper(I) chloride is a good solvent for carbon monoxide, forming an addition compound $CuCl.CO.H_2O$, and as such is used in gas analysis. On passing ethyne through the ammoniacal solution, a red-brown precipitate of hydrated copper(I) dicarbide (explosive when dry) is obtained:

$$2[Cu(NH_3)_2]^+ + HC\equiv CH \rightarrow Cu_2[C\equiv C]\downarrow + 2NH_4^+ + 2NH_3$$

Copper(I) *iodide*, CuI. This is obtained as a white precipitate on addition of potassium iodide to a solution containing copper(II):

$$2Cu^{2+} + 4I^- \rightarrow 2CuI\downarrow + I_2\downarrow$$
$$\text{white}$$

The reaction provides a method of estimating copper(II) since the liberated iodine can be titrated with sodium thiosulphate (p. 285):

$$Cu^{2+} \equiv I \equiv Na_2S_2O_3$$

Copper(I) iodide is used in the extraction of iodine (p. 280).

Copper(I) *cyanide*, CuCN [*and copper*(I) *thiocyanate*]. These are similarly obtained as white precipitates on adding cyanide and thiocyanate ions (not in excess) respectively to copper(II) salts:

$$2Cu^{2+} + 4CN^- \rightarrow 2CuCN + C_2N_2\uparrow$$
$$2Cu^{2+} + 4SCN^- \rightarrow 2CuSCN + (SCN)_2\uparrow$$

Copper(I) chloride, bromide and cyanide were used by Sandmeyer to introduce a chlorine atom, a bromine atom and a cyanide group respectively into a benzene ring by addition to the benzenediazonium salt.

Copper(I) *sulphate*, Cu_2SO_4. This is obtained as a white powder by heating together dimethyl sulphate and copper(I) oxide:

$$(CH_3)_2SO_4 + Cu_2O \rightarrow Cu_2SO_4 + (CH_3)_2O$$
$$\text{dimethyl ether}$$

This copper(I) compound, unlike the above, is soluble in water and therefore in the presence of water liberates copper and forms a copper(II) compound:

$$Cu_2SO_4 \rightarrow CuSO_4 + Cu\downarrow$$

Complexes. The complexes of copper(II) *like* those of silver(I) (p. 374), but *unlike* those of preceding transitions metals, tend to prefer a *linear* coordination of two ligands, i.e. X—Cu—X; thus copper(I) chloride in aqueous ammonia gives the colourless $[Cu(NH_3)_2]^+$ (readily oxidized in air to give blue $[Cu^{II}(NH_3)_4(H_2O)_2]^{2+}$; copper(I) chloride in hydrochloric acid gives $[CuCl_2]^-$, although $[CuCl_3]^{2-}$ is also known.

13.13.3   Tests for copper compounds

Copper(II) ions in aqueous solution are readily obtained from any copper-containing material. The reactions with (a) alkali (p. 358), (b) concentrated ammonia (p. 358) and (c) hydrogen sulphide (p. 360) provide satisfactory tests for aqueous copper(II) ions. A further test is to add a hexacyanoferrate(II) (usually as the potassium salt), whereupon a chocolate-brown precipitate of copper(II) hexacyanoferrate(II) is obtained:

$$2Cu^{2+} + [Fe(CN)_6]^{4-} \rightarrow Cu_2[Fe(CN)_6]$$

13.14   Zinc

13.14.1   The element

The common ores of zinc are *zinc blende*, ZnS, and *calamine*, $ZnCO_3$. The metal is extracted (a) by roasting blende with air or by heating calamine, to give the oxide ZnO, which is then reduced to the metal by heating with coke, or (b) by dissolving out the zinc content of the ore with sulphuric acid, to give a solution of zinc(II) sulphate, $ZnSO_4$, which is electrolysed with an aluminium cathode on which the zinc metal is deposited.

The data provided at the beginning of this chapter show that zinc has a melting point and boiling point much lower than those of the preceding transition metals. This allows zinc to be melted or distilled without difficulty, and distillation can be used to purify zinc from less volatile metals. The low boiling point is an indication of weak metallic bonding, which in turn indicates that the filled $3d$ electron levels are not extensively involved in forming zinc–zinc bonds in the metal. Moreover, zinc in its chemical behaviour shows few characteristics of a transition element; it exhibits only one oxidation state, $+2$, in either ionic or covalent compounds, indicating the involvement only of the two outer, $4s$ electrons. Its compounds are commonly colourless, but it does show a somewhat greater tendency to form complexes than the analogous elements (Ca, Sr, Ba) of Group II.

The metal is not attacked by dry air at ordinary temperature; in moist air it tarnishes, forming a basic carbonate which acts as a coating preventing further corrosion. When heated in air, it burns with a greenish-blue flame giving a fibrous deposit of zinc oxide. This was the 'philosopher's wool' of alchemists. Zinc combines directly with chlorine and sulphur but not with nitrogen (cf. magnesium), although the compound zinc nitride, Zn_3N_2, can be obtained by passing ammonia over red-hot zinc. The metal does not react with water but steam attacks it at red heat (cf. magnesium):

$$H_2O + Zn \rightarrow ZnO + H_2$$

Despite its electrode potential (p. 89), very pure zinc has little or no reaction with dilute acids. If impurities are present, local electrochemical 'cells' are set up (cf. the rusting of iron, p. 349) and the zinc reacts readily evolving hydrogen. Amalgamation of zinc with mercury reduces the reactivity by giving uniformity to the surface. Very pure zinc reacts readily with dilute acids if previously coated with copper by adding copper(II) sulphate:

$$Cu^{2+} + Zn \rightarrow Zn^{2+} + Cu\downarrow$$

This zinc–copper couple reacts with methanol, the mixture reducing an alkyl halide to an alkane:

$$Zn + CH_3OH + C_2H_5I \rightarrow Zn^{2+} + CH_3O^- + I^- + C_2H_6$$

Under no conditions is hydrogen obtained from nitric acid. With the dilute acid, reduction to ammonia occurs:

$$4Zn + 10HNO_3 \rightarrow 4Zn(NO_3)_2 + NH_4NO_3 + 3H_2O$$
i.e.
$$4Zn + 10H^+ + NO_3^- \rightarrow 4Zn^{2+} + NH_4^+ + 3H_2O$$

With more concentrated nitric acid, oxides of nitrogen are formed.

Unlike cadmium and mercury and, in fact, all metals of Group II, zinc dissolves readily in alkalis forming zincates, in which the zinc atom is contained in a complex hydroxo-anion, for example:

$$Zn + 2OH^- + 4H_2O \rightarrow [Zn(OH)_4(H_2O)_2]^{2-} + H_2$$

At ordinary temperatures, zinc forms an addition compound with an alkyl halide (cf. magnesium):

$$Zn + C_2H_5I \rightarrow C_2H_5ZnI$$

The compound breaks up on heating:

$$2C_2H_5ZnI \rightarrow \underset{\text{diethylzinc}}{Zn(C_2H_5)_2} + ZnI_2$$

The zinc alkyls, of which diethylzinc is an example, are vile-smelling inflammable liquids. They were the first *organometallic* compounds prepared by Frankland in 1849. With water, they decompose giving an alkane:

$$Zn(C_2H_5)_2 + 2H_2O \rightarrow Zn(OH)_2 + 2C_2H_6$$

(Cadmium and mercury also form alkyls.)

13.14.2 Uses

Because of its resistance to corrosion, zinc can be used to coat iron. This may be done by dipping the iron into molten zinc or by spraying zinc on the iron articles, for example iron sheets. This is known as *galvanizing*. Smaller iron articles can be coated by heating with zinc dust, a process known as *sherardizing*, or suspensions of zinc may be used in paints.

Sheets of galvanized iron are used for roofing, guttering and the like. Alloys of zinc, notably brass, are used extensively. The metal is used in wet and dry Leclanché batteries.

Zinc oxide or 'zinc white' is used in paints, but lithopone, a mixture of zinc sulphide and barium sulphate, is preferred because of its better covering power. Both paints have the advantage over white lead that they do not 'blacken' in air (due to hydrogen sulphide). Zinc dust and also zinc chromate are constituents of rust-preventing paints. Zinc chromate is a yellow pigment. Lithopone is also used as a filler in linoleum.

Zinc carbonate and zinc oxide are constituents of calamine lotion. Zinc oxide, an antiseptic, is present in 'zinc' ointment and in cosmetic powders.

Zinc is important biologically; there are many zinc–protein complexes, and the human body contains about 2 g. In the human pancreas, zinc ions appear to play an essential part in the storage of insulin.

13.14.3   Chemical properties of zinc compounds

Oxidation state +2

Zinc(II) *oxide*, ZnO. This is prepared by heating the hydroxide $Zn(OH)_2$ or the carbonate $ZnCO_3$. It is a white solid, insoluble in water, but readily soluble in acids to give a solution containing the zinc(II) cation, and in alkalis to give a hydroxozincate(II) anion:

$$ZnO + 2H_3O^+ \rightarrow Zn^{2+}(aq) + 3H_2O$$

e.g.

$$ZnO + 2OH^- + 3H_2O \rightarrow [Zn(OH)_4(H_2O)_2]^{2-}$$

Zinc(II) oxide is therefore amphoteric.

On heating, the oxide becomes yellow, reverting to white on cooling. When zinc oxide is heated, a little oxygen is lost reversibly. This leaves a non-stoichiometric compound. The crystal lattice is disturbed in such a way that electrons from the excess of zinc metal remaining can move in the crystal almost as freely as they can in a metal. This makes zinc oxide a *semiconductor* and gives it a yellow colour, which is lost when oxygen is taken up again on cooling to give zinc oxide.

Zinc(II) *hydroxide* is a white gelatinous solid obtained when the stoichiometric quantity of alkali hydroxide is added to a solution of a zinc salt:

$$Zn^{2+}(aq) + 2OH^- \rightarrow Zn(OH)_2$$

It is soluble in alkali, and in ammonia (*see* below).

Zinc(II) *chloride*, $ZnCl_2$. This is the only important halide; it is prepared by standard methods, but cannot be obtained directly by heating the hydrated salt. It has a crystal lattice in which each zinc is surrounded tetrahedrally by four chloride ions, but the low melting point and solubility in organic solvents indicate some covalent character. In the hydrated salt, and in solution, species such as $[Zn(H_2O)_6]^{2+}$ exist; the latter is slightly acidic, forming $[Zn(H_2O)_5OH]^+$. In presence of excess of chloride ion, tetrahedral complexes such as $[ZnCl_4]^{2-}$ may be formed. Other important zinc salts are the *hydrated sulphate* $ZnSO_4.7H_2O$, isomorphous with the corresponding hydrated sulphates of, for example, iron(II) and nickel, and often used as a source of $Zn^{2+}(aq)$, and the *sulphide*, ZnS, obtained as a white precipitate when hydrogen sulphide is passed through a solution of a zinc(II) salt in presence of ammonia and ammonium chloride.

Complexes. The aqua-complex $[Zn(H_2O)_6]^{2+}$ and the tetrahedral $[ZnCl_4]^{2-}$ have already been mentioned. Numerous hydroxo-complexes, for example $[Zn(OH)_6]^{4-}$, $[Zn(OH)_4]^{2-}$, have been described. Addition of excess of ammonia to an aqueous Zn(II) solution produces the tetraamminezinc cation $[Zn(NH_3)_4]^{2+}$. Zinc tends to form 4-coordinate, tetrahedral or (less commonly) 6-coordinate octahedral complexes.

13.14.4   Tests for zinc

(1)   Alkali hydroxide gives a white precipitate soluble in excess. The white precipitate, $Zn(OH)_2$, gives the oxide when dehydrated; the white $\rightleftharpoons$ yellow reversible colour change observed on heating the oxide is a useful confirmatory test.

(2)   Addition of sulphide ion to a solution of a zinc salt containing ammonia and ammonium chloride gives a white precipitate of zinc sulphide.

Questions

1   Explain the following observations, giving equations wherever possible.

Anhydrous copper(II) sulphate is white but forms a blue hydrate and a blue aqueous solution. The solution turns yellow when treated with concentrated hydrochloric acid, dark blue with ammonia, and gives a white precipitate and brown solution when treated with potassium iodide. A yellow-brown aqueous solution of iron(III) chloride becomes paler on acidification with sulphuric or nitric acid, blood-red on treatment with potassium thiocyanate, gives a white precipitate with hydrogen sulphide and gives a dark blue precipitate with potassium hexacyanoferrate(II).

O, Schol.

2   A chromium atom forms a neutral complex with carbon monoxide molecules and 1,10-phenanthroline molecules. The structure of the complex is:

(a)   Suggest the shape of the complex.

(b)   What feature of the structure of a nitrogen atom makes it possible for it to take part in this sort of complex?

(c) What type of ligand is 1,10-phenanthroline in the complex?
(d) What is the oxidation state of chromium in this complex?
(e) What is the coordination number in the complex?
(f) The complex has no stereoisomers; suggest a reason for this.
(g) Comment briefly on whether or not the complexes could be expected to
      be water soluble.

N,A

3   When cobalt(II) chloride was dissolved in water, a pink solution A was
     formed. The addition of concentrated hydrochloric acid to A gave a blue
     solution B. If solution A was treated with concentrated ammonia solution a
     blue-green precipitate was formed; upon addition of further ammonia
     solution followed by the passage of air through the mixture, an orange-red
     solution C was produced.
     (a) Write down the formulae of the species containing cobalt which is
           present in each of A, B and C.
     (b) How are the ligands arranged spatially around the cobalt in A and B?

JMB,A

4   The transition metals form complexes which are usually different in kind and
     in stability from those formed by the non-transition elements. Give reasons
     for these differences.

Liverpool B.Sc., Part I

5   A compound of cobalt has the formula $Co(NH_3)_xCl_y$. 0.500 g of it was
     dissolved in 50.00 cm^3 M hydrochloric acid; the excess of acid required 40.00
     cm^3 M sodium hydroxide solution to neutralize it. Another 0.500 g portion of
     the compound was dissolved in water and allowed to react with excess of
     silver nitrate solution. 0.575 g of silver chloride was precipitated.
     (a) Calculate the number of moles of ammonia liberated from 0.500 g of the
           cobalt compound.
     (b) Calculate the number of moles of chloride ion released from 0.500 g of
           the cobalt compound.
           (Relative atomic masses: Ag = 108, Cl = 35.5).
     (c) What values for x and y in the original formula do these results suggest?
           (Relative atomic masses: Co = 60, N = 14, H = 1).
     (d) When the compound was decomposed before addition of silver nitrate,
           the value of y was found to be 50 per cent greater than the value you have
           calculated. Offer an explanation for the two values of y.
     (e) Draw the structure of the complex.

Liverpool B.Sc., Inter

6   In what ways do the chemical and physical properties of zinc(II) differ from
     those of iron(II)? Account for these differences. Explain what happens when
     (a) copper(I) oxide is treated with dilute sulphuric acid,
     (b) cobalt(II) chloride solution is treated with an excess of concentrated
           ammonia solution and air is bubbled through the mixture,
     (c) an excess of a concentrated solution of aqueous ammonia is added
           dropwise to an aqueous solution of nickel(II) chloride,

(d) an excess of an aqueous solution of potassium cyanide is added dropwise to an aqueous solution of nickel(II) chloride.

JMB,A

7 (a) Outline the extraction of manganese from pyrolusite and state one important use of the metal. Suggest a method for the preparation of a solution of potassium manganate(VII) starting from manganese, stating the oxidation state of manganese at each stage in the process.
Outline how you would determine the concentration of manganate(VII) ions in the product (practical details are not required).

   (b) Outline the production of (i) chromium, (ii) potassium dichromate, from chromium(III) oxide, stating the oxidation states of chromium at the various stages in (ii). Outline how you would determine the purity of a sample of potassium dichromate (practical details are not required).
Three crystalline compounds, one violet, one pale green, and one deep green in colour, all have the molecular formula $CrCl_3.6H_2O$. When equal masses of the three compounds are separately treated with an excess of aqueous silver nitrate at room temperature, the masses of white precipitate produced are in the ratio 3:2:1. Suggest an explanation for these results.

C,A

8 What do you understand by a complex salt? Give examples, using a different metal in each case, of complex salts that may be formed using the following reagents:
   (a) ammonia   (two examples)
   (b) sodium hydroxide   (two examples)
   (c) potassium cyanide (one example)
   (d) potassium iodide   (one example)
How would you distinguish between the two salts that you have chosen in each of (a) and (b) and how would you convert the examples given in (c) and (d) so that the simple metal ion is obtained in each case?

L,A

9 Write an account of *four* of the following aspects of transition metal chemistry:
   (a) the factors that determine the electrode potential of the metal;
   (b) the preparation of one compound in a high oxidation state;
   (c) the change in the M^{3+}/M^{2+} redox potential as a result of complex ion formation;
   (d) the determination of the formula of any one complex;
   (e) the colour of the compounds of the element;
   (f) the electronic structure and physical properties of the element.

JMB,A

10 Find the element V (vanadium) in the given Periodic Table.
   (a) Write down the electronic configurations of the species (i) V and (ii) V^{2+}.
   (b) What is the highest oxidation state that you expect vanadium to show in its compounds?

(c) Which of the following vanadium species do you expect to be (i) the strongest reducing agent, (ii) the strongest oxidizing agent? V^{3+}, VO^{2+}, V^{2+}, VO^{3+}, V^{4+}.

(d) State two physical properties of the element vanadium.

JMB,A

11   Locate the element titanium (Ti) in the Periodic Table. Read the following paragraph about its chemistry and answer the questions which follow.

When titanium dissolves in dilute hydrochloric acid, a violet solution containing titanium(II) ions is formed. This solution rapidly decolorizes acidified aqueous potassium manganate(VII) at room temperature. Titanium(IV) chloride is a colourless covalent liquid completely hydrolysed by water. Titanium(III) chloride forms hydrated titanium(III) ions in water and disproportionates when heated in a vacuum.

(a) Construct ionic equations for (i) the dissolution of titanium in hydrochloric acid and (ii) the reaction of titanium(III) ions with manganate(VII) ions in acid solution.

(b) Give the formula of the titanium compound formed when titanium(IV) chloride reacts with water.

(c) State briefly what is meant by disproportionation.

(d) Give two physical properties of the element titanium.

JMB,A

12   (a) Show by means of equations and experimental conditions how the following may be prepared:
      (i)   a covalent halide of a Group IV (C—Pb) element:
      (ii) anhydrous iron(II) chloride:

(b) State two chemical differences between anhydrous iron(II) chloride and silicon(IV) chloride.

(c) Explain why
      (i)   a solution of copper(II) chloride in concentrated hydrochloric acid is yellow,
      (ii) the yellow solution turns blue on dilution,
      (iii) the blue solution gives a precipitate with potassium iodide solution.

JMB,A

13   When anhydrous copper(II) sulphate is added to water, solution **A** is obtained. Treatment of solution **A** with an excess of aqueous sodium chloride gives solution **B** which, when treated with an excess of sulphur dioxide followed by dilution with water, gives a precipitate **C**. This precipitate, when filtered off and washed with distilled water, dissolves in aqueous ammonia to give a colourless solution **D** which rapidly becomes a blue-violet solution **E** upon standing in air.

(a) State the colours of solutions **A** and **B** and write formulae for the predominant copper-containing species contained in them.

(b) State the colour and formula of precipitate **C**.

(c) What is the formula of the predominant copper-containing species in **E**?

(d) Explain briefly the changes occurring when solution **D** changes to solution **E**.

JMB,A

Chapter 14
The transition elements of Groups IB and IIB
Silver, gold, cadmium, mercury

14.1 (Copper), silver, gold

These three elements have the outer electronic configuration $d^{10}s^1$ and by analogy with typical elements would be expected to have similar properties. We have already considered copper, as a member of the first transition series. Silver and gold show some resemblances to copper; all three elements exhibit an oxidation state of $+1$; and all three metals have rather similar physical properties (*Table 14.1*). All three metals are difficult to convert into cations, since they have high ionization energies and heats of atomization; they are therefore resistant to attack by aqueous acids or alkalis (increasing resistance from copper to gold); and all three have been used for making coins — hence they are often called collectively the *coinage metals*.

14.2 Silver

14.2.1 The metal

Silver is found in nature as *argentite*, Ag_2S and *horn silver*, AgCl. The extraction of silver depends upon the fact that it very readily forms a dicyanoargentate(I) complex, $[Ag(CN)_2]^-$ (linear), and treatment of a silver ore with aqueous cyanide ion CN^- extracts the silver as this complex. The silver is then displaced from the complex by zinc:

$$2[Ag(CN)_2]^- + Zn \rightarrow 4CN^- + Zn^{2+} + 2Ag$$

(Zinc forms only an unstable complex with the cyanide ion.)

Silver has little tendency to formally lose more than one electron; its chemistry is therefore almost entirely restricted to the $+1$ oxidation state. Silver itself is resistant to chemical attack, though aqueous cyanide ion slowly attacks it, as does sulphur or a sulphide (to give black Ag_2S), hence the tarnishing of silver by the atmosphere or other sulphur-containing materials. It dissolves in concentrated nitric acid to give a solution of silver(I) nitrate, $AgNO_3$.

Oxidation state $+2$
The only important compound is the paramagnetic silver(II) fluoride, AgF_2, prepared by fluorination of the metal; it is used as a convenient fluorinating agent.

Table 14.1 Selected properties of copper, silver and gold

Element	Atomic number	Outer electrons	Atomic* radius/nm	Density g cm^{-3}	m.p./K	b.p./K	First ionization energy kJ mol^{-1}	Heat of atomization kJ mol^{-1}
Cu	29	[Ar]$3d^{10}4s^1$	0.128	8.94	1356	2855	745	339
Ag	47	[Kr]$4d^{10}5s^1$	0.144	10.50	1234	2450	731	286
Au	79	[Xe]$4f^{14}5d^{10}6s^1$	0.144	19.32	1336	2980	889	354

Oxidation state +1

Addition of an alkali hydroxide to a solution of a silver(I) salt gives a brown solid, silver(I) oxide, Ag_2O; when wet, this behaves as 'silver hydroxide' AgOH, for example

$$\text{'AgOH'} + C_2H_5I \rightarrow AgI + C_2H_5OH$$

$\qquad\qquad$ iodethane $\qquad\qquad\qquad$ ethanol

The oxide is soluble in ammonia to give the complex $[Ag(NH_3)_2]^+$ (linear). On heating, silver(I) oxide loses oxygen to give the metal (all the coinage metal oxides have low thermal stability and this falls in the order $Cu > Ag > Au$).

14.2.2 Silver(I) halides

While the chloride, bromide and iodide are insoluble in water, the fluoride, AgF, is very soluble.

The insoluble halides can be prepared by adding the respective halide ion to silver ions:

$$Ag^+ + X^- \qquad \rightarrow AgX\downarrow$$

$\qquad\quad$ (halide)

The chloride is white, the bromide pale yellow and the iodide deeper yellow. These are examples (uncommon) of a coloured compound being obtained from colourless ions. The silver(I) ion intensifies colour in other cases, for example silver chromate(VI), Ag_2CrO_4, is brick-red while potassium chromate(VI), K_2CrO_4, is yellow.

Silver chloride is readily soluble in ammonia, the bromide less readily and the iodide only slightly, forming the complex cation $[Ag(NH_3)_2]^+$. These halides also dissolve in potassium cyanide, forming the linear complex anion $[Ag(CN)_2]^-$ and in sodium thiosulphate forming another complex anion, $[Ag(S_2O_3)_2]^{3-}$.

All the silver halides are sensitive to light, decomposing eventually to silver. In sunlight, silver chloride turns first violet and finally black. The use of these compounds in photography depends on this (*see* below). (All silver salts are, in fact, photosensitive — the neck of a silver nitrate bottle is black owing to a deposit of silver.)

Silver chloride is reduced to the metal by zinc. One of the methods of recovering silver from 'silver residues' depends on this. The residue is first treated with concentrated hydrochloric acid and then sulphuric acid and zinc added:

$$2AgCl + Zn \rightarrow 2Ag + 2Cl^- + Zn^{2+}$$

Photography

It was known in the sixteenth century that silver salts were photosensitive, but it was not until the beginning of the nineteenth century, when Herschel found that silver chloride was soluble in sodium thiosulphate, that photography became possible.

The plate or film of celluloid is coated with a colloidal gelatinized solution containing silver bromide (bromide is used because it is more photosensitive than the original silver chloride). During photographic exposure, decomposition of the bromide occurs to form minute particles of silver. These particles are too small to be seen by the naked eye and are only detectable with the electron-microscope. The number of such nuclei of decomposition in a given area of plate or film depends on the intensity of light falling on the area.

When the film is developed (the developer being a reducing agent), the unchanged silver bromide immediately surrounding these nuclei is reduced to give a visible blackening of the film.

The film is now fixed by washing in sodium thiosulphate ('hypo') solution, whereupon the unchanged bromide is dissolved to form the complex ion

$$AgBr + 2S_2O_3^{2-} \rightarrow [Ag(S_2O_3)_2]^{3-} + Br^-$$

The fixed plate is now a 'negative', for those patches on which most light fell are black. The process is reversed in printing to make the 'positive' — the printing paper having a covering of silver chloride or bromide or a mixture of the two. This, in turn, is developed and fixed as was the plate or film.

The formation of minute specks of silver when silver bromide is exposed to light is known to be aided by the presence of gelatin, which acts as a *sensitizer*. Very pure gelatin does not act in this way; but ordinary gelatin contains a trace of sulphur; because of this, a few sulphide ions, S^{2-}, are introduced into the silver bromide lattice, which is made up of silver and bromide ions. Now a sulphide ion, S^{2-}, must replace *two* bromide ions to keep the crystal electrically neutral, but it only occupies the space of one. Hence a 'vacant anion site', i.e. a 'hole' is left in the crystal. When the crystal is exposed to light, electrons are released from the crystal, and move through it; and some of these, when they reach a 'hole', become 'trapped'. When this happens, neighbouring silver ions unite with these electrons, so forming a nucleus or speck containing a few neutral silver atoms. These nuclei then grow when the silver bromide is reduced by the developer, and form the dark patches of silver where exposure has occurred.

14.2.3   Silver(I) nitrate

Silver nitrate, the most common silver salt, is obtained by dissolving the metal in nitric acid:

$$3Ag + 4HNO_3 \rightarrow 3AgNO_3 + 2H_2O + NO\uparrow$$

Like all nitrates, it is soluble in water; on heating it decomposes evolving nitrogen dioxide and oxygen, but leaving the metal, and not, as is usual with most other nitrates, the oxide:

$$2AgNO_3 \rightarrow 2Ag + 2NO_2 + O_2$$

In ammoniacal solution (in which the ion $[Ag(NH_3)_2]^+$ is formed) it is readily reduced to silver (*see* above) by many organic compounds. The use of silver nitrate for marking clothes depends on its reduction by the material to black silver. The reduction also occurs even when the neutral solution comes in contact with the skin and a black stain is left. Thus solid silver nitrate rubbed on the skin leaves a black deposit and so is used in surgery as a mild caustic — hence the old name for silver nitrate of *lunar caustic*.

If ethyne is passed through an ammoniacal solution of silver nitrate, there is a white precipitate of silver dicarbide [cf. copper(I)]:

$$HC{\equiv}CH + 2[Ag(NH_3)_2]^+ \rightarrow \underset{white}{Ag_2(C{\equiv}C)\downarrow} + 2NH_4^+ + 2NH_3$$

Silver nitrate is used extensively in qualitative and quantitative analysis. In the former, it gives precipitates with halides (except the fluoride), cyanides, thiocyanates, chromates(VI), phosphate(V), and most ions of organic acids. The silver salts of organic acids are obtained as white precipitates on adding silver nitrate to a neutral solution of the acid. These silver salts on ignition leave silver. When this reaction is carried out quantitatively, it provides a means of determining the basicity of the acid.

Gravimetrically, silver nitrate is used to determine the chloride ion.

Silver nitrate is used volumetrically to estimate chloride, bromide, cyanide and thiocyanate ions. Potassium chromate or fluorescein is used as an indicator.

In *neutral* solution, the indicator is potassium chromate(VI). In *acid* solution the CrO_4^{2-} ion changes to $Cr_2O_7^{2-}$ (p. 332), and since silver dichromate(VI) is soluble, chromate(VI) is not a suitable indicator; other methods can be used under these conditions. [In *alkaline* solution, silver(I) oxide precipitates, so silver(I) nitrate cannot be used under these conditions.]

14.2.4   Complexes of silver(I)

Some of these have already been noted as 2-coordinate and linear, for example $[Ag(CN)_2]^-$, $[Ag(NH_3)_2]^+$, $[Ag(S_2O_3)]^{3-}$. Silver(I) halides dissolve in concentrated aqueous halide solutions to give complexes $[AgX_2]^-$, $[AgX_3]^{2-}$, for example $[AgCl_3]^{2-}$.

14.2.5   Tests for silver

(1)   Hydrochloric acid or any soluble chloride gives a white precipitate, soluble in ammonia.
(2)   Hydrogen sulphide gives a black precipitate.
(3)   Potassium chromate(VI) gives a brick-red precipitate of silver chromate(VI) in neutral solution.

14.3   Gold

14.3.1   The element

Metallic gold, which is found free in nature, has always been valued for its nobility, i.e. its resistance to chemical attack. This property is to be expected from its position in the electrochemical series. It can, however, be attacked by certain substances, of which three may be mentioned:

(1)   In the presence of air, it is attacked by potassium cyanide solution, to give the complex *dicyanoaurate*(I) ion, in which gold has an oxidation state +1:

$$4Au + 8CN^- + 2H_2O + O_2 \rightarrow 4[Au(CN)_2]^- + 4OH^-$$

(2)   It is dissolved by 'aqua regia' (a mixture of concentrated hydrochloric and nitric acids). The product here is *tetrachloroauric*(III) *acid*, $HAuCl_4$; in the complex tetrachloroaurate(III) ion $[AuCl_4]^-$ gold is in oxidation state +3, *auric* gold*.

(3)   It is dissolved by bromine trifluoride, to form finally gold(III) fluoride, AuF_3. This is a notable compound, for in it gold exhibits a simple valency of three, whereas in all other gold(III) compounds, gold is 4-coordinate, usually by complex formation (*see* below).

14.3.2   Gold(I) compounds

These all tend to disproportionate into gold and gold(III) compounds, as already stated. Some of those which are insoluble in water, for example gold(I) sulphide, Au_2S, are fairly stable; others, for example gold(I) oxide, Au_2O, readily decompose even on gentle heating. One of the most stable is *gold*(I) *cyanide*, AuCN, which is formed when the ion, $[Au(CN)_2]^-$, is allowed to react with hydrochloric acid. *Gold*(I) *iodide*, AuI, is also formed by the slow loss of iodine from the gold(III) iodide, $(AuI_3)_n$. [The stabilities of gold(I) cyanide and iodide may be compared with those of the corresponding copper(I) salts.]

Gold(I) salts of oxo-acids are not known, but many complexes of gold(I) have been discovered.

14.3.3   Gold(III) compounds

In the gold(III) halides (except the fluoride) there is evidence for the formation of double molecules, Au_2X_6 [cf. chlorides of iron(III) and aluminium] so that the coordination is brought up to four, but with a *planar* structure:

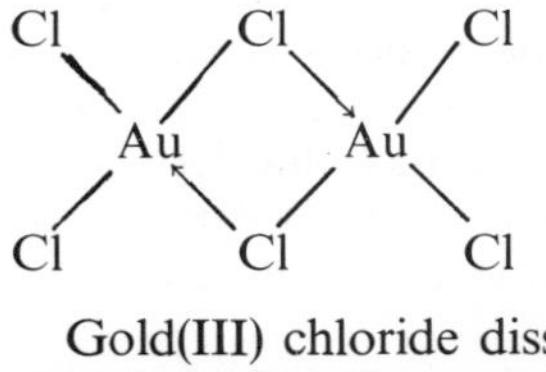

Gold(III) chloride dissolves in hydrochloric acid to form tetrachloroauric acid, $HAuCl_4$. Here again, the gold(III) is 4-coordinate in the ion $[AuCl_4]^-$. If alkali is added to this acid, successive replacement of chlorine atoms by hydroxyl groups occurs, forming finally the unstable *tetrahydroxoaurate*(III)

---

*The ion can be regarded as $(Cl^- \rightarrow AuCl_3)$, and coordination by the chloride ion brings the covalency from three (in $AuCl_3$) to four (in $[AuCl_4]^-$), the oxidation state remaining as +3.

ion, $[Au(OH)_4]^-$:

$$[AuCl_4]^- \rightarrow [AuCl_3OH]^{-\cdots} \rightarrow [Au(OH)_4]^-$$

This ion is very easily reduced to gold, and hence alkaline solutions of chloroaurates(III) (often wrongly called 'gold chloride') are used with a reducing agent to prepare *colloidal gold*.

Other than the fluoride, no compound of gold(III) is known in which gold acts as a metal ion, i.e. there are no gold(III) salts. There are, however, numerous complexes of gold(III) which are 4-coordinate, for example the compound diethylgold(III) sulphate $[(C_2H_5)_2Au]_2SO_4.4H_2O$, which has the structure:

$$\left[\begin{array}{cc} H_5C_2 & OH_2 \\ & Au \\ H_5C_2 & OH_2 \end{array} \right]_2^{2+} \quad SO_4^{2-}$$

14.3.4 Tests for gold compounds

Gold compounds are all easily reduced in alkaline solution to metallic gold which may occur in colloidal form and so be red, blue or intermediate colours. Reduction to gold, followed by weighing of the metal precipitated, can be used in quantitative analysis.

14.4 Zinc, cadmium, mercury

These elements have the outer electronic configuration $d^{10}s^2$. As we have seen in Chapter 13, zinc does not show very marked 'transition-metal' characteristics. The other two elements in this group, cadmium and mercury, lie at the ends of the second and third transition series (Y—Cd, La—Hg) and, although they resemble zinc in some respects in showing a predominantly +2 oxidation state, they also show rather more transition-metal characteristics. Additionally, mercury has characteristics, some of which relate it quite closely to its immediate predecessors in the third transition series, platinum and gold, and some of which are decidedly peculiar to mercury.

Table 14.2 shows that all three elements have remarkably low melting points and boiling points — an indication of the weak metallic bonding, especially notably in mercury. The low heat of atomization of mercury compensates to some extent its higher ionization energies, so that, in practice, all the elements of this group can form cations M^{2+} in aqueous solution or in hydrated salts; *anhydrous* mercury(II) compounds are generally covalent.

Table 14.2 Selected properties of the elements zinc, cadmium and mercury

Element	Atomic number	Outer electrons	Atomic radius*/nm	Density g cm^{-3}	m.p. K	b.p. K	Ionization energies kJ mol^{-1}		Heat of atomization kJ mol^{-1}
							1st	2nd	
Zn	30	[Ar]$3d^{10}4s^2$	0.133	7.13	693	1181	906	1734	131
Cd	48	[Kr]$4d^{10}5s^2$	0.149	8.65	594	1038	876	1630	286
Hg	80	[Xe]$4f^{14}5d^{10}6s^2$	0.152	13.53	234	630	1007	1809	61

* Metallic radius.

14.5   Cadmium

14.5.1   The element

Cadmium is usually found in zinc ores and is extracted from them along with zinc (p. 363); it can be separated from the zinc by distillation (cadmium is more volatile than zinc, *Table 14.2*) or by electrolytic deposition.

Cadmium is a soft metal, which forms a protective coating in air, and burns only on strong heating to give the brown oxide CdO. It dissolves in acids with evolution of hydrogen:

$$Cd^{2+}(aq) + 2e^- \rightarrow Cd(s) \qquad E^{\ominus} = -0.40 \text{ V}$$

It is used as a protective agent, particularly for iron, and is more resistant to corrosion by sea water than, for example, zinc or nickel.

In its chemistry, cadmium exhibits exclusively the oxidation state $+2$ in both ionic and covalent compounds. The hydroxide is soluble in acids to give cadmium(II) salts, and slightly soluble in concentrated alkali where hydroxocadmiates are probably formed; it is therefore slightly amphoteric. It is also soluble in ammonia to give ammines, for example $[Cd(NH_3)_4]^{2+}$. Of the halides, *cadmium*(II) *chloride* is soluble in water, but besides $[Cd(H_2O)_x]^{2+}$ ions, complex species $[CdCl]^+$, $[CdCl_3]^-$ and the undissociated chloride $[CdCl_2]$ exist in the solution, and addition of chloride ion increases the concentrations of these chloro-complexes at the expense of $Cd^{2+}(aq)$ ions.

Solid *cadmium*(II) *iodide* CdI_2 has a 'layer lattice' — a structure intermediate between one containing Cd^{2+} and I^- ions and one containing CdI_2 molecules — and this on vaporization gives linear, covalent I—Cd—I molecules. In solution, iodo-complexes exist, for example

$$3CdI_2 \rightarrow Cd^{2+}(aq) + 2[CdI_3]^-$$

Cadmium(II) *sulphide*, CdS, is a canary-yellow solid, precipitated by addition of hydrogen sulphide (or sulphide ion) to an acid solution of a cadmium(II) salt; presence of chloride ion may reduce the concentration of $Cd^{2+}(aq)$ sufficiently to prevent precipitation.

Complexes of cadmium include, besides those already mentioned, a tetracyanocadmiate $[Cd(CN)_4]^{2-}$ which in neutral solution is sufficiently unstable to allow precipitation of cadmium(II) sulphide by hydrogen sulphide. Octahedral $[CdCl_6]^{4-}$ ions are known in the solid state, as, for example, K_4CdCl_6.

14.5.2   Tests for cadmium

The reaction of $Cd^{2+}(aq)$ with sulphide ion, to give yellow CdS, and with hydroxide ion to give the white $Cd(OH)_2$, soluble in ammonia, provide two useful tests.

14.6 Mercury

14.6.1 The element

Mercury has been known for many centuries, perhaps because its extraction is easy; it has an almost unique appearance, it readily displaces gold from its ores and it forms amalgams with many other metals — all properties which caused the alchemists to regard it as one of the 'fundamental' substances.

It occurs chiefly as *cinnabar*, the red sulphide HgS, from which it is readily extracted either by roasting (to give the metal and sulphur dioxide) or by heating with calcium oxide; the metal distils off and can be purified by vacuum distillation.

Mercury has a large relative atomic mass, but, like zinc and cadmium, the bonds in the metal are not strong. These two factors together may account for the very low melting point and boiling point of mercury. The low boiling point means that mercury has an appreciable vapour pressure at room temperature; 1 m^3 of air in equilibrium with the metal contains about 14 mg of vapour, and the latter is highly toxic. Exposure of mercury metal to any reagent which produces volatile mercury compounds enhances the toxicity.

The metal is slowly oxidized by air at its boiling point, to give red mercury(II) oxide; it is attacked by the halogens (which cannot therefore be collected over mercury) and by nitric acid. (The reactivity of mercury towards acids is further considered on pp. 380, 381. It forms *amalgams* — liquid or solid — with many other metals; these find use as reducing agents (for example with sodium, zinc) and as dental fillings (for example with silver, tin or copper).

14.6.2 Uses

Mercury is extensively used in various pieces of scientific apparatus, such as thermometers, barometers, high vacuum pumps, mercury lamps, standard cells (for example the Weston cell), and so on. The metal is used as the cathode in the Kellner–Solvay cell (p. 119).

Mercury compounds [for example mercury(II) chloride] are used in medicine because of their antiseptic character. The artificial red mercury(II) sulphide is the artist's 'vermilion'. Mercury(II) sulphate is a catalyst in the manufacture of ethanal from ethyne:

$$C_2H_2 \; + \; H_2O \xrightarrow{\;HgSO_4\;} CH_3.CHO$$

14.6.3 Compounds of mercury

The chemistry of mercury compounds is complicated by the equilibrium

$$Hg_2^{2+}(aq) \; \rightleftharpoons \; Hg(s) \; + \; Hg^{2+}(aq)$$

The relevant redox potentials are:

$$Hg^{2+}(aq) \; + \; 2e^- \; \rightarrow \; Hg(I) \qquad E^{\ominus} = 0.85 \text{ V}$$
$$Hg_2^{2+}(aq) \; + \; 2e^- \; \rightarrow \; 2Hg(I) \qquad E^{\ominus} = 0.79 \text{ V}$$

Hence mercury is a poor reducing agent; it is unlikely to be attacked by acids unless these have oxidizing properties (for example nitric acid), *or* unless the acid anion has the power to form complexes with one or both mercury cations Hg^{2+} or Hg_2^{2+}, so altering the $E^\ominus$ values. Nitric acid attacks mercury, oxidizing it to $Hg^{2+}(aq)$ when the acid is concentrated and in excess, and to $Hg_2^{2+}(aq)$ when mercury is in excess and the acid dilute. Hydriodic acid $HI(aq)$ attacks mercury, because mercury(II) readily forms iodo-complexes (*see* p. 382).

Oxidation state +1

The mercury(I) ion has the structure

$$^+Hg:Hg^+$$

so that each mercury atom is losing one electron and sharing one electron, i.e. is 'using' two valency electrons. The existence of Hg_2^{2+} has been established by experiments in solution and by *X*-ray diffraction analysis of crystals of mercury(I) chloride, Hg_2Cl_2, where the mercury ions are in pairs with the chloride ions adjacent, i.e.

$$^-Cl\cdots^+Hg—Hg^+\cdots Cl^-$$

(It is now known that mercury can also form species Hg_3^{2+} up to Hg_6^{2+}; cadmium also gives Cd_n^{2+}, and other *polymetallic cations*, for example Bi_9^{3+} are known.) The ion $Hg_2^{2+}(aq)$ tends to disproportionate, especially if the concentration of $Hg^{2+}(aq)$ is reduced, for example by precipitation or by complex formation. However, the equilibrium can be moved to the left by using excess of mercury, *or* by avoiding aqueous solution. Thus, heating a mixture of mercury and solid mercury(II) chloride gives mercury(I) chloride, which sublimes off:

$$Hg + HgCl_2 \rightarrow Hg_2Cl_2$$

The product, commonly called *calomel*, is a white solid, insoluble in water; in its reactions (as expected) it shows a tendency to produce mercury(II) and mercury. Thus under the action of light, the substance darkens because mercury is formed; addition of aqueous ammonia produces the substance

$$H_2N—Hg—Hg—Cl$$

but this also darkens on standing, giving

$$H_2N—Hg—Cl$$

and a black deposit of mercury.

Mercury(I) ions can be produced in solution by dissolving *excess* of mercury in dilute nitric acid:

$$6Hg + 8H^+ + 2NO_3^- \rightarrow 3Hg_2^{2+} + 2NO + 4H_2O$$

From the acid solution white *hydrated mercury*(I) *nitrate*

$$Hg_2(NO_3)_2.2H_2O$$

can be crystallized out; this contains the ion

$$[H_2O—Hg—Hg—H_2O]^{2+}$$

which is acidic (owing to hydrolysis) in aqueous solution. Addition of chloride ion precipitates mercury(I) chloride.

Oxidation state +2

Mercury(II) *oxide*, HgO. This occurs in both yellow and red forms; the yellow form is precipitated by addition of hydroxide ion to a solution containing mercury(II) ions, and becomes red on heating. Mercury(II) oxide loses oxygen on heating.

Mercury(II) *chloride*. This is obtained in solution by dissolving mercury(II) oxide in hydrochloric acid; the white solid is obtained as a sublimate by heating mercury(II) sulphate and solid sodium chloride:

$$HgSO_4 + 2NaCl \rightarrow HgCl_2 + Na_2SO_4$$

The aqueous solution has a low conductivity, indicating that mercury(II) chloride dissolves essentially as molecules

Cl—Hg—Cl

and these linear molecules are found in the solid and vapour. A solution of mercury(II) chloride is readily reduced, for example by tin(II) chloride, to give first white insoluble mercury(I) chloride and then a black *metallic* deposit of mercury. The complexes formed from mercury(II) chloride are considered below.

Mercury(II) *iodide*, HgI_2. This is coloured either red or yellow, and is precipitated (yellow, turning red) by adding the stoichiometric amount of iodide ion to a solution containing mercury(II):

$$Hg^{2+} + 2I^- \rightarrow HgI_2$$

Addition of excess of iodide gives a complex (*see* below).

Mercury(II) *sulphate and nitrate*. These are each obtained by dissolving mercury in the appropriate hot concentrated acid; the sulphate is used as a catalyst (p. 379).

Mercury(II) *sulphide*, HgS. This again appears in two forms, red (found naturally as cinnabar) and black, as precipitated by hydrogen sulphide from a solution containing Hg(II) ions.

Complexes

Mercury(I) forms few complexes; one example is the linear

$$[H_2O—Hg—Hg—H_2O]^{2+}$$

found in the mercury(I) nitrate dihydrate (p. 380). In contrast, mercury(II) forms a wide variety of complexes, with some peculiarities: (a) octahedral complexes are rare, (b) complexes with nitrogen as the donor atom are common, (c) complexes are more readily formed with iodine than with other halogen ligands.

Mercury(II) halides, HgX_2, can be regarded as neutral, 2-coordinate linear complexes X—Hg—X. X is readily replaced; addition of ammonia to a solution of mercury(II) chloride gives a white precipitate

NH$_2$—Hg—Cl

In the presence of concentrated ammonium chloride, the same reagents yield the diamminemercury(II) cation,

[NH$_3$—Hg—NH$_3$]$^{2+}$

which precipitates as [Hg(NH$_3$)$_2$]Cl$_2$. In presence of excess of chloride ion, mercury(II) chloride gives complexes [HgCl$_3$]$^-$ and [HgCl$_4$]$^{2-}$, but the corresponding iodo-complex [HgI$_4$]$^{2-}$, from mercury(II) iodide and excess of iodide, is more stable. (It is rare for iodo-complexes to form at all and very rare to find them with stabilities greater than those of chloro-complexes.) In both solid HgI$_2$ and the complex [HgI$_4$]$^{2-}$ the mercury is tetrahedrally 4-coordinated. The [HgI$_4$]$^{2-}$ ion has a characteristic reaction with ammonia — a trace produces a yellow colour and more ammonia gives a brown precipitate. An alkaline solution containing [HgI$_4$]$^{2-}$ ions is therefore used as a test for ammonia; it is sometimes called *Nessler's reagent*. Insoluble salts of the anion [HgI$_4$]$^{2-}$ are known, for example Cu$_2$[HgI$_4$] (red).

14.6.4 Tests for mercury

Mercury(I) compounds in solution give a white precipitate with chloride ion, blackened by ammonia (p. 380); alkalis and reducing agents generally produce black or grey mercury from mercury(I) compounds.

Mercury(II) compounds in solution give a black precipitate with hydrogen sulphide or a yellow precipitate with alkali hydroxide (p. 381).

Any solid mercury compound when fused with sodium carbonate yields a grey deposit of mercury. (*Caution*: mercury vapour is formed.)

Questions

1   How would you prepare a specimen of copper(II) sulphate, starting from copper? Indicate the methods you might use to obtain dry crystals of the pentahydrate. What is the structure of the latter?

Liverpool B.Sc., Part I

2   Explain the following observations:
(a) Copper(I) salts disproportionate in solution, but silver(I) salts do not.
(b) Silver chloride is insoluble in water, but is soluble in dilute ammonia.
(c) Copper, silver and gold were all used in ancient times, but aluminium was not used until recent times.

3   Give the name and formula of one ore of mercury. How is the metal (a) extracted from this ore, (b) purified? Starting from the metal, how would you prepare specimens of (c) mercury(I) chloride, (d) mercury(II) chloride? What deductions have been made from a study of the vapour density of mercury(I) chloride at different temperatures?

L,A

Chapter 15
The lanthanides and actinides
Lanthanum to lutetium, actinium to lawrencium

The element lanthanum (atomic number 57) has the electronic configuration

La [Kr core]$4d^{10}5s^25p^65d^16s^2$

and appears as the first element of the third transition series. However, the next element, cerium (58) has the configuration

Ce [Kr core]$4d^{10}4f^15s^25p^65d^16s^2$

and the $4f$ quantum level fills up until lutetium (71) is reached:

Lu [Kr core]$4d^{10}4f^{14}5s^25p^65d^16s^2$

after which the filling of the $5d$ level is resumed. The elements from lanthanum to lutetium are called the *lanthanides* or *lanthanoids*. Similarly the *actinides* or *actinoids* begin at actinium (89).

Ac [Xe core]$4f^{14}5d^{10}6s^26p^66d^17s^2$

after which the $5f$ inner level begins to fill, until lawrencium (103) is reached*:

Lr [Xe core]$4f^{14}5d^{10}5f^{14}6s^26p^66d^17s^2$

Reference has been made already to the existence of a set of 'inner transition' elements, following lanthanum, in which the quantum level being filled is neither the outer quantum level nor the penultimate level, but the next inner. These elements, together with yttrium (a transition metal), were called the 'rare earths', since they occurred in uncommon mixtures of what were believed to be 'earths' or oxides. With the recognition of their special structure, the elements from lanthanum to lutetium were re-named the 'lanthanons' or *lanthanides*. They resemble one another very closely, so much so that their separation presented a major problem, since all their compounds are very much alike. They exhibit oxidation state +3 and show in this state predominantly ionic characteristics — the ions, L^{3+} (L = lanthanide), are indeed similar to the ions of the alkaline earth metals, except that they are tripositive, not dipositive.

Originally, general methods of separation were based on small differences in the solubilities of their salts, for examples the nitrates, and a laborious series of fractional crystallizations had to be carried out to obtain the pure

*These electronic configurations are formal; the orbitals in these heavy atoms are so close in energy that actual electronic configurations are very difficult to determine.

salts. In a few cases, individual lanthanides could be separated because they yielded oxidation states other than three. Thus the commonest lanthanide, cerium, exhibits oxidation states of $+3$ and $+4$; hence oxidation of a mixture of lanthanide salts in alkaline solution with chlorine yields the soluble chlorates(I) of all the $+3$ lanthanides (which are not oxidized) but gives a precipitate of cerium(IV) hydroxide, $Ce(OH)_4$, since this is too weak a base to form a chlorate(I). In some cases also, preferential reduction to the metal by sodium amalgam could be used to separate out individual lanthanides.

When the products of nuclear fission reactions came to be investigated, it was found that the lanthanides frequently occurred among the products. (The lanthanide of atomic number 61, promethium, for instance, probably does not occur naturally and was not discovered until nuclear fission produced it.) Hence it became necessary to devise more effective procedures to separate lanthanides, both from the fission products and from one another. One method used with great success is that of *ion exchange chromatography*; a mixture of (say) lanthanide salts in solution is run into a cation-exchange resin, which takes up the lanthanide ions by exchange. A solution containing negative ions which form complexes with the lanthanide ions (ammonium citrate is used) is then passed into the column and the column is washed ('eluted') with this solution until complexes of the lanthanides begin to emerge. It is found that those of the highest atomic number emerge first, and that the 'zone' of concentration of each lanthanide is separated from that of its neighbour. Some examples are shown in *Figure 15.1.*

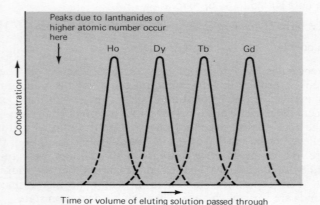

Figure 15.1 Ion-exchange graph for the lanthanides

The appearance of a peak between those for neodymium (60) and samarium (62) was then strong evidence for the existence of promethium (61).

The reason why lanthanides of high atomic number emerge first is that the stability of a lanthanide ion–citrate ion complex increases with the atomic number. Since these complexes are formed by ions, this must mean that the ion–ligand attraction also increases with atomic number, i.e. that the ionic radius decreases (inverse square law). It is a characteristic of the lanthanides that the ionic radius does decrease slightly as the atomic number increases. This effect, called *the lanthanide contraction*, occurs because the nuclear charge rises with rise of atomic number, whereas the two outer electron levels (which largely determine the ionic radius) remain unchanged; hence the ionic radius decreases as the increasing nuclear charge 'pulls in' the outer electrons to an increasing extent.

Another characteristic change across the lanthanide series is that of the paramagnetism of the ions; this rises to a maximum at neodymium, then falls to samarium, then rises to a second maximum at gadolinium before falling finally to zero at the end of the series.

Before it was known that elements beyond uranium were capable of existence, the heaviest known natural elements, thorium, protactinium and uranium, were placed in a sixth period of the periodic classification, corresponding to the elements hafnium, tantalum and tungsten in the preceding period. It was therefore implied that these elements were the beginning of a new, fourth transition series, with filling of the penultimate $n = 6$ level (just as the penultimate $n = 5$ level was being filled for hafnium, tantalum and tungsten). The discovery of many elements beyond uranium (the 'transuranic' elements) and a study of their properties, show that, in fact, a new *inner* transition series is being built up, starting after actinium. Hence the elements beyond actinium are now called the *actinides*.

Initially, the only means of obtaining elements higher than uranium was by α-particle bombardment of uranium in the cyclotron, and it was by this means that the first, exceedingly minute amounts of neptunium and plutonium were obtained. The separation of these elements from other products and from uranium was difficult; methods were devised involving co-precipitation of the minute amounts of their salts on a larger amount of a precipitate with a similar crystal structure (the 'carrier'). The properties were studied, using quantities of the order of 10^{-6} g in volumes of solution of the order of 10^{-3} cm^3. Measurements of concentration could, fortunately, be made by counting the radioactive emissions — a very sensitive method. However, much of the chemistry of plutonium was established on this scale before nuclear fission reactions yielded larger quantities of plutonium, and also yielded the first amounts of americium and curium. It soon became apparent that the ion-exchange chromatography method could be used in the separation of these new elements in just the same way as for the lanthanides. The fact that, when this was done, a series of concentration peaks was obtained exactly similar to those shown in *Figure 15.1*, is in itself strong evidence that the actinides and lanthanides are similar series of elements.

The use of larger particles in the cyclotron, for example carbon, nitrogen or oxygen ions, enabled elements of several units of atomic number beyond uranium to be synthesized. Einsteinium and fermium were obtained by this method and separated by ion-exchange, and indeed first identified by the appearance of their concentration peaks on the elution graph at the places expected for atomic numbers 99 and 100. The concentrations available when this was done were measured not in g cm^{-3} but in '*atoms* cm^{-3}'. The same elements became available in greater quantity when the first hydrogen bomb was exploded, when they were found in the fission products. Element 101, mendelevium, was made by α-particle bombardment of einsteinium, and nobelium (102) by fusion of curium and the carbon-13 isotope.

Evidence other than that of ion-exchange favours the view of the new elements as an inner transition series. The magnetic properties of their ions are very similar to those of the lanthanides; whatever range of oxidation states the actinides display, they always have $+3$ as one of them. Moreover, in the lanthanides, the element gadolinium marks the half-way stage when filling of the inner sub-level is half complete. It is known that this represents a particularly stable electronic configuration — hence gadolinium forms only the ions Gd^{3+} (by loss of three outer electrons) and shows no tendency to add or lose electrons in the half-filled inner level. This behaviour may be compared with the element before gadolinium, europium, Eu, which exhibits an oxidation state of two as well as three, and the element following, terbium, which exhibits states of $+3$ and $+4$.

In the actinides, the element curium, Cm, is probably the one which has its inner sub-shell half-filled; and in the great majority of its compounds curium is tripositive, whereas the preceding elements up to americium, exhibit many oxidation states, for example $+2$, $+3$, $+4$, $+5$ and $+6$, and berkelium, after curium, exhibits states of $+3$ and $+4$. Here then is another resemblance of the two series.

The many possible oxidation states of the actinides up to americium make the chemistry of their compounds rather extensive and complicated. Plutonium being taken as an example, it exhibits oxidation states of $+3$, $+4$, $+5$ and $+6$, four being the most stable oxidation state. These states are all known in solution, for example Pu^{III} as Pu^{3+}, and Pu^{VI} as PuO_2^{2+}. PuO_2^{2+} is analogous to UO_2^{2+}, which is the stable uranium ion in solution. Each oxidation state is characterized by a different colour, for example PuO_2^{2+} is pink, but change of oxidation state and disproportionation can occur very readily between the various states. The chemistry in solution is also complicated by the ease of complex formation. However, plutonium can also form compounds such as oxides, carbides, nitrides and anhydrous halides which do not involve reactions in solution. Hence for example, it forms a violet fluoride, PuF_3, and a brown fluoride, PuF_4; a monoxide, PuO (probably an interstitial compound), and a stable dioxide, PuO_2. The dioxide was the first compound of an artificial element to be separated in a weighable amount and the first to be identified by X-ray diffraction methods.

15.1 The elements beyond the actinides

Element 103, lawrencium, completes the actinides. Following this series, the transition elements should continue with the filling of the $6d$ orbitals. There is evidence for an element 104 (eka-hafnium); it is believed to form a chloride MCl_4 similar to that of hafnium. Less positive evidence exists for elements 105 and 106; attempts (so far unsuccessful) have been made to synthesize element 114 (eka-lead), because on theoretical grounds the nucleus of this element may be stable to decay by spontaneous fusion (as indeed is lead).

'Super-heavy' elements, well beyond this range, may also have nuclear stability, but their synthesis remains as a formidable problem.

Question

1   The lanthanides and actinides are two series of fourteen elements, the members of each series having very similar properties. How do you account for these similarities, and for the fact that all the elements are metals?

Index